Revise
GCSE

Science

Ian Honeysett, nd Emma P

Contents

This book and

	4405	4406
Web Address	www.aqa.org.uk	
Specification Number	4405	4406

Exam Assessed Units and Modules

At least 40% of assessment must be carried out at the end of the course.

For students starting the GCSE course from September 2012 onwards, all assessment (100%) must take place at the end of the course.

Three papers All papers: 1 hr 60 marks 25% of GCSE All papers feature structured and closed questions. **Unit 1: Biology 1** **Unit 2: Chemistry 1** **Unit 3: Physics 1**	Two papers Both papers feature structured and closed questions. **Unit 5:** **Science A 1** 1 h 30 min 90 marks 35% of GCSE Assesses: Biology 2 (B1.1 to B1.3) Chemistry 2 (C1.1 to C1.4) Physics 2 (P1.1 to P1.4) **Unit 6:** **Science A 2** 1 h 30 min 90 marks 40% of GCSE Assesses: Biology 2 (B1.4 to B1.8) Chemistry 2 (C1.5 to C1.7) Physics 2 (P1.4 to P1.5)

Controlled Assessment

Covering:
· Research, planning and risk assessment
· Data collection
· Processing, analysis and evaluation

Unit 4: Controlled Assessment 1hr 35 min, plus time for research / data collection 50 marks 25% of GCSE	

Chapter Map*

1 **Organisms in action**	B1.1, B1.2	B1.1, B1.2
2 **Health and disease**	B1.1, B1.3	B1.1, B1.3
3 **Genetics and evolution**	B1.7, B1.8	B1.7, B1.8
4 **Organisms and environment**	B1.4, B1.5, B1.6	B1.4, B1.5, B1.6
5 **Atoms and materials**	C1.1, C1.5	C1.1, C1.5
6 **The Earth and pollution**	C1.5, C1.6, C1.7	C1.5, C1.6, C1.7
7 **Organic chemistry and analysis**	C1.4, C1.5, C1.6	C1.4, C1.5, C1.6
8 **Metals and tests**	C1.3	C1.3
9 **Acids, bases and salts**	C1.2	C1.2
10 **Energy**	P1.1, P1.2, P1.3, P1.4	P1.1, P1.2, P1.3, P1.4
11 **Waves**	P1.5	P1.5
12 **Electromagnetic waves**	P1.1, P1.5	P1.1, P1.5
13 **Beyond the Earth**	P1.5	P1.5

* There are tick charts throughout the book to show which particular sub-topics in each chapter are relevant to your course.

your GCSE course

Edexcel	OCR A	OCR B	WJEC
www.edexcel.com	www.ocr.org.uk	www.ocr.org.uk	www.wjec.co.uk
2SC01	J241	J261	600/1036/8
Three papers All papers: 1 hr 60 marks 25% of GCSE All papers feature objective, short answer and extended writing questions. **Unit B1** **Unit C1** **Unit P1**	Three papers All papers: 1 hr 60 marks 25% of GCSE All papers feature objective style and free response questions. **Modules B1, B2 and B3** **Modules C1, C2 and C3** **Modules P1, P2 and P3** OR **Modules B1, C1 and P1** **Modules B2, C2 and P2** **Modules B3, C3 and P3**	Two papers Both papers feature structured questions. **Modules B1, C1 and P1** 1hr 15 min 75 marks 35% of GCSE **Modules B2, C2 and P2** 1hr 30 min 85 marks 40% of GCSE Includes data analysis.	Three papers All papers: 1 hr 60 marks 25% of GCSE All papers feature structured questions involving some extended writing. **Biology 1** **Chemistry 1** **Physics 1**
Unit SCA 3 hrs, plus approx. 6 hrs preparation time 50 marks 25% of GCSE	**Unit A144** Approx. 6–7hrs 64 marks 25% of GCSE	**Unit B713** Approx. 6 hrs 48 marks 25% of GCSE	**Unit CA** Approx. 1 hr 15 mins, plus time for initial research 48 marks 25% of GCSE
B1	B2	B1, B2	B1
B1	B2	B1	B1
B1	B1, B3	B1, B2	B1
B1	B3	B2	B1
C1	C2	C1, C2	C1
C1	C1, C2, C3	C1, C2	C1
C1	C1, C2	C1	C1
C1	C1, C3	C1, C2	C1
C1	C3	C1, C2	C1
P1	P3	P1, P2	P1
P1	P1	P1	P1
P1	P2	P1, P2	P1
P1	P1	P2	P1

Preparing for the exams

What will be assessed

In your science exams and controlled assessment, you are assessed on three main criteria called assessment objectives:

- **Assessment Objective 1 (AO1)** – tests your ability to **recall**, select and communicate your knowledge and understanding of science
- **Assessment Objective 2 (AO2)** – tests your ability to **apply** your skills, knowledge and understanding of science in practical and other contexts
- **Assessment Objective 3 (AO3)** – tests your ability to **analyse** and **evaluate** evidence, make reasoned judgements and draw conclusions based on evidence

The exam papers have a lot of AO1 and AO2 questions and some AO3 questions. The controlled assessments focus mainly on AO2 and AO3.

To do well on the exams, it is not enough just to be able to recall facts. You must be able to apply your knowledge to different scenarios, analyse and evaluate evidence and formulate your own ideas and conclusions.

Planning your study

It is important to have an organised approach to study and revision throughout the course.

- After completing a topic in school or college, go through the topic again using this guide. Copy out the main points on a piece of paper or use a pen to highlight them.
- Much of memory is visual. Make sure your notes are laid out in a logical way using colour, charts, diagrams and symbols to present information in a visual way. If your notes are easy to read and attractive to the eye, they will be easier to remember.
- A couple of days later, try writing out the key points from memory. Check differences between what you wrote originally and what you wrote later.
- If you have written your notes on a piece of paper, make sure you keep them for revision later.
- Try some of the questions in this book and check your answers.
- Decide whether you have fully mastered the topic and write down any areas of weakness you think you have.

How this book will help you

This complete study and revision guide will help you because…

- it contains the essential content for your GCSE course without any extra material that will not be examined
- there are regular short progress checks so that you can test your understanding
- it contains sample GCSE questions with model answers and notes, so that you can see what the examiner is looking for.
- it contains exam practice questions so that you can confirm your understanding and practise answering exam-style questions
- the summary table on pages 4-5, and the exam-board tick charts throughout the book, will ensure that you only study and revise topics that are relevant to your course.

Six ways to improve your grade

1. Read the question carefully

Many students fail to answer the actual question set. Perhaps they misread the question or answer a similar question that they have seen before. Read the question once right through and then again more slowly. Underline key words in the question as you read through it. Questions at GCSE often contain a lot of information. You should be concerned if you are not using the information in your answer.

Take notice of the command words used in questions and make sure you answer appropriately:

- **State:** A concise, factual answer with no description or explanation
- **Describe:** A detailed answer that demonstrates knowledge of the facts about the topic
- **Explain:** A more detailed answer than a description; give reasons and use connectives like 'because'.
- **Calculate:** Give a numerical answer, including working and correct units
- **Suggest:** A personal response supported by facts.

2. Give enough detail

If a part of a question is worth three marks, you should make at least three separate points. Be careful that you do not make the same point three times, but worded in a slightly different way. Draw diagrams with a ruler and label with straight lines.

3. Be specific

Avoid using the word 'it' in your answers. Writing out in full what you are referring to will ensure the examiner knows what you are talking about. This is especially important in questions where you have to compare two or more things.

4. Use scientific language correctly

Try to use the correct scientific language in your answers. The way scientific language is used

is often the difference between successful and unsuccessful answers. As you revise, make a list of scientific terms you come across and check that you understand what they mean. Learn all the definitions. These are easy marks and they reward effort and good preparation.

5. Show your working

All science papers include calculations. Learn a set method for solving a calculation and use that method. You should always show your working in full. That way, if you make an arithmetical mistake, you may still receive marks for applying the correct science. Check your answer is given to the correct level of accuracy (significant figures or decimal places) and give the correct units.

6. Brush up on your writing skills

Your exam papers will include specific questions for which the answers will be marked on both scientific accuracy and the quality of the written communication. These questions are worth 6 marks, but it does not matter how good the science is, your answer will not gain full marks unless:

- the text is legible and the spelling, punctuation and grammar are accurate so that your meaning is clear
- you have used a form and style of writing that is fit for purpose and appropriate to the subject matter
- you have organised information in a clear and logical way, correctly using scientific vocabulary where appropriate.

These questions will be clearly indicated on the exam papers.

Exam papers are scanned and marked on a computer screen. Do not write outside the answer spaces allowed, or your work may not be seen by the examiner. Ask for extra paper if you need it. Choose a black pen that will show up – one that photocopies well is a good choice.

How Science Works

The science GCSE courses are designed to help develop your knowledge of certain factual details, but also your understanding of 'How Science Works'.

'How Science Works' is essentially a set of key concepts that are relevant to all areas of science. It is concerned with four main areas:

Data, evidence, theories and explanations

- science as an evidence-based discipline
- the collaborative nature of science as a discipline and the way new scientific knowledge is validated
- how scientific understanding and theories develop
- the limitations of science
- how and why decisions about science and technology are made
- the use of modelling, including mathematical modelling, to explain aspects of science

Practical skills

- developing hypotheses
- planning practical ways to test hypotheses
- the importance of working accurately and safely
- identifying hazards and assessing risks
- collecting, processing, analysing and interpreting primary and secondary data
- reviewing methodology to assess fitness for purpose
- reviewing hypotheses in light of outcomes

Communication skills

- communicating scientific information using scientific, technical and mathematical language, conventions and symbols.
- use models to explain systems, processes and abstract ideas

Applications and implications of science

- the ethical implications of science and its applications
- risk factors and risk assessment in the context of potential benefit

You will be taught about 'How Science Works' throughout the course in combination with the scientific content. Likewise, the different exam boards have included material about 'How Science Works' in different parts of their assessment.

'How Science Works' will be assessed in the controlled assessment, but you will also get questions that relate to it in the exams. If you come across questions about unfamiliar situations in the exam, do not panic and think that you have not learnt the work. Most of these questions are designed to test your skills and understanding of 'How Science Works', not your memory. The examiners want you to demonstrate what you know, understand and can do.

1 Organisms in action

The following topics are covered in this chapter:

- A balanced diet
- Homeostasis 1
- Homeostasis 2
- Hormones and reproduction
- Responding to the environment
- The nervous system
- Plant responses

1.1 A balanced diet

LEARNING SUMMARY

After studying this section you should be able to:

- identify the components of a balanced diet and explain their roles
- realise that dietary requirements vary in different people
- calculate the EAR for protein in the diet and appreciate that there are different types of proteins
- explain how different food substances are stored.

Different food molecules

| AQA | B1 | ✓ |
| OCR B | B1 | ✓ |

All organisms need food to survive. Food provides raw materials for growth and energy.

We take in our food ready-made as complicated organic molecules. These food molecules can be placed into seven main groups (see table below).

> **KEY POINT**
>
> A **balanced diet** needs the correct amounts of each of the types of food molecules in the table.

Remember, a balanced diet is the 'correct' amount of each food type. In exams, candidates can lose a mark by saying a balanced diet contains 'enough' food.

You can use this rhyme to remember the seven types of food molecules: <u>w</u>hen <u>m</u>y <u>p</u>arents <u>c</u>ook, <u>v</u>egetables <u>f</u>eel <u>f</u>unny.

This stands for: <u>w</u>ater, <u>m</u>inerals, <u>p</u>roteins, <u>c</u>arbohydrates, <u>v</u>itamins, <u>f</u>ats and <u>f</u>ibre.

Food type	Made up of	Use in the body
Water	Hydrogen and oxygen	Prevents dehydration
Minerals	Different elements, e.g. iron	Iron is used to make haemoglobin
Proteins	Long chains of amino acids	Growth and repair
Carbohydrates	Simple sugars, e.g. glucose	Supply or store of energy
Vitamins	Different structures, e.g. vitamin C	Vitamin C prevents scurvy
Fats	Fatty acids and glycerol	Rich store of energy
Fibre	Cellulose	Prevents constipation

Different people may have slightly different diets due to a number of factors, including:

- **age** and **gender**
- level of **activity**
- personal preference, e.g. whether they are **vegetarians** or **vegans**
- medical reasons, e.g. if they have any food **allergies**.

Protein in the diet

OCR B   B1   ✓

Proteins are needed for growth and so it is important to eat the correct amount. This is called the **estimated average requirement (EAR)** and can be calculated using the formula:

> **KEY POINT**
>
> **EAR (g) = 0.6 × body mass (kg)**

Too little protein in the diet causes the condition called **kwashiorkor**. This is common in developing countries due to overpopulation and lack of money to improve agriculture.

The EAR is an estimate of the mass of protein needed per day based on the average person. The EAR for protein might be affected by factors such as age, pregnancy or breast feeding (lactation).

> To get an A* you must be able to analyse data about different types of protein.

Although proteins cannot be stored in the body, some amino acids can be converted by the body into other amino acids. However, there are some amino acids that can only be obtained from the diet – they are called **essential amino acids**.

Proteins from meat and fish are called **first class proteins**. They contain all the essential amino acids that cannot be made by the body.

Plant proteins are called **second class proteins** as they do not contain all the essential amino acids.

The amino acid that is in shortest supply is called the limiting amino acid. This will restrict the growth of the person.

Storing food

OCR B B1   ✓
WJEC   B1   ✓

If you eat too much fat and carbohydrate, the excess is stored in the body.

> **KEY POINT**
>
> Carbohydrates are stored in the **liver** as **glycogen** or are converted into fats.

There is a limit to how much glycogen the liver can store, but fat storage is not so limited.

Fats are stored under the skin and around organs as **adipose tissue**.

Although proteins are essential for growth and repair, they cannot be stored in the body.

1. What are proteins made of?
2. Tom has a mass of 55 kg. What is his EAR for protein?
3. What is kwashiorkor?
4. Why is it important to have enough fibre in the diet?
5. Look at the table showing details of four foods.

Food	Protein quality rating	Limiting amino acid
Egg	0.98	None
Beef	0.77	None
Wheat	0.62	Lysine
Peas	0.49	Methionine

a) Why do egg and beef have a higher protein quality rating?

b) Why do many diets often involve eating peas with wheat?

1. Amino acids
2. 0.6 × 55 = 33 g
3. Kwashiorkor is a deficiency disease caused by a lack of protein in the diet.
4. To move food along the gut (avoid constipation).
5. a) Egg and beef are first class proteins so contain all the essential amino acids.
b) Peas and wheat are both deficient in a different amino acid so they complement each other.

1.2 Homeostasis 1

LEARNING SUMMARY

After studying this section you should be able to:

- explain the importance of homeostasis in the body
- explain what is meant by the terms hormone and negative feedback
- explain how blood sugar levels are controlled
- describe the causes and symptoms of diabetes.

Principles of homeostasis

AQA	B1	✓
OCR A	B2	✓
OCR B	B1	✓
EDEXCEL	B1	✓
WJEC	B1	✓

It is vital that the internal environment of the body is kept constant. This state is called **homeostasis.**

The different factors in the body that need to be kept constant include:

- water content
- temperature
- sugar content
- mineral (ion) content.

Many of the mechanisms that are used for homeostasis involve **hormones**.

> **KEY POINT**
>
> Hormones are chemical messengers that are carried in the blood stream.

They are released by glands and passed to their target organ.

Hormones take longer to have an effect compared to nerves, but their responses usually last longer.

Negative feedback

OCR A	B2	✓
OCR B	B1	✓
EDEXCEL	B1	✓
WJEC	B1	✓

The homeostasis control mechanisms in the body work by **negative feedback**. This means that **receptors** in the body detect a change in the body. These changes are then **processed** in the body. Then **effectors** bring about a response that reverses the change so that the normal level is restored.

This is much like many artificial control systems such as the temperature control in a house.

> **Many control devices in the home work by negative feedback. Thinking about how they work might help you to remember what is meant by negative feedback.**

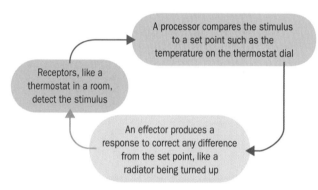

Receptors, like a thermostat in a room, detect the stimulus

A processor compares the stimulus to a set point such as the temperature on the thermostat dial

An effector produces a response to correct any difference from the set point, like a radiator being turned up

Controlling blood sugar levels

OCR B	B1	✓
EDEXCEL	B1	✓
WJEC	B1	✓

It is vital that the sugar or glucose level of the blood is kept constant:

- If it gets too low then cells will not have enough glucose to use for respiration.
- If it is too high then glucose may start to be excreted in the urine.

> **KEY POINT**
>
> **Insulin** is the hormone that controls the level of glucose in the blood.

Insulin is made in the pancreas. When glucose levels are too high, more insulin is released. The insulin acts on the **liver** causing it to convert excess glucose into **glycogen** for storage.

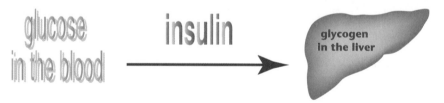

glucose in the blood   insulin   glycogen in the liver

The role of glucagon

EDEXCEL	B1	✓

Some systems have two or more effectors, which can work in opposite directions. This means that the response can happen much faster.

If blood sugar levels are too high then the hormone insulin is released. If levels drop below normal, the pancreas releases another hormone called **glucagon**.

Glucagon will cause the glycogen that is stored in the liver to be converted back to glucose.

Diabetes

OCR B	B1	✓
EDEXCEL	B1	✓
WJEC	B1	✓

KEY POINT

People who cannot control their blood sugar levels have a condition called **diabetes**.

This often causes blood sugar levels to be too high and so glucose is excreted from the body in the urine. This can be tested for using testing strips that are dipped into the urine and change colour if glucose is present.

There are two types of diabetes:

- **Type 1** – A genetic disease that is caused by the pancreas failing to make enough insulin. It is treated with regular insulin injections in order to control the level of glucose in the blood. People with Type 1 diabetes also need to control their diet carefully.
- **Type 2** – Caused by the cells in the body failing to respond to insulin. This is controlled by making sure that the person does not eat too much carbohydrate in meals.

People with Type 1 diabetes need to inject themselves with insulin. It is important that they get the dose right so they have to test their blood to see how much sugar is present. This will vary depending on:

- when they last had a meal
- how much exercise they have done recently.

PROGRESS CHECK

1 What is a hormone?
2 Where in the body is insulin made and released?
3 What effect does insulin have on the liver?
4 Write down one way that a person can be tested for diabetes.
5 What is the difference in function between glucose, glycogen and glucagon?
6 Suggest what effect exercise is likely to have on the blood sugar level.

6. Exercise will reduce the blood sugar level as glucose is used up in respiration.
5. Glucose is a sugar used for respiration in the body, glycogen is a storage carbohydrate and glucagon is a hormone that converts glycogen into glucose.
4. One test for diabetes is using urine testing sticks to check for glucose.
3. Insulin causes the liver to convert glucose into the storage carbohydrate glycogen.
2. Insulin is made and released in the pancreas.
1. A hormone is a chemical messenger that causes a response in the body.

1.3 Homeostasis 2

LEARNING SUMMARY

After studying this section you should be able to:

- explain why and how body temperature is regulated
- describe how the water content of the body is regulated.

Temperature regulation

OCR B	B1	✓
EDEXCEL	B1	✓
WJEC	B1	✓

> **KEY POINT**
>
> It is important to keep our body temperature at about **37°C**.

If the body temperature gets too low this is called **hypothermia** and this can be fatal. If the blood temperature gets too high it could lead to **heat stroke** and **dehydration**.

The body temperature is monitored by the brain and if it varies from 37°C, various changes are brought about.

When we feel hot we need to lose heat faster, as our core body temperature is in danger of rising.

> In addition to knowing about temperature regulation mechanisms, WJEC candidates must have a detailed knowledge of skin structure, including the epidermis, dermis and subcutaneous tissue.

We do this by:

- **Sweating** – as water evaporates from our skin, it absorbs heat energy from the body/skin. This cools the skin and the body loses heat.
- Sending more blood to the skin, so that more heat is lost by radiation. This causes the skin to look red.

When we feel too cold we are in danger of losing heat too quickly and cooling down. This means we need to conserve our heat to maintain a constant 37°C.

We do this by:

- **Shivering** – rapid contraction and relaxation of body muscles. This increases the rate of respiration and more energy is released as heat.
- Sending less blood to the skin, so the blood is diverted to deeper within the body to conserve heat and because of this the skin looks pale.
- Sweating less.

Body temperature needs to be 37°C because it is the best temperature for **enzymes** in the body, which control the rate of chemical reactions in the body, to work.

Any change in body temperature is detected by the **thermoregulatory centre** in the brain. This will bring about the correction mechanisms.

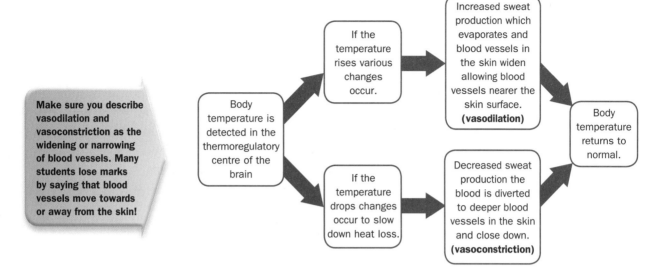

Make sure you describe vasodilation and vasoconstriction as the widening or narrowing of blood vessels. Many students lose marks by saying that blood vessels move towards or away from the skin!

Control of water balance

OCR A B2 ✓
OCR B B1 ✓

It is important to control the amount of water in the body otherwise the blood can become too concentrated or diluted. This is done by making sure that over a certain period of time we take in the same amount of water that we give out.

The body gains water by:

- drinking
- eating food
- respiration which releases water.

The body loses water through:

- sweating
- breathing
- faeces
- excreting urine.

Most of the regulation of water content is done by the **kidneys** altering the volume and concentration of the urine. The kidneys control the water balance of the body by filtering the blood to remove all small molecules.

Then useful molecules (e.g. glucose), and a certain amount of water and salts, are taken back into the blood to keep their levels in balance. The remaining waste is stored in the bladder as urine.

> **KEY POINT**
>
> The amount of water that is taken back into the blood is controlled by a hormone called **antidiuretic hormone (ADH)** which is released by the **pituitary gland**.

To get an A*, you must make sure that you remember how ADH works. More ADH makes the kidney reabsorb more water and so make less urine. Many students get this confused.

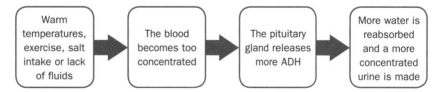

Different drugs can alter ADH release:

- **Alcohol** reduces ADH release and can cause too much urine to be made.
- **Ecstasy** can cause the opposite effect.

1.4 Hormones and reproduction

LEARNING SUMMARY	**After studying this section you should be able to:**
	• describe the role of hormones in controlling reproduction
	• describe how the menstrual cycle is regulated
	• describe how hormones can be used to manipulate fertility.

Reproductive hormones

AQA   B1   ✓

Hormones are responsible for controlling many parts of the reproduction process.

This includes:

• the development of the sex organs
• the production of sex cells
• controlling pregnancy and birth.

The main hormones controlling these processes are shown in the table.

Hormone	Male or female	Produced by	Main function
Testosterone	Male	Testes	Stimulates the male secondary sexual characteristics.
Oestrogen	Female	Ovaries	Stimulates the female secondary sexual characteristics. Repairs the wall of the uterus.
Progesterone	Female	Ovaries and placenta	Prevents the wall of the uterus breaking down.

Testosterone and oestrogen control the changes occurring in the male and female bodies at puberty. These changes are the secondary sexual characteristics.

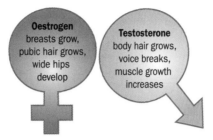

The secondary sexual characteristics also include the production of the sex cells. In the male they are sperm and in females they are eggs.

After puberty in the male, sperm are produced continuously, but in the female one egg is usually released about once a month.

This means that oestrogen and progesterone levels vary at different times in the monthly or menstrual cycle.

- Oestrogen levels are high in the first half of the cycle. The oestrogen prepares the wall of the uterus to receive a fertilised egg. It does this by making it thicker and increasing its supply of blood. It also triggers the release of an egg. This is called ovulation.
- Progesterone is high in the second half of the cycle. It further repairs the wall of the uterus and stops it breaking down.

Changes occur during the monthly cycle.

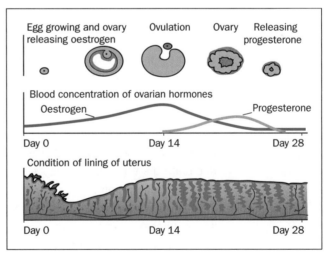

> If a question gives a diagram of the menstrual cycle and asks you when ovulation occurs do not automatically say day 14. Look for the peak of the oestrogen curve or the increase in progesterone. All women are different!

The production of oestrogen and progesterone is controlled by the release of other hormones. These hormones are called luteinising hormone (LH) and follicle stimulating hormone (FSH) and both are made in the pituitary gland in the brain.

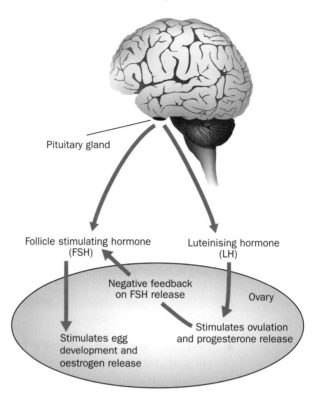

Control of reproduction.

Pituitary gland

Follicle stimulating hormone (FSH)

Luteinising hormone (LH)

Negative feedback on FSH release

Ovary

Stimulates egg development and oestrogen release

Stimulates ovulation and progesterone release

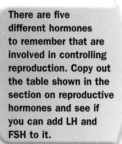

There are five different hormones to remember that are involved in controlling reproduction. Copy out the table shown in the section on reproductive hormones and see if you can add LH and FSH to it.

Treating infertility

AQA   B1   ✓

About one in seven of all couples have difficulty having a baby. There are many reasons for **infertility** and these include:

- a blockage in the Fallopian tubes or in the sperm ducts
- eggs are not developed or released from ovaries
- there is not enough fertile sperm produced by testes.

It is now possible to treat some of these cases of infertility by using hormones:

- Women who do not develop or release eggs from their ovaries can take a **fertility drug**. This contains hormones that are similar to FSH. The drugs stimulate the production of eggs and sometimes a number of eggs are released each month.
- Women who have blocked Fallopian tubes can be treated with fertility drugs and a number of eggs are removed from their body. The eggs can then be fertilised by sperm outside the body. The embryo can then be put back inside the uterus. This process is called **in vitro fertilisation (IVF)**.

Decreasing fertility

AQA   B1   ✓

Some women may want to stop themselves becoming pregnant. They take drugs that are called **oral contraceptives**.

These drugs contain different amounts of the hormones oestrogen and progesterone.

They prevent the pituitary gland releasing FSH. This means that the ovary will not produce eggs.

PROGRESS CHECK

1. Where is testosterone made and what does it do?
2. What is ovulation?
3. What is IVF?
4. How do oral contraceptives work?
5. Normally the progesterone level falls towards the end of the menstrual cycle. Why is it important that it stays high if the egg has been fertilised?
6. The 'morning after pill' contains very high levels of oestrogen. Suggest why many people think that it should not be used regularly for contraception.

1. Testosterone is made in the testes and it causes the development of secondary sexual characteristics in the man including the production of sperm.
2. Ovulation is the release of an egg from an ovary.
3. IVF stands for In Vitro Fertilisation, which is the process by which an egg is artificially fertilised by a sperm outside the body and an embryo re-implanted back into the uterus.
4. Oral contraceptives prevent the release of follicle stimulating hormone (FSH) and so stop ovulation happening, by preventing an egg developing.
5. To prevent the period (menstruation) happening and to maintain the uterus lining.
6. The high levels of oestrogen in the pill might produce side effects.

1.5 Responding to the environment

LEARNING SUMMARY

After studying this section you should be able to:

- explain the role of receptors and effectors in responding to stimuli
- describe the structure and function of the eye as an example of a sense organ
- recall the main eye defects.

Patterns of response

AQA	B1	✓
OCR B	B1	✓
EDEXCEL	B1	✓
WJEC	B1	✓

All living organisms need to respond to changes in the environment. Although this happens in different ways the pattern of events is always the same.

KEY POINT

stimulus → detection → coordination → response

There are three main steps in this process:

- **Detecting the stimulus** – **receptors** are specialised cells that detect a stimulus. Their job is to convert the stimulus into electrical signals in nerve cells. Some receptors can detect several different stimuli, but they are usually specialised to detect one type of stimulus.

Stimulus	Type of receptor
Light	Photoreceptors in the eye
Sound	Vibration receptors in the ears
Touch, pressure, pain and temperature	Different receptors in the skin
Taste and smell	Chemical receptors in the tongue and nose
Position of the body	Receptors in the ears

KEY POINT

A **sense organ** is a group of receptors gathered together with some other structures.

The other structures help the receptors to work more efficiently. An example of this is the eye.

- **Coordination** – the body is receiving information from many different receptors at the same time.
  Coordination involves processing all the information from receptors so that the body can produce a response that will benefit the whole organism.

  In most animals this job is done by the **central nervous system (CNS).** The CNS is made up of the brain and spinal cord.

- **Response** – **effectors** are organs in the body that bring about a response to the stimulus. Usually these effectors are muscles and they respond by contracting. They could however be glands and they may respond by releasing an enzyme.

The eye – an example of a sense organ

OCR B   B1   ✓

The structure of the eye.

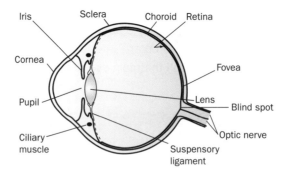

The light enters the eye through the **pupil**.

It is focused onto the **retina** by the **cornea** and the **lens**.

The size of the pupil can be changed by the muscles of the **iris** when the brightness of the light changes. The aim is to make sure that the same amount of light enters the eye.

The job of the lens is to change shape so that the image is always focused on the light sensitive retina.

Remember that both the cornea and the lens bend, or refract, light, but it is the job of the lens to make the fine adjustment to focus the light on the retina.

The receptors are cells in the retina called **rods** and **cones**. They detect light and send messages to the brain along the **optic nerve**.

Accommodation

OCR B   B1   ✓

The lens must be a different shape when the eye looks at a close object compared to a distant object. This is to make sure that the light is always focused on the back of the retina.

The **ciliary muscle** changes the shape of the lens as shown in the diagram.

This is called **accommodation**.

> To get an A*, you must be able to explain how accommodation occurs. Make sure that you remember that contracting the ciliary muscle allows the lens to become rounded and to refract light more.

How the eye focuses.

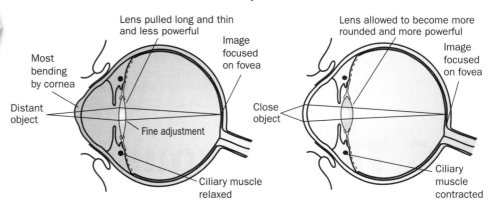

Some people have problems with their eyes. There are a number of different causes:

Condition	Cause	Treatment
Long-sight or short-sight	The eyeball or lens is the wrong shape.	Long-sight and short-sight can be corrected by wearing convex or concave lenses respectively. Cornea surgery can now also be used.
Red-green colour blindness	Lack of certain cones in the retina.	No treatment.
Poor accommodation	Lens becomes less elastic in senior citizens.	Wearing glasses with half convex and half concave lenses.

Judging distance

OCR B   B1, B2   ✓

The eyes are also used to judge distances.

- Animals that hunt usually have their eyes on the front of their head. Each eye has a slightly different image of the object. This is called **binocular vision** and this can be used to judge distance.
- Animals that are hunted usually have eyes on the side of their heads. This gives **monocular vision** and they cannot judge distances so well. They can however see almost all around.

1.6 The nervous system

LEARNING SUMMARY	After studying this section you should be able to:
	• describe the structure and function of different neurones
	• explain how a synapse works
	• describe the role of neurones in reflexes and voluntary actions.

Nerves and neurones

AQA	B1	✓
OCR B	B1	✓
EDEXCEL	B1	✓

To communicate between receptors and effectors the body uses two main methods. These are:

• nerves
• neurones.

KEY POINT

A **neurone** is a single, specialised cell that is adapted to pass electrical impulses.

The brain and spinal cord contains millions of neurones, but outside the CNS neurones are grouped together into bundles of hundreds or thousands. These bundles are called **nerves**.

The three main types of neurones are:

• **Sensory neurones** – they carry impulses from the receptors to the CNS.

Sensory neurone.

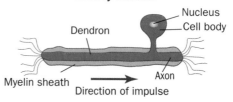

Dendron — Nucleus, Cell body
Myelin sheath — Axon
Direction of impulse

- **Motor neurones** – they carry impulses from the CNS to the effectors.

Motor neurone.

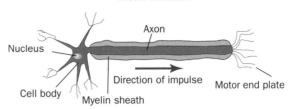

- **Relay neurones** – they pass messages between neurones in the CNS.

Although all neurones have different shapes, they all have certain features in common.

- One or more long projections (**axons** away from cell body and **dendrons** to the cell body) from the cell body to carry the impulse a long distance.
- A fatty covering (**myelin sheath**) around the projection which insulates it and speeds up the impulse.
- Many fine endings (**dendrites**) so that the impulse can be passed on to many cells.

Each neurone does not directly end on another neurone.

> **KEY POINT**
>
> There is a small gap between the two neurones and this is called a **synapse.**

Synapses

AQA	B1	✓
OCR B	B1	✓
EDEXCEL	B1	✓

So that an impulse can be generated in the next neurone, a chemical called a **neurotransmitter** is released when the nerve impulses reaches the synapse.

This then **diffuses** across the small gap and joins with receptors on the next neurone.

This starts a nerve impulse in this cell.

To get an A*, you must be able to explain why certain molecules might affect the working of synapses. Neurotransmitters have a specific shape to fit into receptors, so other molecules that have a similar shape might block the site or even act like the transmitter.

Chemical transmission between nerves.

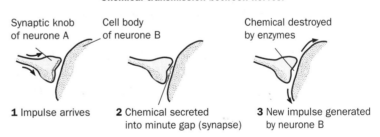

Many drugs work by interfering with synapses. They may block or copy the action of neurotransmitters in certain neurones.

Some of these are discussed on page 41.

Reflex responses

AQA	B1	✓
OCR B	B1	✓
EDEXCEL	B1	✓

> **KEY POINT**
>
> The **peripheral nervous system** is made up of all the nerves that pass information to and from the CNS.

Once impulses reach the CNS from a sensory neurone there is a choice:

- Either the message may be passed straight to a motor neurone via a relay neurone. This is very quick and is called a **reflex action**.
- Or the message can be sent to the higher centres of the brain and the organism might decide to make a response. This is called a **voluntary action**.

All reflexes are:

- fast
- do not need conscious thought
- protect the body.

> Students often lose marks because they say that reflexes 'do not involve the brain'. Some do not, but some such as blinking do. They all do not involve conscious thought.

Examples of reflexes include the knee jerk, pupil reflex, accommodation, ducking and withdrawing the hand from a hot object.

This diagram shows the pathway for a reflex that involves the spinal cord:

A reflex action.

1 Stimulus is detected by sensory cell.

↓

2 Impulse passes down sensory neurone.

↓

3 Relay neurone passes impulse to motor neurone.

↓

4 Motor neurone passes impulse to effector (muscle).

↓

5 Muscle contracts.

> Use this short rhyme to remember the order of events in a reflex action:
>
> **S**ue **R**emembers **S**eeing **R**achel make **E**gg **R**olls
>
> **S**timulus, **R**eceptor, **S**ensory neurone, **R**elay neurone, **E**ffector, **R**esponse

PROGRESS CHECK

1. What is the difference between a nerve and a neurone?
2. What is the job of the fatty sheath around a neurone?
3. What is a synapse?
4. Why is it important to the body that reflexes are fast?
5. Scientists may want to produce a drug that is a painkiller. How can they use their knowledge of neurones and synapses to do this?
6. It is important that the body breaks down neurotransmitter molecules once they have stimulated a nerve impulse in the next neurone. Why is this?

6. It is important that the body breaks down neurotransmitter molecules once they have stimulated a nerve impulse in the next neurone, otherwise they would stay in the receptor site and keep sending impulses. This could lead to convulsions.
5. Scientists could design a painkiller that could block the impulse travelling from the pain receptor, e.g. it might act on the synapses in the pathway, preventing the neurotransmitter from passing.
4. It is important that reflexes are fast so that they can protect the body from damage.
3. A synapse is a small gap between two neurones.
2. The fatty sheath around a neurone is there to insulate the neurone and speed up the rate of conduction.
1. A neurone is a single nerve cell, but a nerve contains thousands of neurones.

1.7 Plant responses

After studying this section you should be able to:

- describe how plants respond to stimuli
- describe the roles of plant hormones in these responses
- describe how plant hormones can be used to manipulate plant growth.

Plant responses

AQA	B1	✓
OCR B	B1	✓
EDEXCEL	B1	✓
WJEC	B1	✓

Plants can also respond to changes in the external environment. These responses are usually slower than animal responses and include:

- roots and shoots growing towards or away from a particular stimulus
- plants flowering at a particular time
- the ripening of fruits.

KEY POINT

The type of response that involves part of the plant growing in a particular direction is called a **tropism**.

If the growth is in response to gravity it is a **geotropism (gravitropism)**.

If it is in response to light it is a **phototropism**.

Stimulus	Growth of shoots	Growth of roots
Gravity	Away = negatively geotropic.	Towards = positively geotropic.
Light	Towards = positively phototropic.	Away = negatively phototropic.

By controlling the growth of plants, **auxins** (a type of **plant hormone**) can allow plants to respond to changes happening around them. This means that the roots and shoots of plants can respond to gravity or light in different ways.

These responses help the shoot to find light for photosynthesis and the root to grow down to anchor the plant in the soil and absorb water and mineral ions.

> Remember it is important for shoots to grow away from gravity.
>
> When a seed germinates it is often under the soil so the shoot cannot be growing towards light as it is dark!

Plant hormones

AQA	B1	✓
OCR B	B1	✓
EDEXCEL	B1	✓
WJEC	B1	✓

Growth in plants is controlled by chemicals called plant growth substances or plant hormones. There are a number of different types, but the main types are called auxins.

Auxins are made in the tip of the shoot and move through the plant acting as the signal to make the shoot grow towards the light.

Auxins change the direction that roots and shoots grow by changing the rate that the cells elongate.

Auxins are responsible for making plant cells increase in length or elongate.

Experiments have shown that a series of steps are involved in the response:

- light is shone on one side of a shoot
- more auxin is sent down the side of the shoot that is in the shade
- this causes cells on the shaded side to elongate more
- the shoot therefore grows towards the light.

How auxins control tropisms.

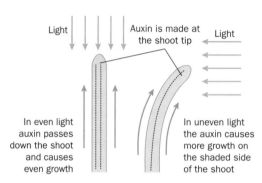

To get an A*, you must be able to look at the results of experiments on shoots and work out which way they will grow.

Light

Auxin is made at the shoot tip

Light

In even light auxin passes down the shoot and causes even growth

In uneven light the auxin causes more growth on the shaded side of the shoot

Applications of plant hormones

AQA	B1	✓
OCR B	B1	✓
EDEXCEL	B1	✓

KEY POINT

Gardeners can use plant hormones such as auxins to help them control the growth of their plants.

Uses of auxins.

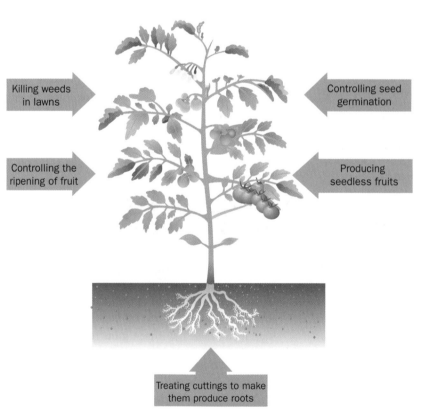

Killing weeds in lawns

Controlling seed germination

Controlling the ripening of fruit

Producing seedless fruits

Treating cuttings to make them produce roots

The plant hormones used by gardeners work in a number of ways:

- Auxins kill weeds because they make them grow too fast so they use up all their food reserves. These weed killers can be selective because they only kill broad leaf weeds, not grass.
- Some seeds need to be in the soil for some time before they germinate. Plant hormones can speed up this process.
- Fruit can be picked unripe so that it can be transported without being damaged. Then it can be ripened using plant hormones.

PROGRESS CHECK

1. Shoots are positively phototropic. What does this mean?
2. Roots are positively geotropic. Why is this important for a plant?
3. Where are auxins made in a plant?
4. Why are shoots dipped into hormone powder when taking cuttings?
5. Placing a foil cap over the tip of a shoot allows it to grow, but stops it bending towards light. Explain why.
6. Write down one advantage and one disadvantage of producing seedless fruits.

1. Phototropic means plants grow towards light.
2. Positively geotropic means roots grow down into the soil anchoring the plant and finding water.
3. Auxins are found in the shoot tip and root tip.
4. Shoots are dipped into hormone powder to make them produce lateral roots.
5. The foil cap blocks the light, so auxin is evenly distributed in the shoot and so the shoot grows upwards.
6. Advantage: more convenient to eat or more flesh to eat; Disadvantage: plant cannot reproduce sexually or cannot collect seeds to grow new plants.

Sample GCSE questions

1 The regulation of body temperature and water content of the body are examples of homeostasis.

(a) What is meant by homeostasis? **[2]**

> This is the regulation of a constant internal environment in the body.

This is an important definition. Make sure that you learn it!

(b) Fill in this table to show ways that water is gained and lost by the body. **[5]**

Ways that water is gained	Ways that water is lost
drinking and eating	sweating
respiration	urine
	breathing

These are all correct points, although there are some others.

The one that is often missed is the production of water by respiration.

(c) The diagram shows sections through the human skin under different conditions.

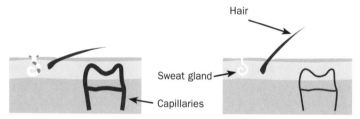

Hair

Sweat gland

Capillaries

Body temperature above normal   Body temperature below normal

A number of changes happen in the skin when the temperature falls below normal.

Describe and explain these changes.

The quality of written communication will be assessed in your answer to this question. **[6]**

> The capillaries in the skin have closed down. This means that less blood flows close to the skin and so less heat is lost.

Good explanation. Many candidates think that the capillaries move but they do not. You could use the term vasoconstriction to describe the closing.

> The sweat gland has also closed down so less sweat is lost. This would mean that less heat is lost by evaporation.

The key word to use when talking about sweating is evaporation. This is what takes heat from the skin.

> The hair stands on end. This is an attempt to trap more air close to the skin which would prevent heat loss.

This still happens in humans but it only really has an effect in hairy mammals. You could mention that air is a good insulator.

Sample GCSE questions

(d) The graph shows the effect of changes in air temperature on sweat and urine production.

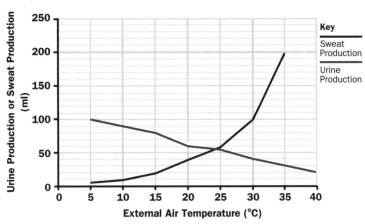

(i) Describe the patterns shown in the graph. **[2]**

As the external air temperature goes up the sweat production goes up and the urine production drops.

The urine production drops in a steady way but the rate of increase in sweat production increases.

(ii) Explain the changes shown by the graph. **[5]**

As it gets hotter the body temperature starts to increase. This is detected by the brain. The body responds with a number of changes aimed at losing more heat. One of these is to produce and release more sweat which evaporates from the skin.

The loss of water from the body makes the blood more concentrated and this is detected by the brain.

The body releases more of the hormone ADH and so less urine is produced and released.

This prevents the body getting too dehydrated.

This is a describe question so the answer needs to just relate to the graph.

This first mark is the easy mark describing the main difference.

Only the better candidates would give this point. The technical term for the shape of the sweat graph is exponential.

This is a good answer to a challenging question which links two topics together.

Remember only a fraction of a change in blood temperature will trigger changes so the blood temperature stays fairly constant.

You could give the site of ADH release which is the pituitary gland. It is also important to mention the kidneys which is where ADH acts.

Exam practice questions

1 Basil is doing an experiment to investigate how shoots respond to light.

He removes the tip from a growing shoot. He places a jelly block containing a certain concentration of auxin on the cut end of the shoot as shown.

After a period of time Basil measures the angle of curvature of the shoot.

He repeats the process for different auxin concentrations.

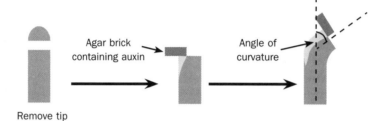

Remove tip

Auxin concentration mg/dm^3	0.05	0.1	0.15	0.2	0.25	0.30
Angle of curvature	4	9	13	19	22	17

(a) **(i)** Plot the results of the experiment on the graph.

Finish the graph by drawing the best curve. **[3]**

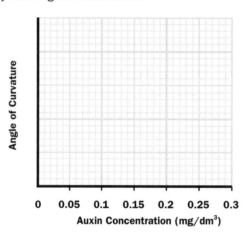

The auxin in the agar block causes the stem to curve.

(ii) Use information from your graph to describe the effect of the auxin concentration on the angle of curvature.

....

.... **[3]**

(b) **(i)** How does auxin cause one side of the shoot to curve over?

....

.... **[2]**

Exam practice questions

(ii) What type of stimulus in nature might cause this type of response in a shoot?

.... **[1]**

(iii) How might the plant gain from this type of response?

....

.... **[2]**

(c) Gardeners often use plant hormones such as auxins.
Write down one possible use.

.... **[1]**

2 The diagram shows a section through a human eye.

(a) **(i)** Label with **A** the part of the eye that carries nerve impulses to the brain.

(ii) Label with **B** the part of the eye that contains light sensitive cells.

(iii) Label with **C** the part of the eye that adjusts the size of the pupil. **[3]**

(b) The diagram shows light rays passing through the eye from a distant object.

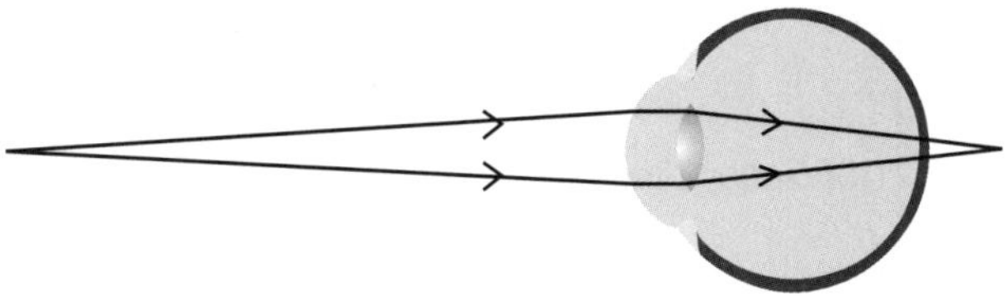

This person is long-sighted.

Explain why they cannot see the object clearly.

....

.... **[2]**

2 Health and disease

The following topics are covered in this chapter:

- Pathogens and infection
- Antibiotics and antiseptics
- Vaccinations
- Drugs
- Smoking and drinking
- Too much or too little

2.1 Pathogens and infection

LEARNING SUMMARY

After studying this section, you should be able to:

- recall some of the main causes of disease
- describe how pathogens can enter the body
- explain how white blood cells respond to antigens.

Causes of disease

AQA	B1	✓
OCR A	B2	✓
OCR B	B1	✓
EDEXCEL	B1	✓

A disease occurs when the normal functioning of the body is disturbed. **Infectious diseases** can be passed on from one person to another, but **non-infectious diseases** cannot. Organisms that cause infectious diseases are called **pathogens.** There are a number of different types of organisms that can be pathogens.

Type of disease	Description	Examples
Non-infectious		
Body disorder	Incorrect functioning of a particular organ	Diabetes, cancer
Deficiency disease	Lack of a mineral or vitamin	Anaemia, scurvy
Genetic disease	Caused by a defective gene	Red-green colour blindness
Infectious disease	Caused by a pathogen: Fungi Viruses Bacteria Protozoa	Athlete's foot Flu Cholera Malaria

Pathogens may reproduce rapidly in the body and may damage cells directly or produce chemicals called **toxins** which make people feel ill.

Viruses damage cells by taking over the cell and reproducing inside them. They then burst out of the cell destroying it in the process.

The entry of pathogens

EDEXCEL B1 ✓

There are a number of different ways that pathogens can be spread from one person to another.

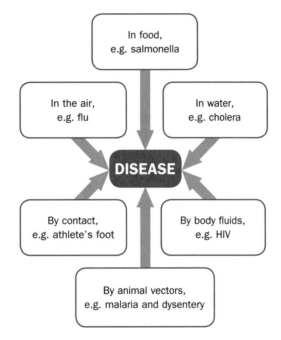

The skin covers most of the body and is very good at stopping pathogens entering the body.

The body has a number of other defences that it uses in order to try to stop pathogens entering.

The body's defences.

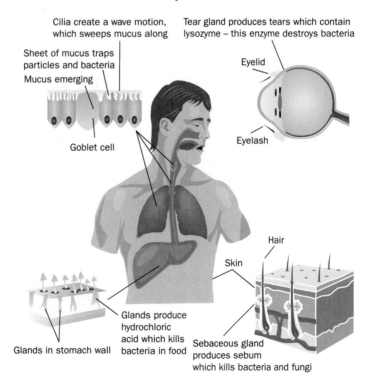

Preventing the spread of disease

AQA	B1	✓
OCR A	B2	✓
OCR B	B1	✓
EDEXCEL	B1	✓

By studying how pathogens are spread from person to person it is possible to find ways of preventing this spread. This will help to reduce the number of people getting the disease.

> Make sure that you know which diseases are mentioned on your specification, which type of organism causes each disease and how they are spread from person to person.

For example, the malaria pathogen is spread by mosquitoes biting, therefore using insect repellents, insect nets and draining swamps where the mosquitoes breed can reduce malaria cases.

The action of white blood cells

AQA	B1	✓
OCR A	B2	✓
OCR B	B1	✓
EDEXCEL	B1	✓

If the pathogens do enter the body then the body will attack them in a number of ways.

The area that is infected will often become inflamed and two types of white blood cells (**phagocytes** and **lymphocytes**) attack the pathogen.

The actions of white blood cells.

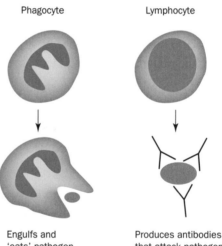

Phagocyte — Engulfs and 'eats' pathogen

Lymphocyte — Produces antibodies that attack pathogens

Pathogens are detected by the white blood cells because the pathogens have foreign chemical groups called **antigens** on their surface.

> Students often lose marks because they confuse 'antibodies', 'antigens', 'antibiotics' and 'antiseptics'. Make sure you know the difference between them all! (Antibiotics and antiseptics are covered on the next page.)

The **antibodies** that are produced are specific to a particular pathogen or toxin and will only attach to that particular antigen.

When an antigen is detected by white blood cells they will produce memory cells as well as antibodies. The memory cells work by:

- living many years in the body
- producing antibodies very quickly if the same type of pathogen reinvades the body.

PROGRESS CHECK

1 Write down one example of a deficiency disease.
2 What type of organism causes malaria?
3 What is an antibody?
4 What is a phagocyte?
5 Releasing thousands of sterile male mosquitoes into the environment helps to reduce the incidence of malaria. Explain why.
6 Why does a person only usually get measles once?

6. Memory cells live for a long time in the body and rapidly produce antibodies if the virus returns. Memory cells are produced and they will produce antibodies quickly if the measles virus re-enters the body.
5. They will mate with females, but no offspring will be produced, therefore there will be fewer mosquitoes to spread the parasite. They cannot reproduce so the population of mosquitoes goes down. Mosquitoes transmit the malarial parasite.
4. A white blood cell that engulfs and destroys pathogens.
3. A molecule that attacks pathogens.
2. Protozoa.
1. Anaemia/scurvy/kwashiorkor.

2.2 Antibiotics and antiseptics

LEARNING SUMMARY	After studying this section, you should be able to: • describe the difference between antibiotics and antiseptics • explain why some microbes are becoming resistant to antibiotics • describe how antibiotics and antiseptics are tested on microbes.

Antibiotics

AQA	B1	✓
OCR A	B2	✓
OCR B	B1	✓
EDEXCEL	B1	✓

Sometimes a pathogen can produce illness before our body's immune system can destroy it. It is sometimes possible for us to take drugs called **antibiotics** to kill the pathogen.

KEY POINT

Antibiotics:

• are chemicals that are usually produced by microorganisms, especially fungi
• kill bacteria and fungi but do not have any effect on viruses.

The first antibiotic to be widely used was penicillin, but there are now a number of different antibiotics that are used to treat different bacteria. This has meant that some diseases that once killed millions of people can now be treated.

There is a problem, however. More and more strains of bacteria are appearing that are resistant to antibiotics.

There are various ways that doctors try to prevent the spread of these resistant bacteria:

"I tell my patients to finish the dose of antibiotics even if they feel better."

"I change the antibiotics that I prescribe regularly and sometimes use combinations of different antibiotics."

"I prescribe antibiotics only in serious cases caused by bacteria."

"I always wash my hands with antiseptic between seeing patients."

Antibiotic resistance first appears due to a genetic change or mutation and soon afterwards a large population of resistant bacteria can appear.

The development of antibiotic resistance.

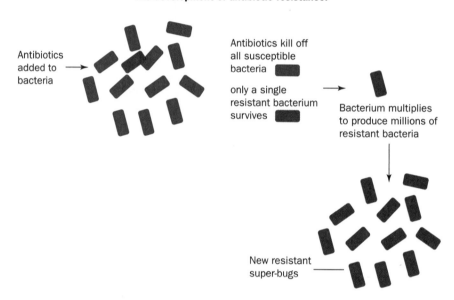

Antibiotics added to bacteria

Antibiotics kill off all susceptible bacteria

only a single resistant bacterium survives

Bacterium multiplies to produce millions of resistant bacteria

New resistant super-bugs

This process has occurred in many different types of bacteria including the TB causing bacterium and one called MRSA. These bacteria are now resistant to many different types of antibiotic and so are very difficult to treat.

Antiseptics

AQA   B1   ✓
EDEXCEL B1   ✓

One important weapon against resistant bacteria is the use of **antiseptics**. Antiseptics:

- are man-made chemicals that kill pathogens outside the body
- were first used by an Austrian doctor called Dr Semmelweis to sterilise medical instruments
- are used widely in hospitals to try and prevent the spread of resistant bacteria.

An antiseptic is usually used on the body and a **disinfectant** is usually used on other surfaces.

> Draw a spider diagram in your revision book to show antibiotics, antiseptics, antibodies and disinfectants. Make sure it shows what they kill and what makes them.

Testing antibiotics and antiseptics

AQA	B1	✓
OCR A	B2	✓
OCR B	B1	✓
EDEXCEL	B1	✓

It is possible to grow microorganisms such as bacteria in laboratories. They are grown on a special jelly called **agar** in a Petri dish. The agar is a culture medium containing an energy source, minerals and sometimes vitamins and protein.

Certain precautions have to be taken:

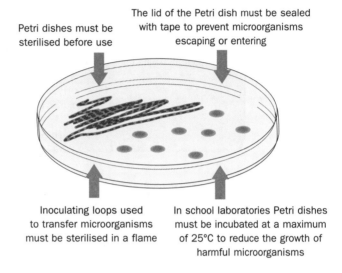

Petri dishes must be sterilised before use

The lid of the Petri dish must be sealed with tape to prevent microorganisms escaping or entering

Inoculating loops used to transfer microorganisms must be sterilised in a flame

In school laboratories Petri dishes must be incubated at a maximum of 25°C to reduce the growth of harmful microorganisms

It is then possible to see what action certain antibiotics or antiseptics have on the microorganisms.

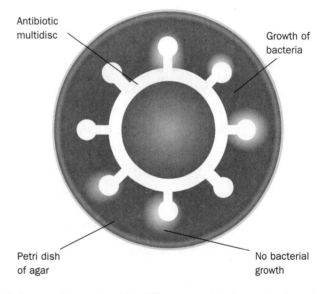

Antibiotic multidisc

Growth of bacteria

Petri dish of agar

No bacterial growth

Filter paper disks can be soaked in different antibiotics and placed on the agar.

The more effective the antibiotic, the wider the area of bacteria that will be killed.

2.3 Vaccinations

LEARNING SUMMARY	**After studying this section, you should be able to:** • explain how a vaccine works • explain the difference between active and passive immunity • discuss some of the risks and advantages associated with vaccinations.

What is a vaccine?

AQA	B1	✓
OCR A	B2	✓
OCR B	B1	✓

When our body encounters a pathogen, white blood cells make antibodies against the pathogen. If they encounter the same pathogen again in the future then antibodies are produced faster and the pathogen is killed quicker. This is called **immunity**. This idea has been used in **vaccinations**.

A vaccine contains harmless versions of the pathogen which stimulate immunity.

The harmless version of the pathogen contained in the vaccine could be:

• dead pathogens
• live, but weakened pathogens
• parts of the pathogen that contain antigens.

Questions often ask why it is necessary to produce a different flu vaccine every year. This is because different strains of the flu virus appear at regular intervals and they have different antigens. This means that the current memory cells would not recognise them.

Types of vaccine producing active immunity.

Bits of bacterial coat   Weakened virus

VACCINE

Dead bacteria

These all contain the specific antigens that are detected by the body's white blood cells. The memory cells that are produced stay in the body and will detect identical antigens in the future. This will lead to a more rapid immune response.

If a new strain of the pathogen appears then the current vaccination may not be effective.

Active and passive immunity

AQA	B1	✓
OCR A	B2	✓
OCR B	B1	✓

> **KEY POINT**
>
> The type of immunity, where the antibodies are made by the person, is called **active immunity**.

Sometimes it might be too late to give somebody this type of vaccination because they already have the pathogen.

> **KEY POINT**
>
> They can be given an injection containing antibodies made by another person or animal. This is called **passive immunity**.

It gives quicker protection but it does not last as long.

A vaccination containing antibodies.

Make a table to show the differences between active and passive immunity. Include who produces the antibodies, an example of when each might occur, how quickly they work and how long they last for.

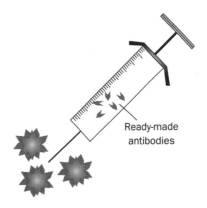

Ready-made antibodies

Passive immunity also occurs when a baby receives antibodies from its mother across the placenta or in breast milk.

Vaccination risks and advantages

AQA	B1	✓
OCR A	B2	✓
OCR B	B1	✓

Whether or not to give your children vaccinations is a difficult decision to make for some people. Diseases like measles, mumps and rubella can have serious effects on the body.

- Measles is a very serious disease – 1 in 2500 babies that catch the disease die.
- Mumps may cause deafness in young children.
- Mumps may also cause viral meningitis which can be fatal.
- Rubella can cause a baby to have brain damage if its mother catches the disease during pregnancy.

The introduction of a combined **measles, mumps and rubella (MMR)** vaccine has led to a decrease in measles, mumps and rubella.

In 1998, a study of autistic children raised the question of a connection between the MMR vaccine and autism. (People with autism have difficulty with communicating and using some thinking skills.) This led to a decrease in the number of parents allowing their children to have the MMR vaccine. This study has been discredited, but it is impossible to say that having a vaccine does not involve a **risk**. Some people say that parents should be forced to allow their children to have the vaccine otherwise the disease will not disappear. Others say that it should be a personal choice.

PROGRESS CHECK

1. What does a vaccine contain?
2. What type of immunity is produced in the following cases:
   a) Antibodies are taken from a horse that has rabies and injected into a person.
   b) A person has chicken pox and is now immune to this disease.
3. Explain your answers to question 2.
4. Why do people sometimes feel ill after having certain vaccines?
5. Some pathogens can change their antigens during their life. What effect does this have?

5. People are not immune to the pathogen anymore, so the disease can reinfect.
4. If the vaccine contains live, but weakened, microbes then the person may get some symptoms of the disease.
3. In **a)** the antibodies have been made by a different organism so it is passive. In **b)** they have been made by the person so it is active.
2. **a)** Passive immunity.
   b) Active immunity.
1. Dead or weakened form of the pathogen.

2.4 Drugs

After studying this section, you should be able to:
- recall the main categories of drugs
- explain the effects that drugs can have on synapses
- discuss some of the issues arising from drug testing.

Types of drugs

AQA	B1	✓
OCR B	B1	✓
EDEXCEL	B1	✓

Drugs are chemicals that alter the functioning of the body. Some drugs such as antibiotics are often beneficial to our body if used correctly. Others can be harmful, particularly those that are used recreationally.

Many drugs are **addictive**. This means that people want to carry on using them even though they may be having harmful effects. If they stop taking them they may suffer from unpleasant side effects called **withdrawal symptoms**. It also means that people develop **tolerance** to the drug, which means that they need to take bigger doses to have the same effect. Heroin and cocaine are very addictive.

Different drugs do different things.

Sedatives/ depressants
slow down the action of the brain, e.g. barbiturates, alcohol, solvents, temazepam

Stimulants
increase the activity of the brain, e.g. nicotine, ecstasy and caffeine

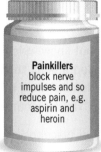
Painkillers
block nerve impulses and so reduce pain, e.g. aspirin and heroin

Performance enhancers
cause muscle growth, e.g. anabolic steroids

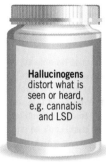
Hallucinogens
distort what is seen or heard, e.g. cannabis and LSD

In order to control drugs many can only be bought with a prescription. Drugs are also classified into groups. Class A drugs are the most dangerous, with Class C being the least dangerous. If people are caught with illegal Class A drugs the penalties are the highest.

Drugs and synapses

| OCR B | B1 | ✓ |
| EDEXCEL | B1 | ✓ |

Stimulants such as nicotine affect synapses (the junction of two neurones) by causing more neurotransmitter substances to cross to the next neurone and bind to the receptor molecules. This makes it more likely for an impulse to be conducted in the next neurone.

KEY POINT

Depressants such as alcohol bind with receptor molecules, so blocking the transmission of impulses.

Testing new drug treatments

AQA	B1	✓
OCR A	B2	✓
OCR B	B1	✓
WJEC	B1	✓

Any new drugs have to be tested before they are used on patients. Doctors need to know:

- if the treatment works
- if it is safe.

There are a number of different ways that a new treatment can be tested:

- Firstly it is tested on cells in a laboratory. This is on human cells to see if it is harmful and on microorganisms in Petri dishes to see if it will kill them.
- If it passes these tests the drug is then tried on animals.
- Then the drug is tested on healthy human volunteers for safety and on people with the illness for safety and effectiveness.

Exam questions often ask about testing drugs on animals or volunteers as this is an ideal 'How Science Works' subject. Be prepared to give both sides of the argument, even if you feel strongly one way or the other.

Many of these tests cause disagreements. Many people think that animals should not be used to test drugs. Some think that it is too cruel, while others think that it is pointless as the effects may be different on animals. Others think that the tests are reasonable because the benefits outweigh the risks of the tests.

Double-blind testing

AQA	B1	✓
OCR A	B2	✓
OCR B	B1	✓

> You must be able to analyse how a drugs test is done and decide if it is an open test, a blind test or a double-blind test. Look to see who knows which the real drug is.

Once a drug is cleared to be tested on patients the trial has to be set up carefully. One group is given the drug and another group has a **placebo**. A placebo looks like the real treatment, but has no drug in it.

If the two groups do not know which treatment they are having, but the doctor does, then this is called a **blind test**. If, in addition, the doctor does not know then this is called a **double-blind test**. It means that the people involved are not influenced by knowing which treatment is being given.

Some people think that placebos should not be used in tests on ill people. They say that it is not right to make people believe that they are receiving a possible cure when they are not.

Controversial drugs

| AQA | B1 | ✓ |

Over the years the use of some drugs has been particularly controversial.

Thalidomide is a drug that was given to pregnant women to try and relieve morning sickness. Thalidomide had been tested on pregnant animals. Unfortunately, many babies born to mothers who took the drug were born with severe limb abnormalities. The drug was then banned. More recently, thalidomide has been used successfully in the treatment of leprosy and other diseases.

Cannabis is an illegal drug. Many people have argued about whether it should be a Class B or Class C drug or possibly made legal. Cannabis smoke does contain harmful chemicals which may cause mental illness in some people.

> **PROGRESS CHECK**
>
> 1. Why is it difficult to stop taking drugs such as cocaine?
> 2. Why are illegal drugs put into different classes?
> 3. Why are drugs tested on healthy volunteers?
> 4. Why do some people object to using animals to test drugs?
> 5. Before anaesthetics were available, surgeons often gave patients brandy to drink before operations. Suggest why they did this.
> 6. Explain why is it important that the doctor treating patients does not know whether the patients are taking the real drug or a placebo.
>
> 1. It is very addictive and changes the body chemistry, so that the body cannot function normally without it.
> 2. To indicate how dangerous they are and give guidance about punishments for illegal use.
> 3. To see if they have any side effects/test for safety.
> 4. They think that it is cruel/they may not have the same effect on animals.
> 5. Alcohol is a depressant. It will reduce synaptic transmission in neurones involved in pain.
> 6. So that the doctor can report the results without any bias and does not subconsciously interpret the same results in a different way.

2.5 Smoking and drinking

LEARNING SUMMARY

After studying this section, you should be able to:

● describe the effects of smoking and drinking alcohol on the body
● explain why smoking is particularly harmful during pregnancy.

Smoking

| OCR B | B1 | ✓ |
| EDEXCEL | B1 | ✓ |

KEY POINT

Many people cannot give up smoking tobacco because it contains the drug **nicotine**. This is addictive.

The nicotine is harmful to the body, but most damage is done by the other chemicals in the tobacco smoke.

Problems resulting from smoking.

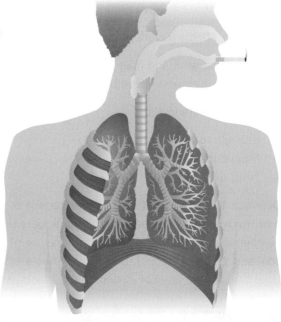

· The heat and chemicals in the smoke destroy the cilia on the cells lining the airways. The goblet cells also produce more mucus than normal. The bronchioles may become infected. This is called **bronchitis**.

· Chemicals in the tar may cause cells in the lungs to divide uncontrollably. This can cause **lung cancer.**

· The mucus collects in the alveoli and may become infected. This may lead to the walls of the alveoli being damaged. This reduces gaseous exchange and is called **emphysema**.

· The nicotine can cause an increase in blood pressure increasing the chance of a **heart attack**.

Smoking and blood pressure

| OCR A | B2 | ✓ |
| OCR B | B1 | ✓ |

As well as the effects described in the diagram, smoking can increase blood pressure. It does this in two main ways:

● Nicotine increases the heart rate directly.
● **Carbon monoxide** reduces the oxygen-carrying capacity of the blood by combining with haemoglobin. This causes the heart rate to increase to compensate.

Smoking and pregnancy

OCR B   B1   ✓

Smoking tobacco is particularly dangerous for pregnant women. Mothers who smoke when they are pregnant are more likely to give birth to babies that have a low birth mass.

The graph shows a good example of a correlation. Although there is quite a spread in the data, the trend shows that the more cigarettes a mother smokes, the lighter her baby is likely to be. You may be given graphs showing similar trends with smoking and lung cancer or heart disease.

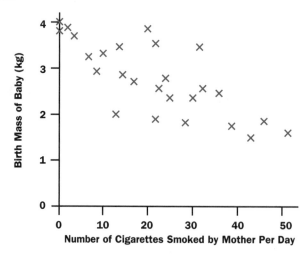

Drinking alcohol

OCR B   B1   ✓
EDEXCEL B1   ✓
WJEC   B1   ✓

Drinking alcohol can have a number of effects on the body.

Short term effects include:

- loss of balance and muscle control
- blurred vision and speech.

Long term effects include:

- damage to the liver (cirrhosis)
- brain damage
- heart disease.

Different drinks have different concentrations of alcohol. To help people judge how much alcohol they have drunk, drinks are described as having a certain number of units of alcohol. A single measure of spirits, or half a pint of beer, contains 1 unit of alcohol. Due to the effects of alcohol on the body there is a legal limit for the level of alcohol in the blood of drivers and pilots.

Alcohol and reaction times

OCR B   B1   ✓
EDEXCEL B1   ✓

KEY POINT

Drinking alcohol increases reaction times.

This means that it is far more likely for drivers to have accidents if they have drunk alcohol recently. The graph on the following page shows this.

When answering questions about reaction times and stopping distances, you must remember that alcohol will increase reaction times and increase stopping distances. Candidates often get confused by this.

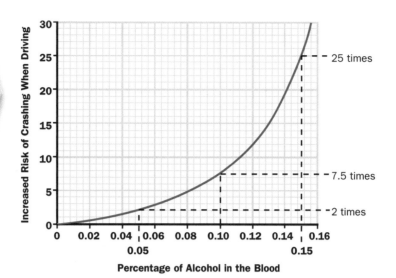

Percentage of Alcohol in the Blood

PROGRESS CHECK

1. What effect does smoking have on mucus production in the lungs?
2. Why is gaseous exchange reduced in emphysema?
3. What name is given to the damage caused to the liver by alcohol?
4. How many units of alcohol are there in two pints of beer and two single whiskeys?
5. If a person smokes, the oxygen content of the blood drops. Why is it necessary for their heart rate to increase to compensate?
6. How many times more likely is a person to have an accident if their blood alcohol level is 0.13% compared to 0.08%?

1. Increases production of mucus.
2. Walls of alveoli are broken down so reducing surface area for gas exchange. Alveoli are damaged so there is less gas exchange surface.
3. Cirrhosis.
4. Six.
5. So that blood is pumped faster around the body and so the cells receive sufficient oxygen to respire aerobically.
6. 15 times more compared with 5 times – so an increase of 3 times.

2.6 Too much or too little

LEARNING SUMMARY

After studying this section, you should be able to:

- recall the problems associated with obesity
- explain how a poor diet can lead to high blood pressure
- describe the risk factors associated with heart disease
- describe the problems associated with certain restricted diets.

Eating too much

OCR B   B1   ✓

It is important to maintain a balanced diet for the healthy functioning of the body. In the developed world many people eat too much food. This can make a person more likely to get various diseases. If a person eats food faster than it is used up by the body then the excess will be stored. Much of this will be stored as fat and can lead to **obesity**.

Obesity can be linked to a number of different health risks:

- arthritis – the joints wear out
- type 2 diabetes – unable to control the blood sugar level
- breast cancer
- high blood pressure
- heart disease.

It is possible to estimate if a person is underweight, normal, overweight or obese by using the formula:

> **KEY POINT**
>
> $$\text{Body Mass Index (BMI)} = \frac{\text{mass in kg}}{(\text{height in metres})^2}$$

The BMI figure can then be checked in a table to see what range a person is in.

Blood pressure

OCR A   B2   ✓
OCR B   B1   ✓

Contractions of the heart pump blood out into the arteries under pressure. This is so it can reach all parts of the body. Doctors often measure the blood pressure in the arteries and give two figures, for example 120 over 80. The highest figure is called the **systolic pressure** and this is the pressure when the heart contracts. The second figure is when the heart is relaxed and this is the **diastolic pressure**.

Blood pressure varies depending on various factors. The following factors can increase blood pressure:

- high salt and fat in the diet
- stress
- lack of exercise

- obesity
- high alcohol intake
- aging.

If left untreated, high blood pressure can cause various problems:

- Small blood vessels may burst, because of the high pressure. If a small blood vessel bursts in the brain, it is called a **stroke**. Brain damage from a stroke can result in some paralysis and loss of speech.
- If a small blood vessel bursts in a kidney, the kidney may be damaged.

Low blood pressure can cause problems such as:

- poor circulation
- dizziness and fainting, because the blood will not be at a high enough pressure to carry enough food and oxygen to the brain.

Heart disease

| OCR A | B2 | ✓ |
| OCR B | B1 | ✓ |

> In heart disease the blood vessels supplying the heart muscle are blocked.
>
> Lots of students lose marks because they say that fat blocks up blood vessels bringing blood back to the heart – do not make this mistake!

The heart is made up of muscle cells that need to contract throughout life. This needs a steady supply of energy so the cells need oxygen and glucose at all times for respiration. This is supplied by blood vessels.

Fatty deposits called **plaques** can form in these blood vessels and reduce the flow of oxygen and glucose to the heart muscle cells. This reduction in blood flow causes heart disease and if an area of muscle stops beating then this is a **heart attack**.

There are many factors that can make it more likely for a person to have heart disease.

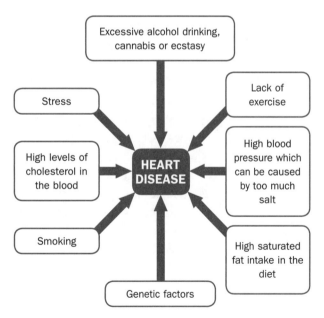

Most of these factors are lifestyle factors and managing these can reduce the risk of heart disease.

Coronary thrombosis

OCR B   B1   ✓

Plaques in the walls of the **coronary arteries** supplying the heart muscle make it more likely that blood will start to clot in the blood vessels. A blood clot inside the vessel is called a **thrombosis.** This blood clot may block the blood vessel. If the heart muscle does not get enough oxygen it will start to die. This leads to a heart attack.

Drugs such as **statins** can be taken to reduce the levels of cholesterol in the blood.

Eating too little

OCR B   B1   ✓

Eating too little of one type of food substance can lead to a deficiency disease.

Examples of deficiency diseases include:

- Anaemia due to a lack of iron.
- Scurvy due to a lack of vitamin C.
- Kwashiorkor due to a lack of protein.

Details of protein requirements and how to work out requirements are on page 10.

There are times when people do not eat enough food although there is food available. They may put themselves on a diet because they have a poor self image or think that they are overweight when they are not. This can reduce their resistance to infection and cause irregular periods in women. It may lead on to illnesses such as **anorexia**.

PROGRESS CHECK

1. A person has a mass of 80 kg and is 1.7 m tall. What is their BMI?
2. Why does a person's blood pressure have two figures?
3. What is a plaque?
4. Write down two ways that a person can try and reduce their risk of heart disease.
5. People with low blood pressure may often experience cold fingers and toes. Suggest why.
6. People who are at risk of heart disease take drugs such as warfarin. This makes the blood less likely to clot. Why do they take this drug?

6. Prevent a thrombosis happening in the coronary arteries which could block them and lead to a heart attack.
5. Poor circulation so limited blood supply to extremities which would usually bring heat.
4. Less stress/do not drink large amounts of alcohol/regular exercise/less saturated fat in diet/do not smoke.
3. A small build up of fat on the inside walls of the arteries.
2. The highest is the systolic when the heart contracts and the lowest is the diastolic when the heart relaxes.
1. $\frac{80}{1.7^2} = 27.7$

Sample GCSE questions

1 Read this newspaper article carefully and use the information to help you answer the questions.

TB bacteria may have met their match

Tuberculosis (TB) is a disease of the lungs.

TB is killing more people now for two main reasons.

Firstly, populations of the bacterium that cause TB are becoming resistant to many antibiotics.

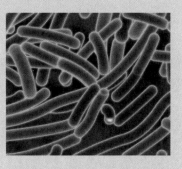

Secondly, more people have the virus called HIV and this makes them much more likely to catch TB.

Scientists think that they have found a new antibiotic that could cure TB. The new antibiotic is being tested in double-blind tests.

(a) TB can usually be treated with antibiotics but HIV or the flu cannot be treated in this way. Explain why. **[2]**

HIV is a virus and flu is caused by a virus.

Antibiotics have no effect on viruses.

> This is correct but would probably only score one mark because it does not say that TB is caused by a bacterium and they are killed by antibiotics.

(b) Explain why antibiotic resistant populations of TB have appeared. **[3]**

Individual bacteria have been produced that have resistance to antibiotics due to mutations.

This means that when antibiotics were used all the non-resistant bacteria were killed leaving the resistant individuals to reproduce. They produced the resistant populations.

> A good answer. The two key ideas are mutations producing the resistance and these bacteria surviving to reproduce.

(c) The formation of resistant populations of bacteria can be slowed down.

Write down **one** way that doctors can help slow this process. **[1]**

Doctors can only prescribe antibiotics when they are really needed.

> This is a correct answer although 'when really needed' is a little vague. It is probably best to say 'only for serious bacterial infections'.

(d) The article says that the new drug will be tested in a double-blind test. What is involved in a **double-blind test**? **[3]**

This is when some patients get the drug and other patients get a blank drug.

Neither the patient nor the doctors giving the drugs know which treatment the patient is receiving.

> This answer is correct although the technical term for a blank drug is called a placebo and this could have been included.

Sample GCSE questions

(e) The first graph shows the percentage resistance to antibiotics of a type of bacteria called MRSA.

The second graph shows the number of new antibiotics that have been given approval to be used.

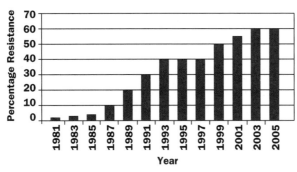

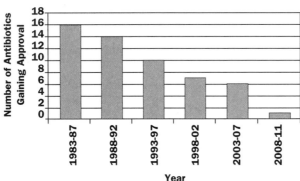

Use data from the two graphs to explain why scientists are concerned by antibiotic resistance in bacteria. **[3]**

Percentage resistance was less than 10% until about 1987, after which it increased dramatically. Although it was constant between 2003 and 2005 it was high at 60%.

The number of new antibiotics being approved is falling steadily. Only one new antibiotic was approved between 2008 and 2011.

To kill the resistant bacteria new antibiotics are needed.

They are not being produced.

This is a good answer, quoting figures from both graphs.
The trends in both graphs are described and there is a conclusion.

Exam practice questions

1 Vijay does not feel well so he visits the doctor.

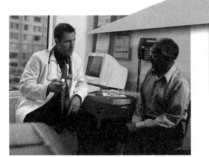

Some bacteria have entered your body.
They are producing chemicals that are making you feel ill.
Your body will soon make cells that will kill the bacteria.
To help kill the bacteria I will give you some medicine.
If you had been given an injection when you were young
then you would not have caught this disease.

(a) The boxes contain descriptions used by the doctor and certain biological terms.

Draw straight lines to join each **description** to the correct **biological** term.

description	biological term
The chemicals made by the bacteria that are making Vijay feel ill	Antibiotics
An injection that could have stopped Vijay getting the disease	Vaccination
The medicine given to Vijay to kill the bacteria	White blood cells
The cells produced by Vijay's body to kill the bacteria	Toxins

[3]

(b) The bacteria entered Vijay's body in his food.

Describe how bacteria in food are usually killed in the stomach.

.... **[1]**

(c) Write down **one** other method that the body uses to try and prevent bacteria entering the body.

.... **[1]**

(d) The doctor told Vijay that the medicine had been tested on animals.

Suggest why Vijay was pleased that the medicine had been tested.

.... **[1]**

Exam practice questions

2 **(a)** MMR is a vaccine that provides protection from three diseases in one injection.

About ten days after having the injection, children might get a measles-like rash.

Then, after three weeks they might get a mild form of mumps.

After six weeks, a rash of small spots like rubella may develop.

(i) People often feel ill after having a vaccination. Explain why.

....

.... **[2]**

(ii) Some parents do not want their children to have the MMR vaccine.

They want their children to visit the doctor three times for three separate vaccinations.

Suggest why they may feel this way.

....

.... **[2]**

(b) The Government has tried to persuade these parents to let their children have the MMR vaccination.

Suggest why the government want children to have one vaccination rather than three separate injections.

....

....

.... **[2]**

(c) Explain how one injection can protect a child from three different diseases.

....

....

....

.... **[3]**

3 Genetics and evolution

The following topics are covered in this chapter:

- **Genes and chromosomes**
- **Passing on genes**
- **Gene technology**
- **Evolution and natural selection**

3.1 Genes and chromosomes

LEARNING SUMMARY

After studying this section, you should be able to:

- explain what is meant by the term gene
- describe the sources of variation produced by sexual reproduction
- explain how sex is determined
- discuss the importance of genes and the environment in variation.

What is a gene?

AQA	B1	✓
OCR A	B1	✓
OCR B	B1	✓
WJEC	B1	✓

Most cells contain a nucleus that controls all of the chemical reactions that go on in the cell. Nuclei can do this because they contain the genetic material. Genetic material controls the characteristics of an organism and is passed on from one generation to the next.

> **KEY POINT**
>
> The genetic material is made up of structures called chromosomes. They are made up of a chemical called **deoxyribonucleic acid** or **DNA**.

The DNA controls the cell by coding for the making of proteins, such as enzymes. The enzymes will control all the chemical reactions taking place in the cell.

> **KEY POINT**
>
> A **gene** is part of a chromosome that codes for one particular protein.

DNA codes for the proteins it makes by the order of four chemicals called **bases**. They are given the letters **A, C, G** and **T**. By controlling cells, genes therefore control all the characteristics of an organism.

Different organisms have different numbers of genes and different numbers of chromosomes. In most organisms that reproduce by sexual reproduction, the chromosomes can be arranged in pairs. This is because one of each pair comes from each parent.

Chromosomes and reproduction

AQA	B1	✓
OCR A	B1	✓
OCR B	B1	✓
WJEC	B1	✓

No living organism can live forever so there is a need to reproduce.

> **KEY POINT**
>
> **Sexual reproduction** involves the passing on of genes from two parents to the offspring.

This is why we often look a little like both of our parents. The genes are passed on in the **sex cells** or **gametes** which join at **fertilisation**. In humans, each body cell has 46 chromosomes in 23 pairs. This means that when the male sex cells (sperm) are made they need to have 23 chromosomes, one from each pair. The female gametes (eggs) also need 23 chromosomes. When they join at fertilisation it will produce a cell called a **zygote** that has 46 chromosomes again. This will grow into an embryo and a baby. This also means that the offspring that are produced from sexual reproduction are all different because they have different combinations of chromosomes from their mother and father.

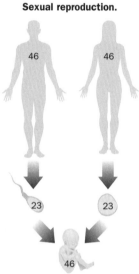

Sexual reproduction.

Because the baby can receive any one of the 23 pairs from mum and any one of the 23 pairs from dad, the number of possible gene combinations is enormous. This new mixture of genetic information produces a great deal of variation in the offspring. This just mixes genes up in different combinations, but the only way that new genes can be made is by **mutation**. This is a random change in a gene.

> You only need to know the number of chromosomes in a human cell. Do not worry if a question asks about a different animal. Look for what information it supplies, for example it might say that a sperm of a fruit fly has four chromosomes. You can then work out that a leg cell would have eight.

Sex determination

OCR A	B1	✓
OCR B	B1	✓
WJEC	B1	✓

> **KEY POINT**
>
> In humans, the chromosomes of one of the 23 pairs are called the **sex chromosomes** because they carry the genes that determine the sex of the person.

There are two kinds of sex chromosome. One is called **X** and one is called **Y**.

- Females have two X chromosomes and are XX.
- Males have an X and a Y chromosome and are XY.

Females produce eggs that contain a single X chromosome and males produce sperm, half of which contain a Y chromosome and half of which contain an X chromosome. The diagram alongside shows the possible zygotes that can be produced by fertilisation.

The reason why the sex chromosomes determine the sex of a person is due to a single gene on the Y chromosome. This gene causes the production of testes rather than ovaries and so the male sex hormone testosterone is made. This will cause the development of all the male characteristics.

Variation

AQA	B1	✓
OCR A	B1, B3	✓
OCR B	B1	✓
EDEXCEL	B1	✓
WJEC	B1	✓

Children born from the same parents all look slightly different. These differences are called **variation**. This can have different causes:

- **Inherited or genetic** – some variation is inherited from our parents in our genes.
- **Environmental** – some variation is a result of our environment.

Often our characteristics are a result of both our genes and our environment. The table shows examples of different kinds of variation.

Inherited	Environmental	Inherited and environmental
Earlobe shape	Scars	Intelligence
Eye colour	Spoken language	Body mass
Nose shape		Height
Dimples		

A good way to think of it, is that the genes provide a height and weight range into which we will fit, and how much we eat determines where in that range we will be.

Nature versus nurture

AQA	B1	✓
OCR A	B1	✓
OCR B	B1	✓

Scientists have argued for many years whether 'nature' or 'nurture' (inheritance or environment), is responsible for characteristics like intelligence, sporting ability and health. Some of the most important work on this subject has been done by studying identical twins that have been separated at birth.

> **PROGRESS CHECK**
>
> 1 What does DNA stand for?
> 2 What does DNA code for?
> 3 Why is it important that a sex cell has only one chromosome from each pair?
> 4 What mechanism can produce new genes?
> 5 Explain why approximately the same number of boys are born as girls.
> 6 Why are identical twins separated at birth so useful when studying nature versus nurture arguments?
>
> 6. Similarities are due to genetics (they have the same alleles) and so any differences must be due to the environment.
> 5. Sperm are either X or Y in even numbers. If a Y sperm fertilises then it is a boy and an X sperm makes a girl.
> 4. Mutation.
> 3. So that at fertilisation the full number of chromosomes can be restored.
> 2. Codes for proteins.
> 1. Deoxyribonucleic acid.

3.2 Passing on genes

LEARNING SUMMARY

After studying this section, you should be able to:

- explain the difference between the terms dominant and recessive
- explain the terms homozygous, heterozygous, genotype and phenotype
- construct genetic diagrams to predict the results of crosses
- recall the symptoms of certain genetic conditions
- discuss the ethical issues arising from genetic screening.

Different copies of genes

OCR A	B1	✓
OCR B	B1	✓
EDEXCEL	B1	✓
WJEC	B1	✓

We have two copies of each chromosome in our cells (one from each parent). This therefore means that we have two copies of each gene. Sometimes the two copies are the same but sometimes they are different.

A good example of this is tongue rolling. This is controlled by a single gene and there are two possible copies of the gene, one that says roll and the other that says do not roll. If a person has one copy of each then they can still roll their tongue. This is because the copy for rolling is **dominant** and the non-rolling copy is **recessive**.

> **KEY POINT**
>
> Each copy of a gene is called an **allele**. If both alleles for a gene are the same this is called **homozygous**. **Heterozygous** means that the two alleles are different.

The only genes that cannot have two alleles present are those found on the X chromosome in men. This is because men only have one X chromosome. These genes are said to be **sex linked**.

The idea that characteristics were passed on as discrete 'factors' or genes was first suggested in 1866 by a monk called **Gregor Mendel**. At that time people believed that reproduction just caused factors to blend together. Using pea plants, Mendel showed that blending did not occur. At the time few scientists took any notice of his work because he was experimenting in a small monastery in the country. His work was rediscovered almost fifty years later.

We usually give the different copies (alleles) of a gene different letters, with the dominant copy a capital letter, for example T = tongue rolling and t = non-rolling.

Let us assume that Mum cannot roll her tongue, but Dad can. Both of Dad's alleles are T so he is homozygous. This is called his **genotype** as it describes what alleles he has. Rolling his tongue is called his **phenotype** as it describes the effect of the alleles. The cross is usually drawn out like this:

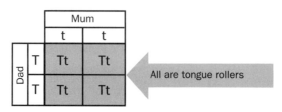

		Mum	
		t	t
Dad	T	Tt	Tt
	T	Tt	Tt

All are tongue rollers

In this cross all the children can roll their tongue.

If both Mum and Dad are heterozygous the children that can produce will be different:

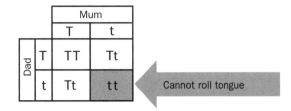

In this cross, 1 in 4 or 25% or a quarter of the children cannot roll their tongue.

Genetic disorders

OCR A	B1	✓
OCR B	B1	✓
EDEXCEL	B1	✓
WJEC	B1	✓

Many **genetic disorders** are caused by certain copies of genes. These can be passed on from mother or father to the baby and lead to the baby having the disorder. Examples of these disorders are cystic fibrosis, Huntington's disease and sickle-cell anaemia. People with these disorders become ill.

Cystic fibrosis	Huntington's disease	Sickle-cell anaemia
Caused by a recessive allele	Caused by a dominant allele	Caused by a recessive allele
Symptoms include: • thick mucus collects in the lung • breathing is difficult • chest infections • food is not properly digested.	Symptoms include: • muscle twitching (tremor) • loss of memory • difficulty in controlling movements • mood changes.	Symptoms include: • feeling tired or weak • coldness in the hands and feet • pain in the bones, lungs and joints

By looking at family trees of these genetic disorders and drawing genetic diagrams (such as the one for tongue rolling) it is possible for people to know the chance of them having a child with a genetic disorder. This may leave them with a difficult decision to make as to whether to have children or not.

Genetic screening

| OCR A | B1 | ✓ |
| OCR B | B1 | ✓ |

Genetic cross diagrams can only work out the probability of a child being affected. It is now possible to test cells directly to see if they contain an allele for a particular genetic disorder. This is called **genetic screening**. This could be done at different stages:

- In an **adult**. This could tell the person if they are a carrier for the disorder and so if they may be able to pass it on. It could also tell if the person was going to develop a certain disorder later in life, for example Huntington's disease.
- In a **foetus**. Some cells can be taken from the foetus whilst the mother is pregnant. The parents can then find out if their baby will have the genetic disorder.
- In an **embryo** before it is implanted in the mother. If an embryo is produced by IVF outside the mother's body, then it can be tested before it is implanted in the mother. It is therefore possible to choose which embryos to put into the mother.

3 Genetics and evolution

To get an A*, you must be able to describe arguments for and against genetic screening in a particular situation. Make sure you give both views.

The process of genetic screening brings with it some difficult ethical decisions:

- In an adult would you want to know if you were going to develop a disease from which there is no cure? Should your employer or your insurance company be told?
- In a foetus the parents could have to decide whether to have a termination or not.
- In an embryo the test is called **preimplantation genetic diagnosis**. Some people think that the destruction of early embryos is wrong. Others worry that the embryos may be tested and chosen for characteristics other than those involving disorders.

PROGRESS CHECK

1. Why can a person roll their tongue even if their cells have an allele for non-rolling?
2. Name a genetic disorder caused by a dominant allele.
3. What is the difference between genotype and phenotype?
4. What is genetic screening?
5. What is the difference between a gene and an allele?
6. Suggest why people may not want their insurance company or employer to have the results of their genetic screening.

6. They may not get insurance or the job they apply for if people know that they will develop a genetic disease in the future.
5. A gene is a length of DNA that codes for a protein, an allele is a particular copy of a gene that codes for a particular variation of the protein.
4. Testing for a genetic disease.
3. Genotype is what alleles a person has and phenotype is how the alleles express themselves (the characteristics of the person).
2. Huntington's disease.
1. The allele for rolling is dominant over the allele for non-rolling.

3.3 Gene technology

LEARNING SUMMARY

After studying this section, you should be able to:

- describe how plants can reproduce asexually
- describe how animals can be cloned
- describe the possible medical uses of stem cells
- discuss some of the uses and issues arising from genetic engineering

Cloning

AQA	B1	✓
OCR A	B1	✓
WJEC	B1	✓

KEY POINT

Bacteria, plants and some animals can reproduce **asexually**. This only needs one parent and does not involve sex cells joining.

All the offspring that are made are genetically identical to the parent.

Gardeners often use **asexual reproduction** to copy plants – they know what the offspring will look like.

Different organisms have different ways of reproducing asexually:

- The spider plant grows new plantlets on the end of long shoots.
- Daffodil plants produce lots of smaller bulbs that can grow into new plants.
- Strawberry plants grow long runners that touch the ground and grow a new plant.

Asexual reproduction produces organisms that have the same genes as the parent.

How Dolly was produced from a cloned cell.

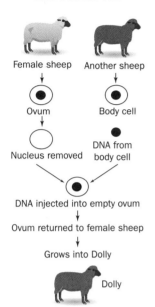

Female sheep   Another sheep

Ovum   Body cell

Nucleus removed   DNA from body cell

DNA injected into empty ovum

Ovum returned to female sheep

Grows into Dolly

Dolly

> **KEY POINT**
>
> Genetically identical individuals are called **clones**.

Many plants, such as the spider plant, clone themselves naturally and it is easy for a gardener to **take cuttings** to make identical plants. Modern methods involve **tissue culture** which uses small groups of cells taken from plants to grow new plants.

Cloning animals is much harder to do. Two main methods are used:

- **Cloning embryos** where embryos are split up at an early stage and the cells are put into host mothers to grow.
- **Cloning adult cells.** The first mammal to be cloned from adult cells was Dolly the sheep.

Since Dolly was born other animals have been cloned and there has been much interest about cloning humans.

There could be two possible reasons for cloning humans:

- **Reproductive cloning** to make embryos for infertile couples.
- **Therapeutic cloning** to produce embryos that can be used to treat diseases.

> Remember that clones have the same genes so any differences between them must be due to their environment.

Stem cells

OCR A   B1   ✓

The use of embryos to treat disease is possible due to the discovery of **stem cells**.

> **KEY POINT**
>
> Stem cells are cells that can divide to make all the different tissues in the body.

They can be extracted from cloned embryos. Scientists think that they could be used to repair damaged tissues such as injuries to the spinal cord.

There are therefore many different views about cloning:

> Both infertility and genetic disease cause much pain and distress. I think that we should be able to use cloning to treat these problems.

> It is not right to clone people because clones are not true individuals and it is not right to destroy embryos to supply stem cells.

There are two main types of stem cells:

- **Embryonic stem cells** can develop into any type of cell. It is easy to extract them from an embryo, but the embryo is destroyed as a result.
- **Adult stem cells** can develop into a limited range of cell types. It is not necessary to destroy an embryo to get them, but they are difficult to find.

Genetic engineering

| AQA | B1 | ✓ |
| WJEC | B1 | ✓ |

All living organisms use the same language of DNA. The four letters A, G, C and T are the same in all living things. Therefore a gene from one organism can be removed and placed in a totally different organism where it will continue to carry out its function. This means, for example, a cow will use a human gene to make the same protein that a human would make.

> **KEY POINT**
>
> Moving a gene from one organism to another is called **genetic engineering**.

Genetic engineering.

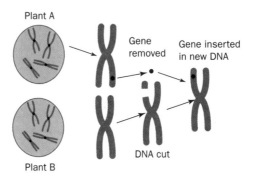

There is also the possibility that genetic engineering may be used to treat genetic disorders like cystic fibrosis. Scientists are trying to replace the genes in people that have the disorder with working genes.

> **KEY POINT**
>
> Using genetic engineering to treat genetic disorders is called **gene therapy**.

GM crops

| AQA | B1 | ✓ |
| WJEC | B1 | ✓ |

New **genetically modified (GM)** plants can be made in this way so that they:

- may be more resistant to insects eating them
- can be resistant to herbicides (weed killers)
- can produce a higher yield.

People often have different views about GM crops. Views against GM crops include:

- Genetic engineering is against 'God and Nature'.
- There may be long-term health problems with eating GM crops.
- Pollen from GM crops may spread to wild crops.

Views for GM crops include:

- More food to supply starving populations.
- Less need to spray harmful insecticides and herbicides.

PROGRESS CHECK

1. Why does a gardener use cuttings rather than seeds to reproduce an attractive plant?
2. What was Dolly?
3. What can stem cells do that normal body cells cannot?
4. Write down one characteristic that is chosen for GM crops.
5. Many people think that using adult stem cells to treat disease is acceptable, but are against using embryonic stem cells. Suggest why this is.
6. Suggest why farmers might want a crop that is resistant to herbicides.

6. They can spray their whole field with weedkiller, killing all the weeds, except the crop.
5. Use of embryonic stem cells involves the destruction of an embryo, but using adult stem cells does not. Some people consider an embryo to be an individual life.
4. Resistance to insects eating them/resistance to herbicides/produce a higher yield.
3. They can differentiate into any other type of cell.
2. Dolly was a sheep and the first mammal that was produced by cloning from an adult cell.
1. Cuttings will produce an identical copy so the gardener can be sure of the characteristic of the plant.

3.4 Evolution and natural selection

After studying this section, you should be able to:
- recall the meaning of the term evolution
- explain Darwin's theory of natural selection
- apply natural selection to recent examples of population changes
- compare Darwin's theories to those of Lamarck.

Evolution and fossils

AQA	B1	✓
OCR A	B3	✓
OCR B	B2	✓
EDEXCEL	B1	✓
WJEC	B1	✓

Most scientists now think that life on Earth started about 3500 million years ago.

How life started and why there is such a great variety of organisms are questions that people have argued over for a long time.

In the 1800s scientists questioned more about what **fossils** were.

Fossils are the remains of organisms from many years ago. Many early life forms did not fossilise because they were soft bodied. However, fossils can be formed in a number of ways:

- From the hard parts of organisms that do not decay.
- From parts of organisms that do not decay because conditions for decay are absent.

An example of the use of fossils is the tracing of the development of the five digits present in all vertebrates. This is called the pentadactyl limb.

- When parts of organisms are replaced by other substances as they decay.
- As preserved traces of organisms, e.g. footprints.

Many people at that time believed in creation. They said that organisms were created as they exist now, by God.

However, scientists found fossils of organisms such as dinosaurs that are not alive today. Some people started to believe the idea that species of organisms could gradually change.

KEY POINT

Evolution is the gradual change in a species over a long period of time.

The problem for the believers in evolution was that at first they could not explain how the gradual changes happened.

Charles Darwin

AQA	B1	✓
OCR A	B3	✓
OCR B	B2	✓
EDEXCEL	B1	✓
WJEC	B1	✓

Charles Darwin (1809–1882) was a naturalist on board a ship called the HMS Beagle. His job was to make a record of the wildlife seen at the places the ship visited.

On his travels, Darwin noticed four things:

- Organisms often produce large numbers of offspring.
- Population numbers usually remain constant over long time periods.
- Organisms are all slightly different – they show variation.
- This variation can be inherited from their parents.

Darwin used these four simple observations to come up with a theory for how evolution could have happened. Darwin said that:

- All organisms are slightly different.
- Some are better suited to the environment than others.
- These organisms are more likely to survive and reproduce.
- They will pass on these characteristics and over long periods of time the species will change.

You need to be able to use Darwin's theory to explain how a group of organisms has evolved. You may not have heard of the organisms before, but just use these main points:

variation → best adapted survive → reproduce → pass on genes.

KEY POINT

Darwin called this theory **natural selection**.

When explaining how natural selection happens, remember to talk about groups or populations of organisms changing over time. One organism does not evolve; it either survives to reproduce or it dies.

Darwin was rather worried about publishing his ideas. When he finally published them they caused much controversy. Many people were very religious and believed in creation. It took many years before Darwin's theory was generally accepted.

Because natural selection takes a long time to produce changes it is very difficult to see it happening. One of the first examples to be seen was the peppered moth. This moth is usually light coloured, but after the Industrial Revolution a black type became common in polluted areas.

This can be explained by natural selection:

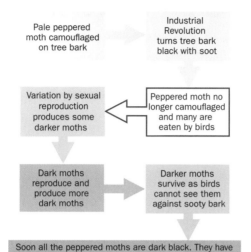

Other examples that can be explained by natural selection include:

- Rats becoming resistant to the rat poison warfarin.
- Bacteria becoming resistant to antibiotics.

Different theories for evolution

AQA	B1	✓
OCR A	B3	✓
OCR B	B2	✓

To get an A*, you must be able to spot an explanation of evolution made using Lamarck's ideas and explain why it is now thought to be wrong. An example might be that giraffes have long necks because they stretched to reach higher leaves and every generation they grew a little longer.

Darwin was not the first person to try and explain how evolution may have happened. A French scientist called **Lamarck** (1744–1829) said that organisms were changed by their environment during their life. They then passed on the new characteristics and so the population would change.

Darwin's and Lamarck's ideas are **theories** that explain **data** known at the time. As different data becomes known then people often start to accept different theories.

Most scientists now think that Lamarck's theory is wrong, because we now know that characteristics are passed on in our genes and genes are not usually altered by the environment.

Most people now accept Darwin's theory because it best explains all the data that has been discovered. However, it is only a theory, it is not fact.

PROGRESS CHECK

1. What does the word extinct mean?
2. Write down one organism that has been investigated by looking at fossils.
3. What advantage did the dark moths have in industrial areas?
4. Why was Darwin worried about publishing his ideas?
5. The terms 'struggle for survival' and 'survival of the fittest' are often used when describing Darwin's ideas. Explain what they mean.

5. The best adapted organisms are the ones that are most likely to survive in an environment.
4. Darwin thought that religious people would be against his ideas because his theory went against the beliefs at the time.
3. They were camouflaged against the polluted buildings and trees, so less likely to be predated on.
2. Any dinosaur species.
1. All the individuals of a species no longer exist.

Sample GCSE questions

1 There are about five million different types of organisms living on Earth.

A number of different theories have been put forward to try and explain how this variety has come about.

Here are three different theories:

> **Creation theory** says that the Earth and all life on it were created by God as described in the Bible. Only small changes have happened since creation and no new species have been created.

> **Darwin** said that all organisms were slightly different. Those organisms that were better suited would pass on their characteristics and so the population would gradually change.

> A French scientist called **Lamarck** said that organisms were changed by their environment during their life. They then passed on the new characteristics and so the population would change.

(a) Which one of these three theories does **not** include evolution in its explanation?

Explain your answer. **[2]**

This is creation. Both of the other theories say that organisms have changed considerably over time. In creation they have not.

Remember that Darwin was not the only person that put forward ideas about evolution.

(b) Why is Darwin's theory still called a theory even though most scientists believe it to be true? **[1]**

It has not been proved correct.

This is an important point. These are all theories that explain data. Darwin's theory is now accepted by many because it best explains the data. It is not fact.

(c) **(i)** People often explain the difference between Lamarck's theory and Darwin's theory by using the example of the long necks of giraffes.

Lamarck's theory would explain this by saying that the necks of giraffes have stretched slightly during life to reach higher leaves.

This increase in length is passed on and after many generations the necks are longer.

Write down the explanation that would be given by Darwin's theory. **[4]**

Giraffes all show variation and so have different length necks. Those with the longer necks can reach more leaves and so get more food. They are more likely to survive and pass on this characteristic. After many generations, the necks of the giraffes are longer.

A good answer but you could include the name of the theory i.e. natural selection. A more modern version of natural selection would talk about mutations and genes but Darwin did not know about them.

Sample GCSE questions

(ii) Explain why most scientists do not believe Lamarck's theory. **[2]**

Lamarck's theory says that characteristics gained during their lifetime are passed on. Characteristics are passed on by genes and these changes would not alter the genes.

The characteristics in Lamarck's theory are often called 'acquired characteristics'.

(d) After Darwin published his theory this cartoon appeared in an important magazine.

PUNCH, OR THE LONDON CHARIVARI.—MAY 25, 1861.

THE LION OF THE SEASON.

ALARMED FLUNKEY. "MR. G-G-G-O-O-O-RILLA!"

Write about why people were upset enough to publish this cartoon and what they were trying to show. **[4]**

Many people at that time were very religious and believed in creation. They did not want to believe in evolution. They were making fun of Darwin's ideas and suggesting that Darwin said that humans are descended from apes.

Remember Darwin never said that humans were descended from apes or monkeys. Humans and apes share a common ancestor.

Exam practice questions

1 **(a)** Peter and Kirsten are expecting a baby.

They know that it has an even chance of being a boy or a girl.

Finish the genetic diagram to show why this is.

Kirsten

Gametes	X	X

Peter

[2]

(b) The table shows the ratio of males to females in different countries and at different ages.

Age	India	Kenya	Russia	UK
at birth	1.12	1.02	1.06	1.05
over 65 years old	0.91	0.83	0.44	0.76
all ages	1.08	1.01	0.85	0.98

(i) In which countries do women live longer than men?

Use data from the table to justify your answer.

....

....

.... [2]

(ii) In some countries parents want to have baby boys rather than girls.

Embryos can be tested to see what sex they are before they are born.

People are worried that this technique might be used to terminate female embryos.

In which country would the data in the table suggest this is possibly happening?

Use data from the table to justify your answer.

....

....

.... [2]

(iii) Suggest **one** reason why people might be concerned about the effect on the country of the termination of female embryos.

....

.... [1]

Exam practice questions

2 Scientists believe that man evolved from ape-like animals several million years ago.

One important change was in the bones which allowed our ancestors to walk upright on two feet.

Scientists think that several millions of years ago the Earth became drier and forests were replaced by grasslands. Before this time all apes walked on four feet. In the grassland, populations of apes developed to walk on two feet. This enabled the ape to see further.

(a) Suggest why it might be an advantage for the ape to be able to see further.

.... **[1]**

(b) Explain how the ape developed so that it walked upright.

Use ideas about natural selection in your answer.

The quality of written communication will be assessed in your answer to this question.

....

....

....

.... **[6]**

(c) Another theory for why humans became upright involves the use of tools.

It suggests that standing on two feet allows the other two limbs to handle tools.

This needs a large brain to control the hands.

Recently a fossil has been found of a human ancestor that has the bones of an upright animal but a small brain.

Explain what this find indicates.

....

....

.... **[2]**

4 Organisms and environment

The following topics are covered in this chapter:

- **Classifying organisms**
- **Competition and adaptation**
- **Living together**
- **Energy flow**
- **Recycling**
- **Pollution and overexploitation**
- **Conservation and sustainability**

4.1 Classifying organisms

LEARNING SUMMARY

After studying this section, you should be able to:

- describe the principles of the modern classification system
- explain how species are defined
- describe the classification of the vertebrates
- describe how organisms are named.

Classifying animals

OCR B	B2	✓
EDEXCEL	B1	✓
WJEC	B1	✓

Humans have been classifying organisms into groups ever since they started studying them:

- This makes it convenient when trying to identify an unknown organism.
- It also tells us something about how closely related organisms are and about their evolution.

The modern system that we use puts organisms into a system of smaller and smaller groups. The groups used are:

There are lots of good ways of remembering the order of the groups from kingdom down to species. One example is **King Phillip Came Over For Great Spaghetti.** You could always make up your own.

- kingdom
- phylum
- class
- order
- family
- genus
- species.

KEY POINT

Kingdoms are the largest groups. The kingdoms are divided into smaller and smaller groups until the smallest group formed is called a **species**.

As you move down the groups there are fewer organisms in the group and they have more similarities.

Artificial versus natural systems

OCR A	B3	✓
OCR B	B2	✓
EDEXCEL	B1	✓
WJEC	B1	✓

The characteristics that are used to classify organisms have changed over time. The system used to be an **artificial system** based on one or two simple characteristics to make identification easier. An example might be the presence of wings on an animal.

Now a **natural system** is used which is based on evolutionary relationships. Animals that are more closely related are more likely to be in the same group. To work out how closely related organisms are it is possible to study their DNA.

The more similar the DNA is, the closer the relationship.

> To get an A*, you must realise that organisms can have similar features for two different reasons. They may be closely related or they may be distantly related, but both adapted for living in a similar environment.

Species

| OCR B | B2 | ✓ |
| EDEXCEL | B1 | ✓ |

Members of a species are very similar, but how do we know if two similar animals are in the same species?

> **KEY POINT**
>
> Members of the same species can breed with each other to produce fertile offspring.

This means that horses and donkeys are different species because although they can mate and produce a mule, mules are infertile. The mule is an example of a **hybrid**.

Horse + donkey = mule!

Horse   +   Donkey   =   Mule

Some organisms cause specific problems when trying to classify them as a species:

- Bacteria do not inter-breed, they reproduce asexually, so they cannot be classified into different species using the 'fertile offspring' idea.
- Hybrids are produced when members of two species inter-breed and so they are infertile. This occurs between many duck species.

Different groups

OCR B	B2	✓
EDEXCEL	B1	✓
WJEC	B1	✓

The first step in classifying an organism is to put it into a kingdom. The five kingdoms are shown in the table:

Kingdom	Features
Prokaryotes (bacteria)	No nucleus
Animals	Multicellular, feed on other organisms
Plants	Cellulose cell wall, use light energy to produce food
Protoctista	Mostly single celled with some plant and some animal characteristics
Fungi	Cell wall of chitin, produce spores

Once an organism is put into the animal kingdom it can be put into the **vertebrate** phylum or one of several invertebrate phyla such as the **arthropods**.

> **KEY POINT**
>
> The vertebrates all have a backbone and the group is divided into five different classes:

OCR B candidates also need to know the main characteristics of the arthropod classes (phyla).

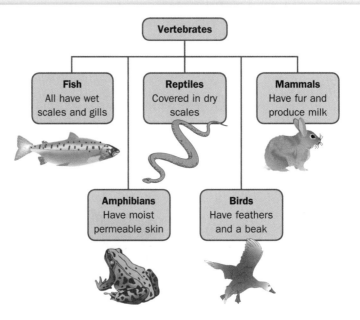

Naming organisms

OCR B	B2	✓
EDEXCEL	B1	✓
WJEC	B1	✓

Organisms are often known by different names in different countries or even in different parts of the same country. All organisms are therefore given a scientific name by the international committees that are used by scientists in every country. This avoids confusion.

> **KEY POINT**
>
> The scientific system of naming organisms is called the **binomial system**.

Each name has two parts. The first part is the name of the genus (the group above species). The second part of the name is the species. For example:

Lion is *Panthera leo* **Tiger is *Panthera tigris***

These animals are in the same genus, but are different species. The genus starts with a capital letter, but the species does not.

PROGRESS CHECK

1. An organism has cell walls made of chitin. What type of organism is it?
2. What is a hybrid?
3. Can tigers and lions mate to produce fertile offspring? Explain your answer.
4. What are the characteristics of mammals?
5. Sharks are fish, but dolphins are mammals. Why are they so similar in appearance?
6. Archaeopteryx is an extinct animal. Fossils show that it had feathers and teeth. Why are there always going to be animals like archaeopteryx that are difficult to classify?

1. A fungus.
2. The offspring of a cross between members of two closely related species.
3. No, because they are not the same species.
4. Have fur and produce milk.
5. They are both adapted to living in the same conditions, i.e. water.
6. Because organisms have evolved from common ancestors by a gradual process there are always going to be organisms that have characteristics that are intermediate between groups.

4.2 Competition and adaptation

LEARNING SUMMARY

After studying this section, you should be able to:

- describe the reasons why organisms compete
- describe adaptation of organisms to extreme climates
- describe adaptations of predators and prey.

Competition

AQA	B1	✓
OCR A	B3	✓
OCR B	B2	✓
WJEC	B1	✓

There are many different types of organisms living together in a habitat and many of them are after the same things.

KEY POINT

This struggle for resources is called **competition**.

4 Organisms and environment

The more similar the organisms, the greater the competition.

Plants usually compete for:

- light for photosynthesis
- water
- minerals.

Organisms of the same species are more likely to compete with each other because they have similar needs.

> **KEY POINT**
>
> A **niche** describes the habitat that an organism lives in and also its role in the habitat.

Organisms that share similar niches are more likely to compete with each other as they require similar resources. There are different types of competition:

- **Intraspecific** is between organisms of the same species and is likely to be more significant as the organisms share more similarities and so need the same resources.
- **Interspecific** is between organisms of different species.

Adaptations to extreme conditions

AQA	B1	✓
OCR A	B3	✓
OCR B	B2	✓
EDEXCEL	B1	✓
WJEC	B1	✓

Because there is constant competition between organisms, the best suited to living in the habitat survive. Over many generations the organisms have become suited to their environment. The features that make organisms well suited to their environment are called **adaptations.** Habitats, such as the Arctic and deserts, are difficult places to live because of the extreme conditions found there. Organisms that are adapted to living in extreme conditions are often called **extremophiles.** Animals and plants have to be well adapted to survive.

Polar bears have:	Cacti have:	Camels have:
A large volume to surface area to minimise heat loss	Leaves that are just spines to reduce surface area to minimise water loss	A hump that stores food as fat
Thick insulating fur	Water stored in the stem	Thick fur on top of the body for shade to protect the skin
A thick layer of fat under the skin		Thin fur on the rest of the body to avoid overheating
White fur that is a poor radiator of heat and provides camouflage		

Be prepared to identify the adaptations on animals that you have not met. Think about size, thickness of fur and body fat.

Adaptation to cold conditions

| AQA | B1 | ✓ |
| OCR B | B2 | ✓ |

To prevent animals losing too much heat in cold climates they are usually quite large, like the polar bear, and have small ears. This helps to decrease the **surface area to volume ratio**. They are more likely to give birth to live young and less likely to lay eggs because the eggs would get too cold before hatching.

To get an A*, you must be able to explain why similar animals tend to be larger in arctic regions and smaller in desert regions. Remember to talk about surface area to volume ratio.

All the members of a population may reproduce at the same time, so that predators would not be able to eat all the young. They may try to avoid the coldest temperatures by changing their behaviour. Some animals will **migrate** long distances to warmer areas. Others may stay in the cold areas, but slow down all their body processes and **hibernate**.

When the sun is shining animals like reptiles will lie in the sun or **bask** to try and increase their body temperature.

Adaptations of predators and prey

| AQA | B1 | ✓ |
| OCR B | B2 | ✓ |

Some animals called **predators** are adapted to hunt other animals for food. The animals that are hunted are called **prey** and are adapted to help them to escape.

Predators are adapted by having:

- Eyes on the front of their head which gives **binocular vision** to judge size and distance.
- Sharp teeth and claws to catch hold of prey.
- A body built for speed to chase prey.
- Stings or **venoms** (poison) to paralyse or poison prey.

Prey animals are adapted by having:

- A body that is **camouflaged** to avoid being seen by predators.
- Eyes on the side of their head to give a view all around.
- A social organisation which involves living in groups which reduces the chance of being caught.
- A body built for speed to outrun predators.
- Defences such as stings or poison to deter predators eating them, along with warning colouration.

Specialists and generalists

| OCR B | B2 | ✓ |

Some organisms, like polar bears, are very well adapted to living in specific habitats. These organisms are called **specialists**. They can survive in these areas when others cannot, but would struggle to live elsewhere.

Other organisms like rats, are not especially adapted to living in one habitat, but can live in many areas. These organisms are called **generalists**. They will be outcompeted by specialists in certain habitats.

1. Why do plants compete for light?
2. Why do camels have thick fur on the top of their body and thin fur underneath?
3. What is special about the leaves of cacti?
4. Why is it difficult to creep up behind a rabbit?
5. Emperor penguins lay eggs and stay very close to the South Pole throughout winter. Why does that make them unusual?
6. Elephants need to be large to digest vast quantities of poor quality food. What problem does this large size lead to in the desert and how does the elephant solve this?

1. Light is needed for photosynthesis.
2. Thick fur on top insulates them from the Sun's heat, thin fur underneath allows heat to escape.
3. They are reduced to spines so that less water is lost.
4. They have eyes on the side of their heads so that they have virtually all round vision.
5. Many animals that live near the poles give birth to live young and often migrate away from the pole in the winter. Most animals in cold regions give birth to live young because eggs are likely to get too cold and the foetus may die.
6. Large animals have a small surface area to volume ratio and so could overheat. Elephants have big ears to increase their surface area but could overheat, so they have large ears to increase surface area and lose excess heat.

4.3 Living together

LEARNING SUMMARY

After studying this section, you should be able to:

- explain the shape of predator-prey graphs
- recall the meaning of the terms parasite and host
- explain the term mutualism and describe examples.

Predators and prey

OCR B   B2   ✓

Organisms form different types of relationships with other organisms in their habitat. One of the most common is that of predator and prey. The numbers of predators and prey in a habitat will vary and will affect each other. The size of the two populations can be plotted on a graph that is usually called a predator–prey graph.

In the graph the peaks of the predators curve occur a little while after the peaks of the prey curve. This is because it takes a little while for the increase in food supply to allow more predators to survive and reproduce.

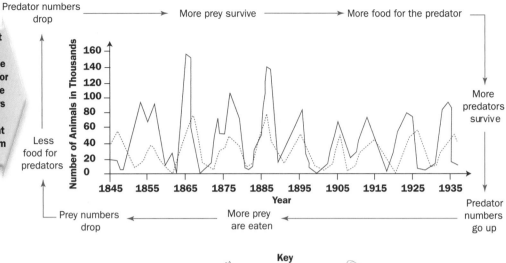

A predator–prey graph for lynx and hares.

> Sometimes two different y axes are given on these graphs, one for the predator and the other for the prey. This is because the numbers of predators and prey may be very different. Make sure that you read any figures from the correct scale.

Parasites and hosts

| OCR B | B2 | ✓ |
| EDEXCEL | B1 | ✓ |

Sometimes one organism may not kill another organism, but it may take food from it while it is alive.

> **KEY POINT**
>
> A **parasite** lives on, or in, another living organism called the **host**, causing it harm.

Fleas are parasites that live in an animal's fur.

Tapeworms are parasites that may live in an animal's gut.

Many diseases, such as **malaria**, are caused by parasites feeding on a host. The parasite in malaria is a single-celled species called Plasmodium that feeds on humans, who are the host. The organism is injected into the bloodstream by a mosquito. This is also acting as a parasite, but is known as a **vector** for malaria because it spreads the disease causing organism, without being affected by it.

Mistletoe is a partial parasite. It grows on trees such as apple trees. It is green so it can photosynthesise and make its own food, but it also takes food from the apple tree.

Mutualism

OCR B	B2	✓
EDEXCEL	B1	✓

Instead of trying to eat each other some different types of organisms work together.

> **KEY POINT**
>
> When two organisms of different species work together so that both gain, it is called **mutualism.**

Examples of this type of relationship are:

- Oxpeckers and buffalo: the oxpecker birds eat the parasites on the backs of the buffalo. So the birds get food and the buffaloes get their parasites removed.
- Cleaner fish: these fish live in certain areas of the reef and are visited by larger fish. They do the same job as oxpeckers.
- Pollinating insects: they visit flowers and so transfer pollen allowing pollination to happen. They are 'rewarded' by sugary nectar from the flower.

To get an A*, you must be able to link the presence of legumes with their nitrogen fixing bacteria to the nitrogen cycle. This is discussed on page 81.

Pea plants and certain types of bacteria also benefit from mutualism. Pea plants are **legumes** and have structures on their roots called nodules. **Nitrogen fixing bacteria** live in these nodules. The bacteria turn nitrogen gas into nitrogen containing chemicals and give some to the pea plant. The pea plant gives the bacteria some sugars that have been produced by photosynthesis.

Tube worms live deep in the ocean and cannot feed themselves. They have chemosynthetic bacteria living inside them. They can make their own food using the energy from chemical reactions. They give some of this to the worms in return for a safe place to live.

> **PROGRESS CHECK**
>
> 1 When prey numbers are high then predator numbers start to increase. Why is this?
> 2 Why are fleas described as parasites?
> 3 Why is mistletoe called a partial parasite?
> 4 Why do flowers produce nectar?
> 5 Lichens have mutualistic relationships. Algae grow inside the cells of fungi and get water and minerals from the fungi. Suggest what the fungi get in return.
> 6 Why is there so little food available deep in the oceans?
>
> 1. Predators have more food, so are able to reproduce more.
> 2. They live on a living organism and take food from them so cause them harm.
> 3. It can make some of its own food by photosynthesis, but also takes some food from the tree it grows on.
> 4. To attract and reward insects so they pollinate them.
> 5. Fungi cannot photosynthesise so they get food from the algae.
> 6. Very little sunlight can penetrate there so there are no plants as photosynthesis cannot occur.

4.4 Energy flow

After studying this section, you should be able to:

- explain what is meant by a food web
- construct a pyramid of biomass
- calculate the efficiency of energy flow through a food chain.

Food webs

AQA	B1	✓
OCR A	B3	✓
OCR B	B2	✓
EDEXCEL	B1	✓
WJEC	B1	✓

A food web shows the feeding relationships between organisms in a habitat.

KEY POINT

Each stage, or feeding level, in a food chain or food web is called a **trophic** level.

Producers are at the start of a food web because they can make their own food. Most producers are green plants or algae that make food by photosynthesis. Very few are bacteria, such as the ones that live in tube worms, who make food using energy from chemical reactions (chemosynthesis). Very few organisms only eat one type of food. Most will eat several types and the food might be from different trophic levels. For example in this food web the birds eat both ladybirds and blackfly. When they eat blackfly they are secondary consumers and when they eat ladybirds they are tertiary consumers.

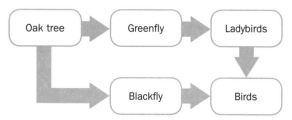

If one organism is reduced or increases in numbers in a food web it can alter the numbers of other organisms in the food web.

Pyramids of biomass

AQA	B1	✓
OCR B	B2	✓
EDEXCEL	B1	✓
WJEC	B1	✓

The mass of all the organisms at each step of the food chain can be estimated. This can be used to draw a diagram that is similar to a pyramid of numbers. The difference is that the area of each box represents the mass of all the organisms not the number. This type of diagram is called a **pyramid of biomass**.

The reason that a pyramid of biomass is shaped like a pyramid is that energy is lost from the food chain in different ways as the food is passed along. Often the waste from one food chain can be used by decomposers to start another chain.

Where energy is wasted in the food chain.

Reflection   Waste and uneaten parts   Waste, uneaten parts, and heat through respiration

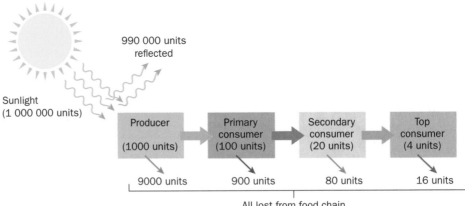

> Remember excretion is the removal of waste products made by the body, e.g. urine, whereas egestion is food material that passes straight through. Candidates often get these two confused.

The diagram shows that biomass and energy are lost from the food chain in a number of ways:

- In waste from the organisms by **excretion** and **egestion**.
- As heat when organisms **respire**. Birds and mammals that keep a constant body temperature will often lose large amounts of energy in this way.

Measuring biomass

OCR B	B2	✓
CCEA	B1	✓
WJEC	B1	✓

Although pyramids of biomass are a better way of representing trophic levels they are difficult to construct. This is because:

- Some organisms feed on organisms from different trophic levels.
- Measuring dry mass is difficult as it involves removing all the water from an organism which will kill it.

Calculating efficiency

AQA	B1	✓
OCR A	B3	✓
OCR B	B2	✓
EDEXCEL	B1	✓
WJEC	B1	✓

The diagram shows the flow of energy through a food chain.

990 000 units reflected

Sunlight (1 000 000 units)

| Producer (1000 units) | Primary consumer (100 units) | Secondary consumer (20 units) | Top consumer (4 units) |

9000 units   900 units   80 units   16 units

All lost from food chain

> To get an A*, you must be able to work out the percentage efficiency of energy transfer in different food chains and suggest reasons for differences. For example, farmers often keep their cattle indoors so that they lose less heat keeping warm.

Of one million units of light that hit the surface of the plant, only 4 units are used for growth in the top consumer. This loss of energy also explains why food chains usually only have four or five steps. By then, there is so little energy left the animals would not be able to find enough food.

The percentage efficiency of transfer from producer to primary consumer in the diagram is:

$$\frac{100}{1000} \times 100\% = 10\%$$

This percentage is quite low because it is difficult to digest plant material.

PROGRESS CHECK

1. Why are food webs more common than simple food chains in nature?
2. Look at the food web on page 77. What might happen to the numbers of ladybirds if a gardener killed all the blackfly in his garden with insecticide?
3. What does the size of a box represent in a pyramid of biomass?
4. Write down two ways that energy is lost from a food web.
5. Calculate the percentage efficiency of the energy transfer from secondary to top consumer in the above food chain.
6. Compare your answer from question 5 with the percentage efficiency from producer to primary consumer. Suggest reasons for the difference.

1. Most organisms eat more than one type of food.
2. They might decrease because the birds would eat more of them as there are no blackfly to eat.
3. The amount of biomass of living material at each trophic level.
4. Heat/excretion/egestion/uneaten parts from respiration.
5. $\frac{4}{20} \times 100\% = 20\%$
6. This is much more efficient. This is because meat contains more energy and it is easier to digest.

4.5 Recycling

LEARNING SUMMARY

After studying this section, you should be able to:

- describe the conditions needed by decomposers
- interpret diagrams of the carbon and nitrogen cycles.

Decay

AQA	B1	✓
OCR A	B3	✓
OCR B	B2	✓
WJEC	B1	✓

Some animals and plants die before they are eaten. They also produce large amounts of waste products. This waste material must be broken down or **decayed** because it contains useful minerals. If this did not happen, organisms would run out of minerals. Ecosystems are therefore called **closed loop systems** as the minerals are constantly recycled and not lost.

KEY POINT

Organisms that break down dead organic material are called **decomposers**.

The main organisms that act as decomposers are bacteria and fungi.

They release enzymes on to the dead material that then digest the large molecules. They then take up the soluble chemicals that are produced. The bacteria and fungi use the chemicals in respiration and for raw materials. For decomposers to decay dead material they need certain conditions:

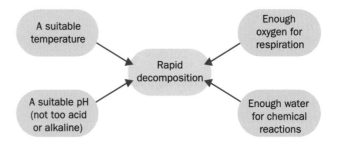

Gardeners try to produce ideal conditions for decay in their compost heaps. Make sure you can explain how they do this.

A suitable temperature

Enough oxygen for respiration

Rapid decomposition

A suitable pH (not too acid or alkaline)

Enough water for chemical reactions

Earthworms are important for decomposition in the soil. This is because they drag dead leaves below the surface and also aerate the soil.

The carbon cycle

AQA	B1	✓
OCR A	B3	✓
OCR B	B2	✓
EDEXCEL	B1	✓
WJEC	B1	✓

It is possible to follow the way in which each mineral element passes through living organisms and becomes available again for use. Scientists use nutrient cycles to show how these minerals are recycled in nature. One of these is the **carbon cycle**.

Carbon dioxide is returned to the air in a number of different ways:

- Plants and animals respire.
- Soil bacteria and fungi acting as decomposers.
- The burning of fossil fuels (combustion).

The main process that removes carbon dioxide from the air is photosynthesis.

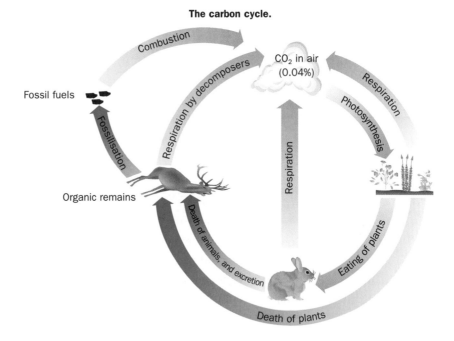

The carbon cycle.

The carbon cycle in the sea

OCR B	B2	✓

Carbon dioxide is absorbed from the air by oceans. Much of this is by algae. Some marine organisms use the carbon dioxide and make shells made of carbonate which, over millions of years, become **limestone** rocks.

The carbon in limestone can return to the air as carbon dioxide during volcanic eruptions or weathering. The action of acid rain on buildings will speed up the weathering process due to the reaction with the limestone.

The nitrogen cycle

OCR A	B3	✓
OCR B	B2	✓
EDEXCEL	B1	✓
WJEC	B1	✓

Plants take in nitrogen as **nitrates** from the soil to make protein for growth. Feeding passes nitrogen compounds along a food chain or web. The nitrogen compounds in dead plants and animals are broken down by decomposers and returned to the soil.

The nitrogen cycle is more complicated than the carbon cycle because as well as the decomposers, it involves three other types of bacteria:

- **Nitrifying bacteria** – these bacteria live in the soil and convert ammonium compounds to nitrates. They need oxygen to do this.
- **Denitrifying bacteria** – these bacteria in the soil are the enemy of farmers. They turn nitrates into nitrogen gas. They need conditions without oxygen, rather than needing oxygen.
- **Nitrogen fixing bacteria** – they live in the soil or in special bumps called nodules on the roots of plants from the pea and bean family. They take nitrogen gas and convert it back to useful nitrogen compounds.

To get an A*, you must be able to recognise parts of the nitrogen cycle. You are unlikely to have to describe it all, but you might, for example, have to explain how the protein in fallen leaves gets converted to nitrates.

The nitrogen cycle.

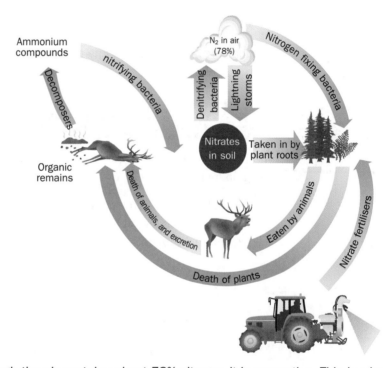

Although the air contains about 78% nitrogen it is unreactive. This is why lightning and nitrogen fixing bacteria are so important. They **fix** the nitrogen back into chemicals that can be used by plants.

PROGRESS CHECK

1 Gardeners water their compost heaps in dry weather. Why do they do this?
2 Write down two ways that carbon dioxide is returned to the atmosphere.
3 What is the main nitrogen containing compound taken up by plants?
4 What do plants need nitrogen for?
5 Explain why acid rain releases carbon dioxide when it falls onto certain buildings.
6 Farmers try to make sure that their soils are well drained so that they contain plenty of air. Explain why they do this. **(cont.)**

4.6 Pollution and overexploitation

LEARNING SUMMARY

After studying this section, you should be able to:

- describe problems associated with an increase in the human population
- describe sources and effects of different pollutants
- compare indicator organisms and direct methods of measuring pollution.

Population increase

| OCR B | B2 | ✓ |
| EDEXCEL | B1 | ✓ |

The human population on Earth has been increasing for a long time, but it is now going up more rapidly than ever:

- This is because of an increasing birth rate and decreasing death rate.
- The rate of increase of the population is increasing and this is called **exponential growth**.

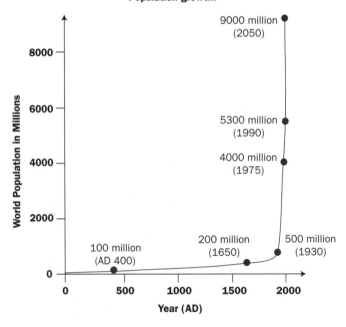

Population growth.

This increase in the population is having a number of effects on the environment:

- More raw materials are being used up such as fossil fuels and minerals.
- More waste is being produced which can lead to pollution.
- More land is being taken up to be used for activities such as building, quarrying, farming and dumping waste.

Pollution

OCR B	B2	✓
EDEXCEL	B1	✓
WJEC	B1	✓

Modern methods of food production and the increasing demand for energy have caused many different types of **pollution**.

> **KEY POINT**
>
> Pollution is the release of substances into the environment that harm organisms.

The table shows some of the main polluting substances that are being released into the environment.

Polluting substance	Main source	Effects on the environment
Carbon dioxide	Burning fossil fuels	Greenhouse effect
Sulfur dioxide	Burning fossil fuels	Acid rain
Chlorofluorocarbon (CFCs)	Fridges and aerosols	Destroys the ozone layer
Fertilisers including nitrates and phosphates	Intensive farming	Pollutes rivers and lakes
Domestic waste	Households	Landfill sites release gases
Heavy metals	Industry	Accumulates in food chains
Sewage	Human and farm waste	Pollutes rivers and lakes

The **greenhouse effect** is caused by a build-up of gases, such as carbon dioxide and methane, in the atmosphere. These gases trap the heat rays as they are radiated from the Earth. This causes the Earth to warm up. This is similar to what happens in a greenhouse. This could lead to changes in the Earth's climate and a large rise in sea level.

The greenhouse effect.

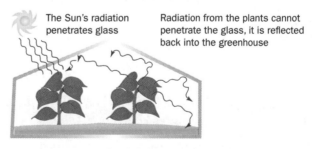

The Sun's radiation penetrates glass

Radiation from the plants cannot penetrate the glass, it is reflected back into the greenhouse

Acid rain is caused by the burning of fossil fuels that contain sulfur impurities. These give off sulfur dioxide, which dissolves in rainwater to form sulfuric acid. This falls as acid rain.

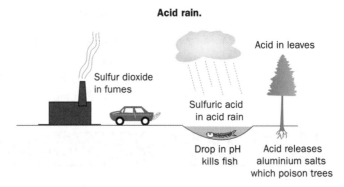

Acid rain.

Sulfur dioxide in fumes

Acid in leaves

Sulfuric acid in acid rain

Drop in pH kills fish

Acid releases aluminium salts which poison trees

> Remember that CFCs are greenhouse gases as well as breaking down the ozone layer, but it is the lack of the ozone layer that can cause skin cancer.

Ozone depletion is caused by the release of chemicals such as CFCs which come from the breakdown of refrigerators and aerosol sprays. Ozone helps protect us from harmful ultraviolet (UV) radiation and so depletion may lead to more skin cancer.

Carbon footprints

OCR B   B2   ✓

The world population figures show that the greatest rise in population is occurring in countries such as Africa and India. However, the countries that use the most fossil fuels are developed countries, such as the USA and Europe.

A useful way of measuring how much pollution is caused per person is the **carbon footprint**. This measures the total greenhouse gas given off by a person, or organisation, over a certain period.

Eutrophication

EDEXCEL B1   ✓
WJEC   B1   ✓

Rain water containing fertilisers can run-off from fields into rivers. Similarly, sewage also pollutes rivers. This can result in **eutrophication** of the river or lake:

- Nitrates and phosphates enter rivers and are absorbed by plants and algae. This makes them grow.
- Algae float near the water surface and their population increases dramatically. A 'blanket' of algae soon covers the surface.
- Other plants beneath the algae die as the surface algae block out the sunlight.
- Bacteria and other decomposers begin to break down the dead plants using more oxygen for respiration. Fish die as the oxygen content of the water becomes too low.

> To get an A*, you must be able to link the nitrogen cycle to eutrophication. Remember that nitrates in fertilisers are needed by plants to produce protein and are also produced when sewage is decomposed to ammonium compounds and then converted to nitrates by nitrifying bacteria.

Indicators of pollution

AQA   B1   ✓
OCR B   B2   ✓
EDEXCEL B1   ✓
WJEC   B1   ✓

Some organisms are more sensitive to pollution than others. If we look for these organisms it can tell us how polluted an area is. On land, lichens grow on trees and stone. Some lichens are killed by lower levels of pollution than other types. Black spot fungus grows on roses in areas with less sulfur dioxide pollution.

In water some animals, for example rat-tailed maggots, can live in polluted water, but other animals like mayfly larvae can only live in clean water.

There are advantages to the different methods of measuring pollution:

- Using **indicator organisms** is cheaper, does not need equipment that can go wrong and monitors pollution levels over long periods of time.
- Using **direct methods** can give more accurate results at any specific time.

PROGRESS CHECK

1 The world's population is showing an exponential increase. What does this mean?
2 Write down **two** gases that can cause the greenhouse effect.
3 What is the main gas that causes acid rain?
4 Write down one indicator organism that is found in polluted water.
5 Explain why eating food that is grown in another country will result in a higher carbon footprint.
6 Nitrate fertilisers cause eutrophication. Explain how sewage can also cause eutrophication.

6. Sewage contains nitrogen containing compounds, so can also cause an algal bloom as the algae use it for growth.
5. Transportation of that food to us involves the burning of fossil fuels that release carbon dioxide.
4. Rat-tailed maggots.
3. Sulfur dioxide.
2. Carbon dioxide/methane.
1. The rate of increase is increasing.

4.7 Conservation and sustainability

LEARNING SUMMARY

After studying this section, you should be able to:

- explain why some organisms are at risk of extinction
- discuss reasons for maintaining biodiversity
- describe the principles of conservation programmes
- explain the importance of maintaining genetic variation
- explain what is meant by sustainable development.

Organisms at risk

OCR B   B2   ✓

As well as causing pollution, the increasing demands for food, land and timber have caused people to cut down large areas of forests. Deforestation has led to:

- Less carbon dioxide being removed from the air by the trees and carbon dioxide being released when the wood is burnt.
- The destruction of habitats which contain rare species.

Some animals have been hunted, so their numbers have been dramatically reduced, for example, species of whales which have been hunted for food, oil and other substances. Their numbers now are very low and people are trying to protect them. Other organisms have not been so lucky. Their numbers have decreased so far that they have completely died out. This is called **extinction**. Organisms do become extinct naturally, but man has often increased the rate either directly or indirectly by:

- over-hunting
- destroying habitats
- pollution
- competition
- changing the climate.

Other organisms are at risk of becoming extinct and are **endangered**.

Biodiversity

| OCR A | B3 | ✓ |
| OCR B | B2 | ✓ |

Many people believe that it is wrong for humans to damage natural habitats and cause the death of animals and plants. They believe that it is important to keep a wide variety of different animals and plants alive.

> **KEY POINT**
>
> The variety of different organisms that are living is called **biodiversity**.

There are many reasons given for trying to maintain biodiversity, such as:

- Losing organisms may have unexpected effects on the environment, such as the erosion caused by deforestation.
- Losing organisms may have effects on other organisms in their food web.
- Some organisms may prove to be useful in the future, such as for breeding, producing drugs or for their genes.
- Organisms may be needed for food.
- People enjoy looking at and studying different organisms.

Conservation programmes

| OCR A | B3 | ✓ |
| OCR B | B2 | ✓ |

To help save and preserve habitats and organisms, people have set up many different **conservation** schemes. There are a number of different ways that conservation programmes can work:

Questions on this part of the course could use an animal or plant that you have never heard of. You may need to use the data that you are provided with to try and work out why it became endangered and what could be done to try and protect it.

How to save an endangered species.

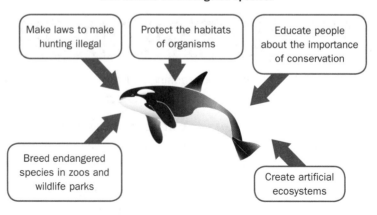

Make laws to make hunting illegal

Protect the habitats of organisms

Educate people about the importance of conservation

Breed endangered species in zoos and wildlife parks

Create artificial ecosystems

Genetic variation

| OCR B | B2 | ✓ |

If populations become small then the variety of different alleles in the population might be quite low. The population has low **genetic variation**. This makes it more likely to become extinct because:

- It will be harder for it to adapt to any changes in the environment because there is little variation.
- There is more chance of organisms being produced that have two identical harmful recessive alleles.

> **KEY POINT**
>
> Reproducing with an organism that has similar alleles is called **inbreeding**.

To get an A*, you must be able to explain why it is so difficult to try and save endangered species once their numbers get below a certain level. Many studies indicate that about 500 individuals are needed to provide enough variation.

Zoos try and move animals to other zoos to breed with less related organisms to avoid this happening. It is also more likely to happen when populations become isolated.

Sustainable development

OCR A	B3	✓
OCR B	B2	✓
WJEC	B1	✓

If the human population is going to continue to increase, it is important that we meet the demand for food and energy without causing pollution or over-exploitation.

> **KEY POINT**
>
> Providing for the increasing population without using up resources or causing pollution is called **sustainable development**.

Fish stocks and woodland can be managed sustainably by:

- Educating people about the importance of controlling what they take from the environment.
- Putting quotas on fishing.
- Re-planting woodland when trees have been removed.

A decrease in the use of packaging materials and recycling would also help by:

- Cutting down the energy needed to make them and transport them.
- Reducing the problem of disposing of the waste.

Make sure that you can suggest why it is difficult to get people to agree to plans for sustainable development. Different people and different countries have different requirements. Some think that it is their right to hunt, fish or farm certain animals. Developing countries may not have enough money to provide alternatives.

Alternatives to peat composts must also be found. This will help to prevent the destruction of peat bogs. These are rare habitats and the removal and decomposition of the peat adds carbon dioxide to the air.

To make sure that development is sustainable a lot of planning is needed at local, national and international levels.

PROGRESS CHECK

1. Write down two ways that man has caused extinctions.
2. What is biodiversity?
3. What is conservation?
4. Why does recycling help to improve sustainability?
5. Areas of tropical rainforest are being cleared, but small patches are being left. Explain why small isolated areas may not be very useful in conserving organisms.
6. About 10 000 years ago the cheetah nearly became extinct. Zoos find it very difficult to get cheetahs to produce healthy offspring. To try and make sure this happens they try and artificially inseminate them using sperm from around the world. Explain these observations.

1. Overhunting/destroying habitats/causing pollution/changing of climate.
2. The variety of different organisms in an environment.
3. Trying to preserve a habitat so that the organisms that live there are protected.
4. Fewer resources are used to make new materials and there is less waste.
5. The small patches may only contain small numbers of individuals of a species. There might not be enough genetic diversity.
6. Cheetahs do not have much genetic diversity as they are all related to a small number of individuals. They try and reproduce them with other cheetahs that are not closely related and so have fewer similarities in their genes. Using artificial insemination from less closely related individuals will help reduce inbreeding problems.

Sample GCSE questions

1 The graph shows how the levels of carbon dioxide have changed in the atmosphere over the past thousand years.

It also shows an estimate of the global temperature.

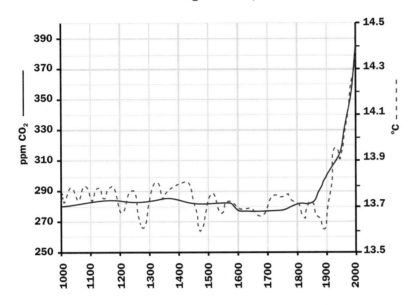

(a) Some scientists say that there is a correlation between carbon dioxide levels and the temperature.

What does this mean? **[2]**

This means that as the carbon dioxide levels go up so does the global temperature.

> It is important that you know the difference between a correlation and a cause. This answer describes a correlation, it does not say that one factor causes the other.

(b) Use ideas about the greenhouse effect to explain a possible cause of this correlation. **[3]**

Increasing levels of carbon dioxide cause the greenhouse effect.

The gas allows the Sun's radiation through to the Earth but prevents it being re-radiated back out into space. This causes the global temperature to increase.

> This is a good summary of the cause of the greenhouse effect but you could say that short wavelength radiation can enter but long wavelength cannot escape.

(c) An alternative theory says the Earth warmed up naturally, allowing more animals to survive.

How could this explain the correlation? **[3]**

More animals survive and so there is more respiration.

This produces carbon dioxide and so levels in the air will increase.

> A good answer. Some candidates may just say that respiration increases and not link it to increased carbon dioxide. Others may just say that there is more carbon dioxide given out.

Exam practice questions

1 The diagram shows part of the nitrogen cycle.

(a) The letters **A**, **B** and **C** represent three chemicals that contain nitrogen.

Write down the names of these three chemicals.

A =_____

B =_____

C =_____

Diagram boxes: Denitrifying bacteria → B; C; Nitrogen fixing bacteria; Decomposing bacteria; Nitrates (NO$_2$); Free living in the soil [3]; Nitrifying bacteria; Animals - proteins; A; Plants - convert to amino acids and proteins

(b) **(i)** The cycle shows bacteria decomposing dead material.
Name one other type of organism that decomposes dead material.

.... [1]

(ii) For decomposers to break down dead material they need certain conditions.

Write down three of these conditions.

....

....

.... [3]

(c) The nitrogen fixing bacteria shown on the diagram live free in the soil.

Others live in plants such as peas and beans.

Write about where in the plant they live and about the relationship that they have with the plant.

The quality of written communication will be assessed in your answer to this question.

....

....

....

.... [6]

5 Atoms and materials

The following topics are covered in this chapter:

- Atomic structure
- Chemical reactions and atoms
- Balancing equations
- Smart materials

5.1 Atomic structure

LEARNING SUMMARY

After studying this section, you should be able to:

- Name the three types of particle present in an atom.
- Describe the three types of particle in terms of mass, charge and where found.
- Use the atomic number and mass number to work out how many of each type of particle is present.
- Work out the electron arrangement for an atom of a given element.

Elements

| AQA | C1 | ✓ |
| EDEXCEL | C1 | ✓ |

KEY POINT

A substance that is made of only one type of **atom** is called an **element**.

Elements cannot be broken down chemically. Atoms of different elements have different properties. About 100 different elements have been discovered. The elements can be represented by **symbols**.

Approximately 80% of the elements are **metals**. Metals are found on the left-hand side and in the centre of the periodic table. The **non-metal** elements are found on the right-hand side of the periodic table. Elements with **intermediate properties** such as germanium are found in group 4.

Structure of the atom

AQA	C1	✓
EDEXCEL	C1	✓
WJEC	C1	✓

An atom has a very small, central **nucleus** that is surrounded by shells of **electrons**. The nucleus is found at the centre of the atom. It contains **protons** and **neutrons**.

- Protons have a mass of 1 **atomic mass unit (amu)** and a charge of 1+.
- Neutrons also have a mass of 1 amu but no charge.
- Electrons have a negligible mass and a charge of 1–.

Structure of an atom

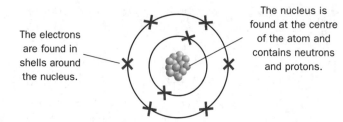

The electrons are found in shells around the nucleus.

The nucleus is found at the centre of the atom and contains neutrons and protons.

> Atoms are very small. They have a radius of about 10^{-10} m and a mass of about 10^{-23} g.

All atoms are **neutral**: there is no overall charge, so the number of protons must be equal to the number of electrons.

You may have seen two numbers written next to an element's symbol. These numbers are the **mass number** and the **atomic number**. They provide information about the particles inside the atom.

Mass number and atomic number

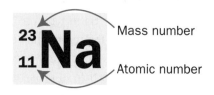

$_{11}^{23}\text{Na}$

Mass number

Atomic number

The mass number is the number of protons added to the number of neutrons. The atomic number is the number of protons (so it is also known as the **proton number**). All the atoms of a particular element have the same number of protons, for example, carbon atoms always have six protons. Atoms of different elements have different atomic numbers.

> Be familiar with the mass and charge of the three types of particle found inside an atom. All atoms of the same element have the same number of protons and electrons. For example, all atoms of oxygen contain 8 protons and 8 electrons.

Sodium has an atomic number of 11, so every sodium atom has 11 protons. A sodium atom has no overall charge, so the number of electrons must be the same as the number of protons. Sodium atoms therefore have 11 electrons. The number of neutrons is given by the mass number minus the atomic number. In sodium that is 23 – 11 = 12 neutrons.

Electron structure

AQA   C1   ✓

Electrons occupy the lowest available **shell** (or energy level). This is the shell that is closest to the nucleus. When this is full the electrons start to fill the next shell. In the diagram, the first shell may contain up to two electrons while the second and third shells may contain up to eight electrons.

A model of electron shells

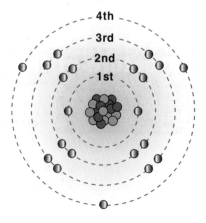

KEY POINT

The electron structure of an atom is important because it determines how the atom (and, therefore, the element) will react.

Groups

AQA   C1   ✓
WJEC C1   ✓

KEY POINT

Elements in the same **group** (the same vertical column) of the periodic table have similar chemical properties because they have the same number of electrons in their outer shells.

Element	Number of protons	Number of electrons	Electronic structure	Number of shells of electrons	Group of periodic table	Period of periodic table	Diagram
Lithium	3	3	2, 1	2	1	2	
Magnesium	12	12	2, 8, 2	3	2	3	

Across a **period** (the same horizontal row in the periodic table), each consecutive element has one extra proton in its nucleus and one extra electron in its outer shell of electrons. This means an electron shell is filled with electrons across a period.

PROGRESS CHECK

1 What does the nucleus of an atom contain?
2 Which particles are found in shells around the nucleus?
3 What is the charge and mass of a proton?
4 What is the charge and mass of an electron?
5 What is the charge and mass of a neutron?
6 What is the mass number of an atom?
7 Calcium and magnesium both belong to group 2 of the periodic table. Why does the element calcium react in a similar way to the element magnesium?

7. As both elements are in group 2 of the periodic table they have a similar electron configuration; they both have two electrons in their outer shell.
6. The number of protons plus the number of neutrons.
5. No charge, mass 1 amu.
4. Charge −1, mass negligible.
3. Charge +1, mass 1 amu.
2. Electrons.
1. Protons and neutrons.

5.2 Chemical reactions and atoms

LEARNING SUMMARY	After studying this section, you should be able to:
	• Use symbols and formulae to represent elements and chemical compounds.
	• Interpret a chemical formula in terms of the type and ratio of the atoms that have combined.
	• Recall the two different ways atoms can bond together to form compounds.

Chemical symbols and formulae

AQA	C1	✓
OCR A	C2	✓
OCR B	C1	✓
EDEXCEL	C1	✓
WJEC	C1	✓

In science, elements are represented by **symbols**. Each element has its own unique symbol that is recognised all over the world, e.g. the element magnesium is represented by the symbol Mg.

> **KEY POINT**
>
> A **compound** can be represented using a chemical **formula**. The formula shows the type and ratio of the atoms that are joined together in the compound.

A model of ammonia

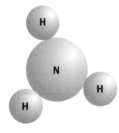

Ammonia has the chemical formula NH_3. This shows that in ammonia, nitrogen and hydrogen atoms are joined together in the ratio of one nitrogen atom to three hydrogen atoms.

You should take care when writing out the symbols for chemical compounds as some of them are very similar to elements. For example:

- The element carbon has the symbol C.
- The element oxygen has the symbol O.
- The element cobalt has the symbol Co.

> Take care when writing formulae with subscript numbers. They will need to be perfect to get the mark awarded in the exam.

The formula CO shows that a carbon atom and an oxygen atom have been chemically combined in a 1 : 1 ratio. This is the formula of the compound carbon monoxide. The symbol Co represents the element cobalt. Notice how the second letter of the symbol is written in lower case. If it wasn't, it would be a completely different substance. The formula CO_2 shows that carbon and oxygen atoms have been chemically combined in a 1 : 2 ratio. This is the formula of the compound carbon dioxide.

Chemical reactions

AQA	C1	✓
OCR A	C2	✓
OCR B	C1	✓
WJEC	C1	✓

Atoms of different elements can join together by forming new chemical **bonds**.

> **KEY POINT**
>
> Atoms can join together by:
>
> - **covalent bonding** – sharing electrons
> - **ionic bonding** – transferring electrons.

Compounds consist of two or more different types of atom that have been chemically combined. Compounds formed from metals and non-metals consist of ions. These compounds are held together by strong electrostatic forces of attraction. Compounds formed from non-metals consist of molecules. Giant molecules are held together by strong **covalent** bonds.

Word and symbol equations

AQA	C1	✓
OCR B	C1–C2	✓
EDEXCEL	C1	✓
WJEC	C1	✓

Symbol equations can be used to explain what happens during a chemical reaction. When magnesium burns in air the magnesium metal reacts with the non-metal atoms in oxygen molecules to form the **ionic** compound magnesium oxide. This reaction can be shown in a word or symbol equation:

magnesium + oxygen → magnesium oxide

$$2Mg + O_2 \rightarrow 2MgO$$

When carbon reacts with oxygen the non-metal carbon atoms react with the non-metal oxygen atoms to form molecules of the covalent compound carbon dioxide. This reaction can be shown in a word or symbol equation:

carbon + oxygen → carbon dioxide

$$C + O_2 \rightarrow CO_2$$

KEY POINT

Atoms are not created or destroyed during a chemical reaction: the atoms are just rearranged. This means that the total mass of the **reactants** is the same as the total mass of the **products**.

PROGRESS CHECK

1. How can atoms join together?
2. Give the name of the element with the symbol Na.
3. Give the name of the element with the symbol Cr.
4. A water molecule has the formula H_2O. Explain what this formula tells us.
5. Sodium nitrate has the formula $NaNO_3$. Explain what this formula tells us.
6. Give the formula for the following compounds:
   a) Potassium chloride.
   b) Sodium bromide.

6. a) KCl. b) NaBr.
5. It consists of sodium atoms, nitrogen atoms and oxygen atoms in the ratio 1 : 1 : 3.
4. It consists of 2 hydrogen atoms and 1 oxygen atom.
3. Chromium.
2. Sodium.
1. Atoms can be joined by sharing electrons or by transferring electrons.

5.3 Balancing equations

LEARNING SUMMARY

After studying this section, you should be able to:

- Recall that mass is always conserved in chemical reactions.
- Understand the advantage of using a symbol equation over a word equation.
- Decide if an equation is balanced, by counting atoms on both sides.
- Balance an equation that is not balanced, by adding numbers in front of symbols.
- Understand the use of state symbols in a chemical equation.

Conservation of mass

AQA	C1	✓
OCR B	C1–C2	✓
EDEXCEL	C1	✓
WJEC	C1	✓

Symbol equations show the type and ratio of the atoms involved in a reaction. The **reactants** are placed on the left-hand side of the equation. The **products** are placed on the right-hand side of the equation. Overall, mass is **conserved** because atoms are never made or destroyed during chemical reactions. This means that there must always be the same number of each type of atom on both sides of the equation.

Reactants	$\longrightarrow$	Products
Magnesium + Oxygen	$\longrightarrow$	Magnesium Oxide
$2Mg(s) + O_2(g)$	$\longrightarrow$	**$2MgO(s)$**

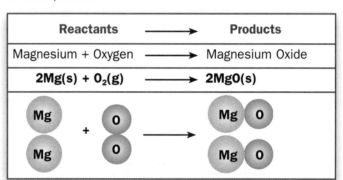

Balancing the equation

AQA	C1	✓
OCR B	C1–C2	✓
EDEXCEL	C1	✓
WJEC	C1	✓

Hydrogen burns in air to produce water vapour. This can be shown using a word equation.

Hydrogen + Oxygen → Water

The word equation is useful but it doesn't give the ratio of hydrogen and oxygen molecules involved. Balanced symbol equations show this extra information. First, replace the words with symbols. Hydrogen and oxygen both exist as molecules.

$$H_2 + O_2 \rightarrow H_2O$$

The formulae are all correct, but the equation does not balance because there are different numbers of atoms on each side of the equation. The formulae cannot be changed, but numbers can be added in front of the formulae to balance the equation.

The equation shows that there are two oxygen atoms on the left-hand side of the equation but only one oxygen atom on the right-hand side.

A number 2 is therefore placed in front of the H_2O:

$$H_2 + O_2 \rightarrow 2H_2O$$

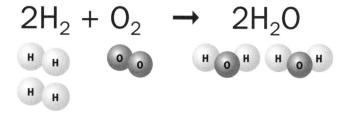

Now the oxygen atoms are balanced: there is the same number of oxygen atoms on both sides of the equation. However, the hydrogen atoms are no longer balanced. There are two hydrogen atoms on the left-hand side and four hydrogen atoms on the right-hand side. So a 2 is placed in front of the H_2:

$$2H_2 + O_2 \rightarrow 2H_2O$$

> To get a top mark, you need to be able to balance equations. This skill just needs a little practice. Deal with each type of atom in turn until everything balances.
>
> Remember to write any subscripts below the line:
>
> H_2O is correct while H^2O and H2O are wrong.

The equation is now balanced.

State symbols

EDEXCEL   C1   ✓
WJEC   C1   ✓

State symbols can be added to an equation to show extra information. They show what physical state the reactants and products are in. The symbols are:

- (s) for solid
- (l) for liquid
- (g) for gases
- (aq) for aqueous, or dissolved in water.

> Aqueous comes from the Latin *aqua* meaning water. Aqueous means dissolved in water.

For example, magnesium metal can be burned in air to produce magnesium oxide. Magnesium and magnesium oxide are both solids. The part of the air that reacts when things are burned is oxygen, which is a gas.

magnesium + oxygen → magnesium oxide

$$2Mg(s) + O_2(g) \rightarrow 2MgO(s)$$

> **KEY POINT**
>
> When balancing equations, always check that the formulae you have written down are correct.

Some equations involve formulae that contain brackets, for example, calcium hydroxide: $Ca(OH)_2$. This means that calcium hydroxide contains calcium, oxygen and hydrogen atoms in the ratio 1 : 2 : 2. These equations can be balanced normally. Calcium reacts with water to form calcium hydroxide, which is slightly soluble, and hydrogen gas.

calcium + water → calcium hydroxide + hydrogen

$$Ca(s) + 2H_2O(l) \rightarrow Ca(OH)_2(aq) + H_2(g)$$

Precipitation reactions

AQA   C1   ✓
EDEXCEL C1   ✓

Some insoluble salts can be made from the reaction between two solutions. Barium sulfate is an insoluble salt. It can be made by the reaction between solutions of barium chloride and sodium sulfate.

barium chloride + sodium sulfate → barium sulfate + sodium chloride

$$BaCl_2(aq) + Na_2SO_4(aq) \rightarrow BaSO_4(s) + 2NaCl(aq)$$

The insoluble barium sulfate can be filtered off, washed and dried. Overall, the two original salts, barium chloride and sodium sulfate, have swapped partners. Barium chloride solution can be used to test whether a solution contains sulfate ions. If sulfate ions are present, a white precipitate of barium sulfate will be seen. The chloride ions and sodium ions are **spectator ions**. They are present but they are not involved in the reaction. The ionic equation for the reaction is:

$$Ba^{2+}(aq) + SO_4{}^{2-}(aq) \rightarrow BaSO_4(s)$$

Precipitation reactions are very fast. When the reactant solutions are mixed, the reacting ions collide together very quickly and react together to form the insoluble solid.

Barium sulfate is used in medicine as a **barium meal**. The patient is given the insoluble salt and then X-rayed. The barium sulfate is opaque to X-rays so doctors can detect digestive problems without having to carry out an operation. Although barium salts are toxic, barium sulfate is so insoluble that very little dissolves and passes into the bloodstream of the patient.

PROGRESS CHECK

1. Why must there be the same number of each type of atom on both sides of an equation?
2. Balance the equation Na + Cl_2 → NaCl.
3. Balance the equation H_2 + Cl_2 → HCl.
4. Balance the equation C + CO_2 → CO.
5. What does the state symbol (l) indicate?
6. Explain why precipitation reactions happen very quickly.

6. The reacting ions collide together and react very quickly
5. It is a liquid.
4. C + CO_2 → 2CO.
3. H_2 + Cl_2 → 2HCl.
2. 2Na + Cl_2 → 2NaCl.
1. Atoms cannot be created or destroyed during chemical reactions.

5.4 Smart materials

After studying this section, you should be able to:

- Understand that new materials need to be developed for new uses.
- Describe the properties of photochromic and thermochromic materials.
- Relate the properties of new materials to their uses.

Smart materials

AQA   C1   ✓

Many scientists are involved in making new materials. These materials can have very special properties. Smart materials have one or more property that can be dramatically and reversibly altered by changes in the environment. A whole variety of smart materials already exist including:

- shape-memory alloys
- thermochromic materials
- photochromic materials.

Scientists are working to find more applications for existing smart materials and to discover new materials.

Photochromic glasses

Photochromic materials

Photochromic materials change colour when exposed to bright light. They are widely used to make lenses for glasses. The lenses adapt to light conditions: when it is bright, the lenses get darker.

Hydrogels

Hydrogels are a new type of polymer. They are able to absorb water and swell up as the result of changes in pH or changes in temperature. Hydrogels are being used to make special wound dressings. Hydrogels help to:

- stop fluid loss from the wound
- absorb bacteria and odour molecules
- cool and cushion the wound
- reduce the number of times the wound has to be disturbed (e.g. to change the dressing).

The hydrogel is transparent, so medical staff can monitor the wound without having to remove the dressing.

PROGRESS CHECK

1. Why are smart materials special?
2. What is special about a photochromic material?

2. Photochromic materials change colour when exposed to bright light.
1. They have one or more property that responds to changes in the environment.

Sample GCSE questions

1 Use the periodic table in the data sheet to help answer these questions.

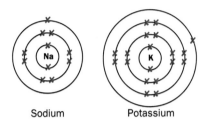

Sodium   Potassium

(a) **(i)** Complete the diagrams to show the electron arrangements of both atoms. **[2]**

(ii) Why are sodium and potassium in the same group of the periodic table? **[1]**

Both atoms have the same number of electrons in their outer shells, i.e. one electron.

(iii) Why are sodium and potassium in different periods on the periodic table? **[1]**

Sodium has three shells containing electrons, while potassium has four.

(b) Sodium has mass number 23, potassium has mass number 39.

(i) How many protons are in an atom of sodium? **[1]**

11

(ii) How many neutrons are in an atom of potassium? **[1]**

The number of neutrons is mass number - atomic number: 39 - 19 = 20 neutrons.

(c) Sodium metal reacts with water to produce hydrogen gas and sodium hydroxide:

$2Na(s) + 2H_2O(l) \rightarrow 2NaOH(aq) + H_2(g)$

(i) Which gas would be produced when potassium reacts with water? **[1]**

Hydrogen.

(ii) Give the name and formula of the other product. **[1]**

If sodium produces sodium hydroxide, potassium will produce potassium hydroxide.

The formula for potassium hydroxide is KOH.

Mark the electrons as clear Xs on the circles. Sodium should have the arrangement 2, 8, 1, while potassium has the arrangement 2, 8, 8, 1. Remember shells fill from the inside outwards.

Remember that the number of outer shell electrons is the same as the group number.

Remember that the period number is the same as the number of shells the atom has.

Be careful! The number of protons is the same as the number of electrons you drew in part a(i). The mass number is not needed to calculate the number of protons!

If you read the question properly, you will notice that it is now asking about potassium, not sodium.

Elements in the same group have similar reactions, so the gas will be hydrogen again.

Check the symbol for potassium, using the periodic table, before writing the formula (it is K!)

The formula doesn't need a 2 in front, because you aren't balancing an equation.

Exam practice questions

1 The nucleus of a neon atom has 10 protons and 10 neutrons.

(a) What is the atomic number of neon?

.... [1]

(b) What is the atomic mass of a neon atom?

.... [1]

(c) What is the electron arrangement of a neon atom?

.... [1]

(d) Where would you expect to find neon on the periodic table?

....

.... [2]

2 **(a)** Write the balanced symbol equation for the following reaction.

Magnesium + Chlorine ⟶ Magnesium chloride

.... [2]

(b) Write the balanced symbol equation for the following reaction.

Iron + Oxygen ⟶ Iron(III) oxide

.... [2]

3 In the production of ammonia, nitrogen reacts with hydrogen according to this equation:

$N_2(g) + \ldots H_2(g) \rightarrow \ldots NH_3(g)$

(a) In which physical state are the reactants and products?

.... [1]

(b) What do we call a particle of nitrogen where two atoms are bonded together?

.... [1]

(c) Balance the equation by putting numbers into the gaps.

(d) Suggest what ammonia would react with to make ammonium hydroxide, NH_4OH.

.... [1]

6 The Earth and pollution

The following topics are covered in this chapter:

- **Evolution of the atmosphere**
- **Atmospheric gases**
- **Pollution of the atmosphere**
- **The greenhouse effect**
- **Pollution of the environment**
- **Evidence of plate tectonics**
- **Consequences of plate tectonics**
- **The carbon cycle**

6.1 Evolution of the atmosphere

LEARNING SUMMARY	After studying this section, you should be able to:
	- Describe the composition of the Earth's early atmosphere.
	- Compare the early atmosphere to today's atmosphere.
	- Relate changes in the atmosphere to specific processes.
	- Understand the significance of the Miller-Urey experiment.
	- List natural processes that reduce atmospheric carbon dioxide.

The atmosphere today

AQA	C1	✓
OCR A	C1	✓
OCR B	C1	✓
EDEXCEL	C1	✓
WJEC	C1	✓

> **KEY POINT**
>
> Today, the **atmosphere** is composed of: about 78% **nitrogen**, about 21% **oxygen**, small amounts of **other gases**, such as carbon dioxide, water vapour and **noble gases**, for example, argon and neon.

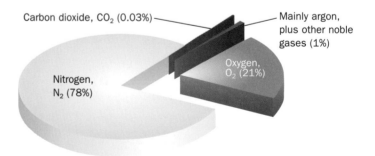

Carbon dioxide, CO_2 (0.03%) — Mainly argon, plus other noble gases (1%)

Nitrogen, N_2 (78%)

Oxygen, O_2 (21%)

Changes in the atmosphere

AQA	C1	✓
OCR A	C1	✓
OCR B	C1	✓
EDEXCEL	C1	✓
WJEC	C1	✓

Small changes in today's atmosphere can be caused by **volcanic activity** or by human activities, such as **deforestation** or farming. Throughout the history of the Earth, the composition of the atmosphere has changed.

The effect of volcanic activity

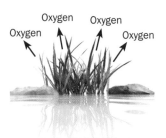

The first billion years

During the first billion years of the Earth's life, there was enormous volcanic activity. Volcanoes belched out carbon dioxide (CO_2), steam or water vapour (H_2O), ammonia (NH_3) and methane (CH_4). The atmosphere consisted mainly of carbon dioxide and there was very little oxygen. In fact, Earth's atmosphere was very similar to the atmosphere of the planets Mars and Venus today. The steam **condensed** to form the early oceans.

Later

During the two billion years that followed, **plants** and **algae** evolved and began to cover the surface of the Earth.

> **KEY POINT**
>
> The plants grew very well in the carbon dioxide-rich atmosphere. They steadily removed carbon dioxide and produced oxygen (O_2).

Later still

Remember that it is difficult for scientists to be completely precise about all the details above because different sources of information suggest slightly different things may have happened.

Most of the carbon dioxide in the early atmosphere dissolved into the oceans. The carbon gradually became locked up in the shells and skeletons of marine organisms and, when the organisms died, as **carbonate** minerals. Some of the carbon from the early atmosphere is also stored in fossil fuels. The ammonia in the early atmosphere reacted with oxygen to release nitrogen. Living organisms, such as denitrifying bacteria, also produced nitrogen. As the amount of oxygen increased, an **ozone layer** (O_3) developed. This layer filtered out harmful **ultraviolet (UV) radiation** from the Sun, enabling new, more complex life forms to develop.

Chemical theories for the origins of life

AQA	C1	✓
EDEXCEL	C1	✓

Historically, people believed that life started when living things were spontaneously generated from non-living materials. These ideas are part of the teaching of many religions. Today, many scientists believe that life started because of chemical reactions taking place, possibly between hydrocarbons, ammonia and lightning. The Earth's early environment would have provided the necessary conditions and raw materials (or **primordial soup**) for life to develop. There are many theories about how life first evolved.

In the **Miller–Urey experiment**, water, methane, ammonia and hydrogen were placed into sterile flasks and exposed to electrical sparks. Miller and Urey found that the reaction produced amino acids.

Carbon dioxide in the atmosphere

AQA	C1	✓
OCR A	C1	✓
OCR B	C1	✓
EDEXCEL	C1	✓
WJEC	C1	✓

KEY POINT

The level of carbon dioxide in our atmosphere has increased since the **Industrial Revolution** as we have burned more fossil fuels.

These fossil fuels had stored carbon from the Earth's early atmosphere for hundreds of millions of years.

There is a mismatch, however, between the amount of carbon dioxide released into the atmosphere by the burning of fossil fuels and the actual increase in the amount of carbon dioxide in the atmosphere. A great deal of the carbon dioxide appears to be missing.

Carbon dioxide is removed from the atmosphere by:

- **photosynthesis** by plants on land
- photosynthesis by phytoplankton in the oceans
- dissolution of carbon dioxide molecules from the atmosphere to the oceans.

The carbon dioxide reacts with seawater to produce:

- **insoluble** (does not dissolve) carbonate salts, which are deposited as sediment
- **soluble** (does dissolve) calcium and magnesium hydrogencarbonate salts.

Much of the carbon dioxide is, therefore, locked up in sediment for long periods of time. Some of this carbon dioxide is later released back into the atmosphere when the sediment is forced underground by geological activity and then released when volcanoes erupt.

However, not all of the carbon dioxide released by the burning of fossil fuels is removed in these ways. Many people are concerned about rising levels of carbon dioxide in the Earth's atmosphere and the possible link between these increased levels and **global warming**. The theories about the evolution of the Earth's atmosphere come from scientific studies of rocks formed millions of years ago. Scientists' ideas evolve as more evidence becomes available.

PROGRESS CHECK

1. Approximately how much of today's atmosphere is made up of oxygen?
2. What was the main gas in the Earth's early atmosphere?
3. How did the evolution of plants affect the Earth's atmosphere?
4. What happened to most of the carbon from the carbon dioxide in the Earth's early atmosphere?

1. 21%
2. Carbon dioxide.
3. It removed carbon dioxide and produced oxygen.
4. It became locked up in sedimentary rocks and fossil fuels.

6.2 Atmospheric gases

LEARNING SUMMARY

After studying this section, you should be able to:

- Recall the percentage composition of air.
- Describe an experiment to show that air is 20% oxygen.
- Understand the separation of air by fractional distillation.
- Explain the low reactivity of the noble gases.
- List some uses of noble gases.

The level of oxygen present in air

AQA	C1	✓
OCR B	C1	✓
EDEXCEL	C1	✓
WJEC	C1	✓

Air is a mixture of different gases. About 78% of air is **nitrogen**, about 21% is **oxygen** and about 1% is a mixture of **other gases** including argon, neon, water vapour and carbon dioxide. All of these molecules and atoms are very small. There are large spaces between them. Nitrogen is an element. Nitrogen exists as molecules, with the formula N_2. Oxygen is also an element and exists as molecules, with the formula O_2. Argon and neon are both elements that exist as single atoms. They are represented by the symbols Ar and Ne.

Learn the percentage of nitrogen and oxygen in the air and be prepared to recall the information in the exam. Nitrogen and oxygen are both diatomic molecules. A diatomic molecule consists of two atoms joined together.

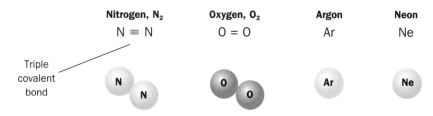

Water vapour is a molecular compound, with the formula H_2O. Carbon dioxide is also a molecular compound, with the formula CO_2.

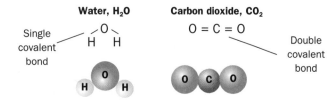

Combustion reactions

OCR A	C1	✓
OCR B	C1	✓
EDEXCEL	C1	✓

Combustion, or burning reactions, needs oxygen. In fact, fuels will burn better in pure oxygen than they do in air. Oxygen can be mixed with the fuel acetylene in welding torches.

Combustion

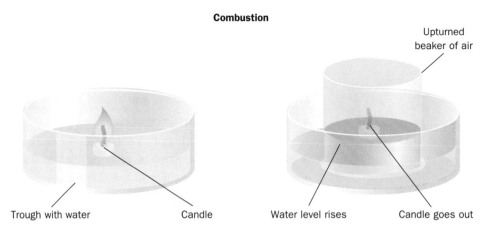

Trough with water   Candle   Water level rises   Candle goes out

If an upturned beaker is placed over a candle, the oxygen in the air is used up as the candle burns and the water level inside the beaker moves up. When the candle uses up all the oxygen in the air the candle goes out. The water level moves about a fifth of the way up the beaker. This shows that about a fifth, or around 20%, of the air is oxygen.

Fractional distillation of liquid air

AQA   C1   ✓

Fractional distillation separates mixtures into different fractions, or parts, because the fractions have different boiling points. Both oxygen and nitrogen can be extracted from air by fractional distillation.

First, the air is filtered to remove dust and other impurities. Next, the air is cooled until it reaches −200°C. The gases condense to form liquids. Carbon dioxide and water are removed as they condense, leaving a mixture of liquid nitrogen and oxygen. Oxygen turns from a liquid to a gas at −183°C, while nitrogen turns from a liquid to a gas at −196°C. The **liquefied** air mixture is placed into a **fractionating column**.

Separating oxygen and nitrogen

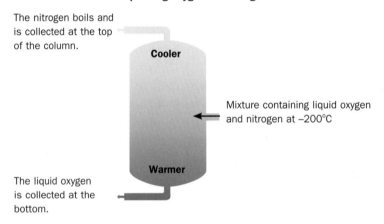

The nitrogen boils and is collected at the top of the column.

Cooler

Mixture containing liquid oxygen and nitrogen at −200°C

Warmer

The liquid oxygen is collected at the bottom.

> Design a flow diagram to show each step in the fractional distillation of air.

A final step is required to remove traces of argon from the oxygen. These two gases have such similar boiling points that a second fractional distillation step is required to separate them. The gases separated from air are useful raw materials that are used in many industrial processes.

Noble gases

AQA	C1	✓
WJEC	C1	✓

A model showing outer shell of electrons of the noble gases

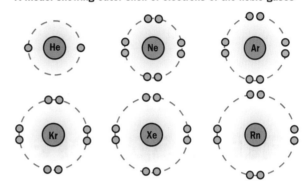

Notice that the noble gases have eight electrons in their outer shell, except helium. Helium only has two electrons but that still gives it a full outer shell.

Noble gases are useful to us precisely because they do not react. They are inert, have a **low density** and are **non-flammable**. The table shows some uses of noble gases.

Gas	Use	Image
Helium	Used in balloons and in airships because it is less dense than air. It is not flammable. (Early airships used hydrogen, which is flammable, and this could be disastrous if a fault occurred and the hydrogen caught fire.)	
Neon	Used in electrical discharge tubes in advertising signs.	
Argon	Used in filament light bulbs. The hot filament is surrounded by argon. This stops the filament from burning away and breaking the bulb.	

1. What percentage of the air is nitrogen?
2. What is the formula of carbon dioxide?
3. Why can liquid air be separated by fractional distillation?
4. How many electrons does a helium atom have?
5. Why is it better to use helium than hydrogen in balloons?

5. Hydrogen is a flammable gas while helium, which also has a low density, is extremely unreactive and so much safer.
4. 2 electrons.
3. The different components have different boiling points.
2. CO₂.
1. 78%.

6.3 Pollution of the atmosphere

LEARNING SUMMARY

After studying this section, you should be able to:

- List the fossil fuels burned to provide energy.
- Write balanced equations for the combustion of hydrocarbons.
- Explain how sulfur impurities cause acid rain.
- Understand why limiting oxygen supply can produce carbon monoxide.
- Describe how a catalytic converter removes pollutants from car exhaust fumes.

Fossil fuels

AQA	C1	✓
OCR A	C1	✓
OCR B	C1	✓
EDEXCEL	C1	✓
WJEC	C1	✓

Coal is mainly carbon. Petrol, diesel, oil and natural gas are **hydrocarbons**. When hydrocarbons are burned in a good supply of oxygen, water vapour and carbon dioxide are produced. The carbon and hydrogen atoms in the hydrocarbon fuels combine with oxygen atoms. This is an example of an **oxidation** reaction.

methane + oxygen → carbon dioxide + water vapour

$$CH_4 + 2O_2 \rightarrow CO_2 + 2H_2O$$

Practise writing balanced symbol equations for combustion of fuels.

Fuels will burn more quickly in pure oxygen than they will in air. The products made in these reactions can be **pollutants** that affect air quality.

Acid rain

AQA	C1	✓
OCR A	C1	✓
OCR B	C1	✓
EDEXCEL	C1	✓
WJEC	C1	✓

KEY POINT

Fossil fuels, such as coal, oil and gas, often contain small amounts of sulfur. When these fuels are burned, the gas sulfur dioxide, SO_2, is produced. This gas can dissolve in rainwater to form **acid rain**.

Acid rain can affect the environment by damaging statues and buildings, as well as harming plant and aquatic life and corroding metals.

Fossil fuels are burned in power stations to produce electricity. Using less electricity, by turning off lights when they are not in use and not leaving everyday appliances on standby mode, will help to reduce the amount of acid rain produced.

Removing sulfur

OCR A	C1	✓
EDEXCEL	C1	✓
WJEC	C1	✓

Alternatively, sulfur compounds can be removed directly from oil and gas before they are burned so that they do not produce sulfur dioxide as they burn. The sulfur that is removed is a valuable material that can be sold on.

> Remember, sulfur dioxide causes acid rain. You could be asked to recall the chemical responsible for this environmental problem.

It is more difficult to remove sulfur from the fossil fuel coal. However, the sulfur dioxide produced by burning coal can be removed from the waste gases before they are released into the atmosphere. This process is carried out by scrubbers in power stations. The scrubbers react sulfur dioxide (from the waste gases) with calcium carbonate to produce gypsum and carbon dioxide. Sulfur dioxide can also be removed by oxidation and reaction with ammonia or by using seawater.

Carbon monoxide

OCR A	C1	✓
OCR B	C1	✓
EDEXCEL	C1	✓

The gas carbon monoxide, or CO, can be a dangerous pollutant. When fossil fuels containing carbon and hydrogen are burned, carbon dioxide and water vapour are produced. However, if carbon is burned in an **insufficient** supply of oxygen, the gas carbon monoxide can also be produced. Carbon monoxide is colourless, odourless and very poisonous. Faulty gas appliances can produce carbon monoxide, so it is important that they are regularly serviced. **Incomplete combustion** is undesirable because:

- It produces carbon monoxide.
- Less heat than expected is given off when the fuel is burned.
- Soot is produced, which must then be cleaned. A sooty flame has a yellow colour.

Global dimming is caused by smoke particles that are released into the atmosphere. Scientists believe that these smoke particles reduce the amount of sunlight that reaches the Earth's surface and may even affect weather patterns.

Catalytic converters

OCR A	C1	✓
OCR B	C1	✓

In the UK, modern, petrol-fuelled cars are fitted with **catalytic converters** or 'cats'. The catalytic converter is part of a car's exhaust system and helps to reduce the amount of harmful gases that the car releases into the atmosphere. Catalytic converters work best at high temperatures and have a high surface area to increase the rate at which harmful gases are converted.

Catalytic converters work in several ways:

- They help to convert carbon monoxide to carbon dioxide. The carbon monoxide is oxidised and the nitrogen monoxide is reduced.

$$2CO + 2NO \rightarrow N_2 + 2CO_2$$

- They help to convert nitrogen oxides to nitrogen.
- They oxidise unburned hydrocarbons to carbon dioxide and water vapour.

Nitrogen oxide is produced when nitrogen from air reacts with oxygen from air at the high temperatures reached when fuels are burned inside internal combustion engines. The nitrogen oxide reacts with oxygen to form nitrogen dioxide. Nitrogen oxide and nitrogen dioxide are referred to as nitrogen oxides or NOx. Nitrogen oxides cause acid rain and photochemical smog.

Atmospheric pollution caused by cars can also be reduced by:

- having more efficient car engines
- encouraging people to make more use of public transport
- setting legal limits for the levels of pollutants in exhaust gases (these levels are checked during MOT tests).

> Design a spider diagram to show how the amount of pollution produced by cars can be reduced.

PROGRESS CHECK

1. What is the name of the gas produced when sulfur is burned?
2. How can you tell from the flame that a fuel is being burned in a poor supply of oxygen?
3. What gas is produced when carbon is burned in a good supply of oxygen?
4. What gas is produced when carbon is burned in an insufficient supply of oxygen?
5. What causes global dimming?
6. Use a balanced symbol equation to show how a catalytic converter can help to remove carbon monoxide and nitrogen oxide from the exhaust gases of a car.

6. $2CO + 2NO \rightarrow N_2 + 2CO_2$.
5. Smoke particles.
4. Carbon monoxide.
3. Carbon dioxide.
2. It will have a yellow colour.
1. Sulfur dioxide.

6.4 The greenhouse effect

LEARNING SUMMARY

After studying this section, you should be able to:

- Explain what is meant by 'the greenhouse effect'.
- Recall examples of ways to reduce atmospheric carbon dioxide.

Carbon dioxide and the greenhouse effect

OCR B	C1	✓
EDEXCEL	C1	✓
WJEC	C1	✓

The **greenhouse effect** is believed to be slowly heating up the Earth. When fossil fuels are burned, the gas carbon dioxide is produced. Although some of this carbon dioxide is removed from the atmosphere by the reaction between carbon dioxide and seawater, the overall amount of carbon dioxide in the atmosphere has increased over the last 200 years.

> Remember that the levels of carbon dioxide in the atmosphere are rising as more fossil fuels are burned.

KEY POINT

Carbon dioxide traps the heat energy that has reached the Earth from the Sun.

Global warming may mean that the polar ice caps will eventually melt and this could cause massive flooding.

The greenhouse effect

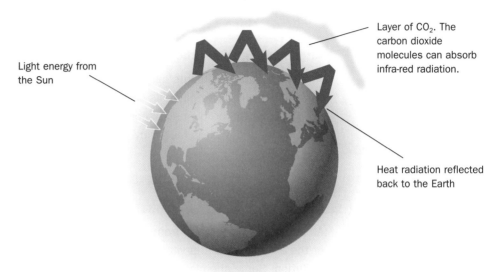

Layer of CO_2. The carbon dioxide molecules can absorb infra-red radiation.

Light energy from the Sun

Heat radiation reflected back to the Earth

Plants use the gas carbon dioxide during photosynthesis so **deforestation** reduces the amount of carbon dioxide that can be removed from the air. Organisms release carbon dioxide during respiration. Methane and water vapour are also greenhouse gases.

Reducing carbon dioxide levels

OCR B	C1	✓
EDEXCEL	C1	✓
WJEC	C1	✓

In **carbon capture and storage**, the carbon dioxide produced by power stations is captured and then stored safely. The carbon dioxide can be stored in **porous** rocks. Carbon dioxide can also be converted into **carbonate** rocks and then stored.

Not all scientists believe that human activity is causing global warming. Other factors, such as solar cycles, may also be important. Scientists are also investigating ways to control the amount of carbon dioxide by:

- adding iron to the oceans to encourage algae to **photosynthesise**
- converting carbon dioxide into useful hydrocarbons.

> **PROGRESS CHECK**
>
> ① How does adding iron to oceans reduce levels of carbon dioxide?
> ② List three greenhouse gases
>
> 1. It encourages algae to photosynthesise.
> 2. carbon dioxide; methane; water vapour

6.5 Pollution of the environment

LEARNING SUMMARY

After studying this section, you should be able to:

- Describe the problems caused by over-use of nitrate fertilisers.
- Explain why crude oil spills cause damage to the environment.
- Describe the problems associated with the disposal of plastics.
- Understand what is meant by the 'Life cycle assessment' of an object.

Pollution

| OCR B | C1 | ✓ |
| WJEC | C1 | ✓ |

All substances are made from matter obtained from the Earth's crust, the sea or the atmosphere. It is vital that we protect the environment from harmful **pollution**. Some chemicals persist for long periods of time in the environment. Such chemicals can be carried over large distances and may even accumulate in human tissues because of food consumption. Today, there are a large number of chemicals in the environment that may adversely affect the environment or human health, but scientists do not have enough data yet to be sure of all their effects.

Problems with nitrate fertilisers

| OCR B | C2 | ✓ |

Nitrogen, potassium and phosphorus are all needed for plants to grow. Nitrate **fertilisers** help plants to grow well and this means that farmers are able to produce more food. Nitrate fertilisers can cause problems if they are washed into lakes or streams:

- Algae (small plants) thrive in the fertiliser-rich water and grow very well.
- Eventually, the algae die and bacteria start to decompose (break down) the algae.
- As the bacteria decompose the algae, they use up the oxygen in the water.
- Fish and other aquatic life cannot get enough oxygen, so they die.

This process is called **eutrophication**.

Nitrate fertilisers can also find their way into drinking water supplies. There have been health concerns over the levels of nitrates in water and the prevalence of stomach cancer and 'blue baby' disease. Babies suffering from blue baby disease have elevated levels of nitrates in their blood. These nitrates reduce the amount of oxygen that the blood can carry, so the baby's skin looks blue. Although no firm links have yet been proved, it seems sensible to limit the levels of nitrate in drinking water until more is known.

Problems with oil exploitation

| OCR B | C1 | ✓ |
| EDEXCEL | C1 | ✓ |

Oil is an extremely important raw material. It is found in porous rocks in the

Earth's crust. Sometimes, the crude oil has to be pumped up to the surface before it can be collected. It is often transported around the world in giant oil tankers. When accidents occasionally occur, crude oil can escape. The oil forms a slick that can devastate animal and plant life. For example, sea birds can die if their feathers become covered in oil. These oil slicks can do great damage to affected beaches; this can have serious consequences for local people, particularly in holiday areas. If detergents are used to break up the oil slicks, the **detergents** may also affect wildlife.

In addition to the environmental problems associated with the exploitation of crude oil, there are also political problems that must be considered. Oil reserves are often found in politically sensitive areas. These countries may not want to sell great quantities of oil as a shortage in the world supply will naturally lead to an increase in the price of the oil. In other areas the situation can be even more unstable: battles in areas around oil fields can make it too dangerous for the oil to be extracted safely.

Plastics

AQA	C1	✓
OCR A	C2	✓
OCR B	C1	✓
EDEXCEL	C1	✓
WJEC	C1	✓

Plastics are very useful materials:

- They are very stable and unreactive, and waterproof.
- Most plastics do not react with water, oxygen or other common chemicals.
- Plastics are also non-biodegradable, which means that they are not decomposed by microorganisms.

> **KEY POINT**
>
> When plastic objects are no longer needed, they do not rot away but remain in the environment. Plastic objects now fill many landfill sites.

Plastics can be disposed of by burning, but this solution may also cause pollution problems. Although some plastics burn quite easily, they can give off harmful gases. The common plastic PVC releases the gas hydrogen chloride when it is burned. The plasticisers added to PVC sometimes leach out of the plastics and have harmful effects in the environment.

In response to these problems, scientists have developed new, biodegradable plastics that will eventually rot away. Some biodegradable plastics have been made from corn starch and some can be disposed of by dissolving them in water.

Glass and plastic bottles can be recycled but they can also be reused to store other liquids.

In addition, scientists are developing ways to recycle plastics. Polyesters, which can be used to make fabrics and bottles, can be recycled to form fleece material to make new clothes. Currently, recycling plastics is difficult because the different types of polymer have to be sorted by hand, and this is very expensive. **Recycling** also means that our finite resources of crude oil will last longer.

Life cycle assessment (LCA)

OCR A	C3	✓

Life cycle assessment (LCA) is used to assess the environmental impact an object has over its whole lifetime. This is sometimes referred to as **from cradle to grave**. LCAs are an effective way of comparing several possible alternative products to see which one has the least impact on the environment.

To calculate the overall effect, scientists measure the impact of:

- extracting the raw materials
- the manufacturing process
- any packaging used
- how the product is transported
- how it is used
- what happens to the object when it is no longer useful.

Recycling an object, if possible, will reduce its adverse effect on the environment.

PROGRESS CHECK

1. How is crude oil transported around the world?
2. What does the term 'non-biodegradable' mean?
3. What is another term used to describe the different stages of a LCA?

3. From cradle to grave.
2. It is not decomposed by microorganisms.
1. Using oil tankers.

6.6 Evidence of plate tectonics

LEARNING SUMMARY

After studying this section, you should be able to:

- Describe the structure of the Earth and its composition.
- Understand the evidence that has led to this model of Earth's structure.
- Explain the movement of tectonic plates floating on the liquid mantle.
- Recall that Alfred Wegener originally proposed his theory of 'continental drift'.
- Describe the evidence supporting Wegener's theory.

The structure of the Earth

AQA	C1	✓
OCR B	C2	✓
WJEC	C1	✓

Scientists believe that the Earth has a layered structure. The outer layer, called the **crust**, is very thin and has a low **density**. The next layer down is called the **mantle**. This layer extends almost halfway to the centre of the Earth. The rock in the mantle is mainly solid, but small amounts must be liquid as the mantle flows very slowly. At the centre of the Earth is the **core**. The core consists of two parts: the outer core is liquid; the inner core, which is under even greater pressure, is solid.

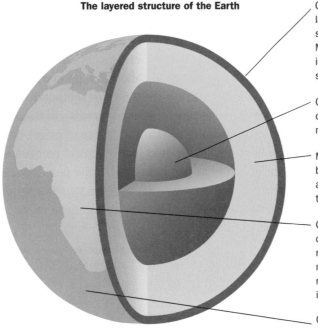

The layered structure of the Earth

> Make sure you can recall the names and details of the different layers of the Earth.

Crust: The crust is the outermost layer of the Earth, and is rich in silicon, oxygen and aluminium. Much of the silicon and oxygen in the Earth's crust is present as silicon dioxide or silica.

Core: The core lies at the centre of the Earth. It is thought to be made of iron and nickel.

Mantle: The mantle is found between the crust and the core and is partially liquid. Rocks in the mantle flow slowly.

Continental crust: The continental crust consists of sedimentary rock, igneous rock and metamorphic rock. The igneous rock found in the continental crust is mainly granite.

Oceanic crust: The oceanic crust consists mainly of basalt.

Evidence of the structure of the Earth

| OCR B | C2 | ✓ |
| WJEC | C1 | ✓ |

The Earth's crust is too thick to drill through so evidence for the layered structure of the Earth comes from studies of the way that **seismic waves** (the shock waves sent out by earthquakes) travel through the Earth.

The material through which the shock waves travel affects the speed of these waves. These studies show that the outer core of the Earth is liquid while the inner core is solid. The overall **density** of the Earth is greater than the density of the rocks that make up the Earth's crust. This means that the rocks in the mantle and the core must be much denser than the rocks we observe in the crust. Scientists believe that the core is mainly made of iron and nickel.

Movement of the crust

AQA	C1	✓
OCR A	C3	✓
OCR B	C2	✓
WJEC	C1	✓

People used to believe that the features of the Earth's surface, such as the mountain ranges, were formed when the surface of the Earth shrank as it cooled down. However, scientists now believe that the Earth's geological features can be explained using a single, unifying theory called **plate tectonics**.

> **KEY POINT**
>
> In 1914, the scientist Alfred Wegener first proposed **continental drift**, the idea behind plate tectonics. Initially, these ideas were resisted, particularly by religious groups. Scientists examining Wegener's theory could not, at first, explain how or why the plates moved, but as more evidence emerged, the theory of plate tectonics was gradually accepted.

Plate movement

AQA	C1	✓
OCR A	C3	✓
OCR B	C2	✓
WJEC	C1	✓

> Learn what the Earth's lithosphere is made up of.

The main idea behind plate tectonics is that the Earth's **lithosphere** (the crust and upper mantle) is split up into 12 large **plates**. Each plate moves slowly over the Earth's surface at a rate of a few centimetres each year. The movement of the plates is caused by convection currents in the mantle. These currents are caused by the natural **radioactive** decay of elements deep inside the Earth that release heat energy. By studying geological processes, scientists have been able to explain what has happened in the past. These scientists believe that at one time all the continents were joined together to form a **supercontinent** called **Pangea**. Since that time, the continents have moved apart and are now at their maximum separation.

How the continents once looked

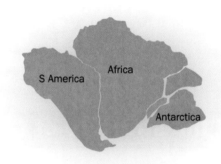

Evidence to support the theory

AQA	C1	✓
OCR A	C3	✓
OCR B	C2	✓
WJEC	C1	✓

There are many clues that support our ideas about plate tectonics:

- When the South American coast was first mapped, people noticed that the east coast of South America and the west coast of Africa fitted together like pieces of an enormous jigsaw.

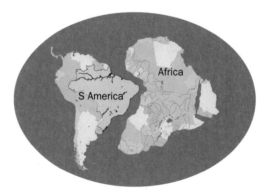

- The examination of fossil remains in both South America and Africa showed that rocks of the same age contained the remains of an unusual freshwater crocodile-type creature.
- Further evidence that South America and Africa were once joined was uncovered when scientists discovered that rock strata of the same age were strikingly similar on both sides of the Atlantic.

Strata layers in British sedimentary rocks

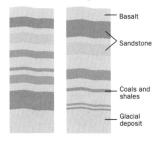

— Basalt

— Sandstone

— Coals and shales

— Glacial deposit

- British rocks that were created in the **Carboniferous period** (300 million years ago) must have formed in tropical swamps. Yet rocks found in Britain, which formed 200 million years ago, must have formed in deserts. This shows that Britain must have moved through different climatic zones as the tectonic plate that Britain rests on moved across the Earth's surface.

Ideas about plate tectonics have changed over time. Scientists build a model that fits with the evidence currently available to them. When new evidence is discovered they must re-evaluate their existing models and, if necessary, change them to take in the new evidence.

PROGRESS CHECK

1. What name is given to the outer layer of the Earth?
2. In which state is the Earth's inner core?
3. Which elements are abundant in the Earth's crust?
4. Which elements are abundant in the Earth's core?
5. Where does our evidence for the structure of the Earth come from?
6. What is the Earth's lithosphere?

6. The crust and upper mantle.
5. It comes from the study of seismic waves.
4. Iron and nickel.
3. Silicon, oxygen and aluminium.
2. Solid.
1. The crust.

6.7 Consequences of plate tectonics

LEARNING SUMMARY

After studying this section, you should be able to:

- Recall that volcanoes, earthquakes and tsunamis are caused by events at plate boundaries.
- Understand why these events are very difficult to predict.
- Describe the differences between different types of lava.
- Explain how mountain ranges are formed when plates converge.
- Explain how mid-oceanic ridges are formed when plates move apart.

Plate movements

AQA	C1	✓
OCR B	C2	✓
WJEC	C1	✓

KEY POINT

The movement of tectonic plates causes many problems, including earthquakes and volcanoes. These tend to be worse near the edges of plates, known as the plate boundaries.

The plates can move in three different ways:

1 They can slide past or over each other.
2 They can move towards each other.
3 They can move away from each other.

These diagrams show how the Earth's plates can move.

Earthquakes

AQA	C1	✓
OCR B	C2	✓
WJEC	C1	✓

Earthquakes are caused by tectonic plates sliding past or over each other. The San Andreas Fault in California is a famous example of where this occurs.

The San Andreas Fault

San Andreas Fault

The plates in this area have fractured into a very complicated pattern. As the plates try to move past each other, they tend to stick together rather than slide smoothly past. When the plates stick together, forces build up until eventually the plates suddenly move. The strain that has built up is released in the form of an earthquake. If this happens beneath the oceans, it can result in catastrophic tsunami waves.

> **KEY POINT**
>
> Scientists have studied earthquakes in an effort to predict when they will occur and so warn people to move away from the affected areas. However, with so many factors involved, it is not always possible to predict exactly when an earthquake or a volcanic eruption will happen.

When they do happen, they can cause massive destruction and loss of life.

The results of an earthquake

Volcanoes

AQA	C1	✓
OCR B	C2	✓
WJEC	C1	✓

Like earthquakes, volcanoes are sometimes found in locations around the Earth where two plates are moving towards each other. By studying where most earthquakes and volcanoes happen, scientists have been able to identify plate boundaries.

These convergent plate boundaries often involve the collision between an oceanic and a continental plate. Oceanic plates contain minerals that are rich in the elements iron and magnesium, and are denser than continental plates. When an oceanic plate and a continental plate converge, the denser, oceanic plate is forced beneath the continental plate. The continental plate is stressed, and the existing rocks are folded and metamorphosed.

Diagram showing a convergent plate boundary

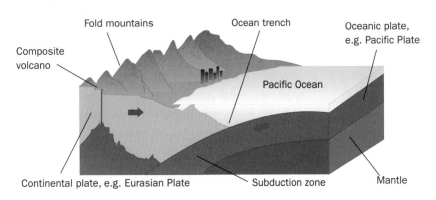

As the oceanic plate is forced down beneath the continental plate, seawater lowers the melting point of the rock and some of the oceanic plate may melt to form magma. If the magma has a lower density than the surrounding rock in the Earth's crust it can rise up through weaknesses or cracks in the crust to form volcanoes. Magma is molten rock below the Earth's surface; it becomes lava as it reaches the Earth's surface. Lava erupts from volcanoes. Some iron-rich basaltic lavas are runny and are relatively safe. Elsewhere, silica-rich viscous lavas are produced. These lavas are much more dangerous: they explode violently, often producing pumice, clouds of choking ash and throwing out pieces of rock called bombs. Volcanoes that erupt this way are much more dangerous.

When the lava cools down and solidifies, it forms igneous rocks. The faster the lava cools down the smaller the crystals in the rock will be. Some people choose to live near to volcanoes, even though they might erupt, because the soils formed when the igneous rocks are weathered are very fertile.

Diagram showing the Earth's plate boundaries

As the plates are moving past each other, earthquakes are also common in these areas.

A convergent plate boundary along the Western coast of South America is responsible for the formation of the Andes mountain range.

Mid-ocean ridge basalts

OCR B   C2   ✓

Another consequence of plate tectonics is the formation of mid-ocean ridge basalts.

Diagram showing a divergent plate boundary

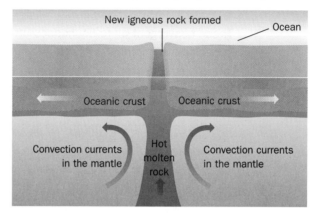

When tectonic plates move apart, magma comes to the surface. This usually occurs under oceans. As the molten rock cools, it solidifies and forms the igneous rock, basalt. These plate boundaries are often referred to as constructive plate boundaries, because new crust is being made. Basalt is rich in iron, which is magnetic. As the basalt cools down, the iron-rich minerals in the basalt line up with the Earth's magnetic field. By examining the direction in which these minerals have lined up, scientists in the 1960s discovered that they were able to work out the direction of the Earth's magnetic field. However, examination of the basalt rocks on either side of a mid-ocean ridge shows a striped magnetic reversal pattern. The pattern is symmetrical about the ridge and provides evidence that the Earth's magnetic field periodically changes direction. This reversal appears to be very sudden and occurs about every half a million years. According to the rock record, another reversal is now well overdue!

PROGRESS CHECK

1. What causes earthquakes?
2. Why can't scientists predict the exact date of an earthquake?
3. Why do earthquakes sometimes occur near volcanoes?
4. Why do oceanic plates move below continental plates when they collide?
5. Where is the Andes mountain range?
6. Explain how magnetic reversal patterns are formed near ocean ridges.

6. When the Earth's magnetic field reverses, the iron minerals in the solidifying lava line up with the Earth's magnetic field in the new opposite direction, forming a symmetrical pattern about the ridge.
5. The Western coast of South America.
4. The oceanic plates are denser.
3. Earthquakes sometimes occur near volcanoes because plates are moving past or over each other, having been restricted and causing stress to build up. The sudden release of this stress results in an earthquake.
2. There are too many factors involved.
1. Earthquakes are caused when plates suddenly move past or over each other, having been restricted and causing stress to build up. The sudden release of this stress results in an earthquake.

6.8 The carbon cycle

LEARNING SUMMARY

After studying this section, you should be able to:

- Understand that carbon dioxide is a very small, but increasing, proportion of air.
- List processes that release carbon dioxide into the air.
- List processes that remove carbon dioxide from the air.
- Explain how human activities are upsetting the balance of the carbon cycle.
- Describe the properties of a good fuel.

Moving carbon around the carbon cycle

AQA	C1	✓
OCR A	C1	✓
OCR B	C1	✓
EDEXCEL	C1	✓
WJEC	C1	✓

KEY POINT

The level of carbon dioxide in the atmosphere is fairly constant. This is because of the carbon cycle.

This cycle moves carbon between the atmosphere, the oceans and rocks.

The carbon cycle

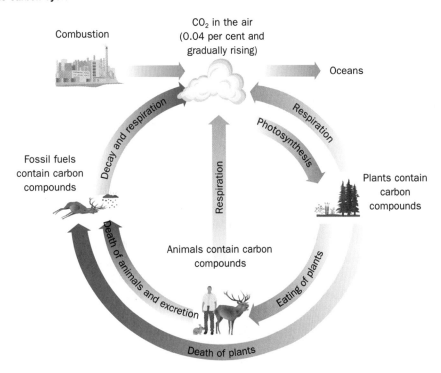

- Plants take in carbon from the atmosphere during photosynthesis.
- Plants and animals return carbon to the atmosphere during respiration.
- Fossil fuels release carbon into the atmosphere during combustion (burning).

Carbon is also recycled in the sea.

> **Make a poster to show how carbon is moved between the atmosphere, oceans and rocks. Make sure you annotate each stage.**

1 Marine organism shells are made of carbonates. The shells drop to the sea bed as the organisms die.

2 The shells fossilise to become limestone rock.

3 Volcanic eruptions heat the limestone and release carbon dioxide into the atmosphere. Carbon dioxide is also released during weathering of the limestone rock.

4 Oceans absorbing carbon dioxide act as **carbon sinks**.

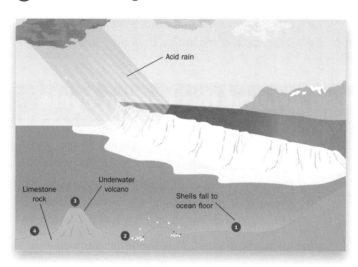

Acid rain
Underwater volcano
Limestone rock
Shells fall to ocean floor

The carbon cycle and fossil fuels

OCR B	C1	✓
EDEXCEL	C1	✓
WJEC	C1	✓

As the world's population expands, and with greater worldwide industrialisation, the overall levels of fossil fuels being burned is increasing. This means more carbon dioxide is being released into the atmosphere. As fossil fuels are thought to contribute towards the greenhouse effect, alternative fuels are being developed. A good fuel should be:

- easy to store and transport
- inexpensive to buy
- non-polluting
- easy to burn
- produce little ash or smoke
- non-toxic
- widely available
- efficient when it is burned (produce lots of energy).

> **PROGRESS CHECK**
>
> **1** Name three places where large amounts of carbon are found.
> **2** Why is more carbon dioxide now being released into the atmosphere?
> **3** Name three fossil fuels.
> **4** How do plants take in carbon?
> **5** What is happening to the world's population?
>
> 5. It is increasing.
> 4. By photosynthesis.
> 3. Coal, oil and gas.
> 2. More fossil fuels are being burned.
> 1. In the atmosphere, oceans and in rocks.

Sample GCSE questions

1 The majority of soft drinks sold in the UK are now sold in plastic bottles. Although most plastic bottles carry the recycling symbol, a large number end up in conventional rubbish bins, from which they are taken and dumped in landfill sites.

(a) Why is it a problem that plastic bottles are dumped in landfill sites? **[2]**

The bottles are non-biodegradable, so they will remain in the landfill for many years.

(b) As an alternative to dumping the bottles in landfill sites, the bottles could be:

- reused by being refilled with drinks
- recycled by melting the plastic and making new plastic products
- burned to provide heat energy in power stations.

Use your knowledge and understanding to compare the advantages and disadvantages of these three alternatives, in relation to their cost and their impact on the environment. **[6]**

The quality of written communication will be assessed in your answer to this question.

The advantage of reusing would be that no more bottles would have to be made, saving resources and energy.

Bottles would not be dumped in landfill unless damaged.

To reuse bottles they would have to be undamaged. They would have to be collected, cleaned and sterilised, which could cost a lot.

The advantage of recycling is that the plastic is not wasted or dumped in landfill.

To recycle the bottles, different plastics have to be sorted and separated. It takes energy to melt the plastic.

Burning provides energy which would otherwise come from fossil fuels, a non-renewable resource.

Burning plastics causes pollution as they do not burn with a clean flame.

Marks will be awarded depending on the number of relevant points included in the answer and the spelling, punctuation and grammar. In this question there are 9 relevant points, so 7 or 9 with good spelling, punctuation and grammar will gain full marks.

When you have written your answer, check that you have covered every aspect you were asked to write about. Read it back, silently to yourself, to ensure it makes sense.

Exam practice questions

1 Earth's early atmosphere contained a much higher proportion of carbon dioxide than it does, today.

(a) What name is given to the process by which green plants remove carbon dioxide from the atmosphere?

.... [1]

(b) Which gas is produced and released into the atmosphere by this process?

.... [1]

(c) How might deforestation increase the atmospheric carbon dioxide?

....

.... [2]

2 Air is a mixture of gases.

(a) What is the name of the technique which can be used to separate the gases?

.... [1]

(b) What property of the gases allows them to be separated in this way?

.... [1]

(c) Which two gases are the most abundant in air?

.... [2]

3 Clean air contains a mixture of gases. The proportions of these gases are shown in the pie chart below.

Nitrogen (78%)
Oxygen
Other gases (1%)

(a) Which gas makes up most of the air?

.... [1]

(b) What percentage of the air is made up of oxygen?

.... [1]

(c) Give an example of a gas that would be found in 'other gases'.

.... [1]

Exam practice questions

4 Many non-biodegradable plastics end up in landfill sites, where they will persist for many hundreds of years.

   (a) What do you understand by the term 'non-biodegradable'?

   .... **[1]**

   (b) Plastics are flammable, but burning is not a good way to dispose of them. Why not?

   .... **[1]**

   (c) Give two examples of ways people can avoid disposing of plastics in landfill sites.

   .... **[2]**

5 The ozone layer is made of O_3 molecules and stops UV light hitting the surface of the Earth.

   Explain why CFCs are harmful to the ozone layer.

   ....

   .... **[2]**

6 David and Lisa measure the concentration of sulfur dioxide gas in the air starting at the centre of town and moving out into the countryside. Their results are shown in the table.

Distance from town centre (km)	0	2	4	6	8	10
Sulfur dioxide level (μg/m^3)	122	113	95	83	116	82

   David claims the results show that the greater distance you are from the town centre the less air pollution there is. Comment on David's claim and discuss how they could improve their evidence.

   ....

   ....

   .... **[3]**

7 Explain how cutting down large areas of rainforest in South America affects the Earth's atmosphere.

   ....

   ....

   ....

   ....

   .... **[5]**

8 Helium is a noble gas. It is very unreactive and it does not form compounds with other elements.

   (a) Why is helium preferred to hydrogen for use in modern airships?

   .... **[2]**

   (b) Argon can be extracted from air. Why can it not be used in airships?

   .... **[1]**

7 Organic chemistry and analysis

The following topics are covered in this chapter:

- Organic chemistry
- Fuels
- Vegetable oils
- Plastics
- Ethanol

7.1 Organic chemistry

LEARNING SUMMARY

After studying this section, you should be able to:

- Understand that 'organic' chemicals are compounds of carbon covalently bonded to other elements.
- Recognise an alkane from its general formula.
- Understand the term 'homologous series'.
- Recognise the differences between the formulae of alkanes and alkenes.
- Describe how bromine water can be used to test for an alkene.

The importance of carbon

| AQA | C1 | ✓ |
| OCR B | C1 | ✓ |

KEY POINT

Carbon atoms have the ability to form four bonds with other atoms. This means that carbon atoms can be made into a large range of compounds. These compounds are the basis of life and the chemistry of these compounds is called **organic** chemistry.

Organic compounds contain **covalent bonds**.

Covalent bonding involves the sharing of electrons. The shared pairs of electrons hold the atoms together.

Alkanes

AQA	C1	✓
OCR B	C1	✓
EDEXCEL	C1	✓

The **alkanes** are a family of **hydrocarbon** molecules. Most of the compounds in crude oil are hydrocarbons. This means that alkanes only contain hydrogen and carbon atoms. Scientists describe alkanes as **saturated** hydrocarbons. This is because they contain no carbon double bonds (C=C bonds) and so already contain the maximum number of hydrogen atoms. The alkanes are an example of an **homologous series**: all alkanes have the same general formula and similar chemical properties. Their physical properties, for example, boiling points, gradually vary down the series.

Name	Methane	Ethane	Propane	Butane
Chemical Formula	CH_4	C_2H_6	C_3H_8	C_4H_{10}
Structure	H │ H−C−H │ H	H H │ │ H−C−C−H │ │ H H	H H H │ │ │ H−C−C−C−H │ │ │ H H H	H H H H │ │ │ │ H−C−C−C−C−H │ │ │ │ H H H H

> **Practise drawing out the different alkane molecules shown in the table.**

Alkanes are useful fuels: complete combustion of alkanes produces carbon dioxide and water.

Alkanes have the general formula C_nH_{2n+2}. **Ball and stick models** are a useful way of showing the three-dimensional position of atoms and bonds. The ball and stick model of methane, CH_4, is shown below.

Ball and stick model of methane

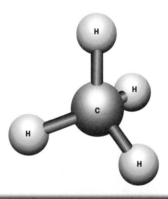

> **If you are given a molecular formula that obeys the rules for the general formula of an alkane, then you can tell it is an alkane molecule without having to draw it out.**

Alkenes

AQA	C1	✓
OCR B	C1	✓
EDEXCEL	C1	✓

The **alkenes** are also hydrocarbon molecules. Scientists describe alkenes as **unsaturated** hydrocarbons because they all contain one or more C=C bond. They are produced by cracking longer chain alkane molecules. The single lines in the diagrams represent a single covalent bond while the double lines represent a double covalent bond.

Name	Ethene	Propene
Chemical Formula	C_2H_4	C_3H_6

Structure	H H
	  \ /
	   C = C
	  / \
	H H
		H H
		  \ /
		   C = C − C − H
		  / \ \
		H H H

Alkenes are more reactive than alkanes owing to the presence of C=C bonds. This means alkenes are more useful because they can be used to make new substances. Alkenes have the general formula C_nH_{2n}. Butene has the formula C_4H_8.

Reaction of alkenes with bromine

OCR B   C1   ✓
EDEXCEL C1   ✓

> **KEY POINT**
>
> Alkenes also react with bromine water. Bromine water is **decolourised** in the presence of alkenes.

When alkenes react with bromine water an addition reaction occurs (the two molecules add together to form one molecule).

Learn the product made when alkenes react with bromine.

The bromine from the bromine water adds to the alkene: one bromine atom is added to each of the carbon atoms involved in the double bond. This forms a colourless dibromo compound. In the diagram below, ethene is reacting with bromine to form a dibromo compound.

When describing the test for unsaturation, make sure you describe the resulting solution as colourless, not clear.

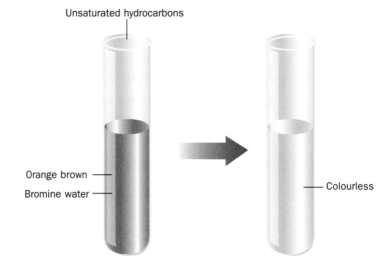

Unsaturated hydrocarbons

Orange brown
Bromine water

Colourless

> **KEY POINT**
>
> Alkanes do not contain C=C bonds so they do not react with bromine water.

> **PROGRESS CHECK**
>
> 1 How many bonds can carbon atoms form?
> 2 Why are alkanes described as saturated hydrocarbons?
> 3 What is the name of the first member of the alkane family?
> 4 Which family does ethene belong to?
> 5 What is the formula of butane?
> 6 Consider these compounds:
> $C_{56}H_{112}$ C_2H_5OH $C_{18}H_{38}$
>   **a)** Which of these compounds belongs to the alkene family?
>   **b)** Which of these compounds belongs to the alkane family?
>
> 6. a) $C_{56}H_{112}$ b) $C_{18}H_{38}$
> 5. C_4H_{10}
> 4. Alkenes.
> 3. Methane.
> 2. 'Saturated' means they contain no double bonds; 'hydrocarbons' contain hydrogen and carbon atoms only.
> 1. Four.

7.2 Fuels

LEARNING SUMMARY

After studying this section, you should be able to:

- Explain how fossil fuels were formed.
- Recall that crude oil is a mixture of hydrocarbons.
- Explain how fractional distillation is used to separate crude oil.
- Describe how differences in chain length determine the properties of hydrocarbons.
- Understand how and why cracking of hydrocarbons is carried out.

Formation of fossil fuels

OCR A	C1	✓
OCR B	C1	✓
EDEXCEL	C1	✓
WJEC	C1	✓

> Coal is mainly carbon. Petrol, diesel and oil are hydrocarbons.

Fuels are burned to release energy. In the UK, the **fossil fuels** coal, oil and natural gas are widely used. The burning of fuels is an **exothermic** reaction. The products of crude oil can also be used to make a wide range of useful materials. Fossil fuels are formed over millions of years from the fossilised remains of dead plants and animals. When the plants and animals died, they fell to the sea or swamp floor. Occasionally, the remains were covered by **sediment** very quickly. In the absence of oxygen, the remains did not decay. Over time, more layers of sediment gradually built up. The lower layers became heated and **pressurised**. Over millions of years, fossil fuels formed. Fossil fuels are **non-renewable** so crude oil is a **finite** resource. These take millions of years to form, but are being used up very quickly.

Crude oil

AQA	C1	✓
OCR A	C2	✓
OCR B	C1	✓
EDEXCEL	C1	✓
WJEC	C1	✓

Crude oil is a mixture of many substances but the most important are **hydrocarbons**. Hydrocarbons are molecules that only contain carbon and hydrogen atoms. Some of the hydrocarbons have very short chains of carbon atoms. These hydrocarbons:

- are not very **viscous** (i.e. runny)
- are easy to **ignite**
- have low boiling points
- are valuable fuels.

Other hydrocarbon molecules have much longer chains of carbon atoms. These hydrocarbon molecules:

- are more viscous (less runny) than shorter chain ones
- are harder to ignite
- have higher boiling points.

These longer hydrocarbon molecules are less useful as fuels than shorter chain ones. However, before any of these hydrocarbon molecules can be used, they must first be separated into groups of molecules with a similar number of carbon atoms, called fractions.

In compounds, the atoms of two or more different elements are chemically combined. In mixtures, two or more different elements or compounds are simply mixed together. Each constituent part of the mixture has its original chemical properties. This makes it quite easy to separate mixtures.

Fractional distillation of crude oil

AQA	C1	✓
OCR A	C2	✓
OCR B	C1	✓
EDEXCEL	C1	✓
WJEC	C1	✓

The components of crude oil can be separated by fractional distillation. First, the crude oil is heated until it **evaporates** and enters the fractionating column. The diagram of the fractionating column shows that the bottom of the column is much hotter than the top of the column.

KEY POINT

This means that short hydrocarbon molecules can reach the top of the column before they **condense** and are collected. Longer hydrocarbon molecules condense at higher temperatures and are collected at different points down the column.

Remember, in the fractional distillation of crude oil, the crude oil mixture is first vaporised. The mixture is then separated because the different fractions condense at different temperatures. Do not confuse fractional distillation with cracking or with the blast furnace.

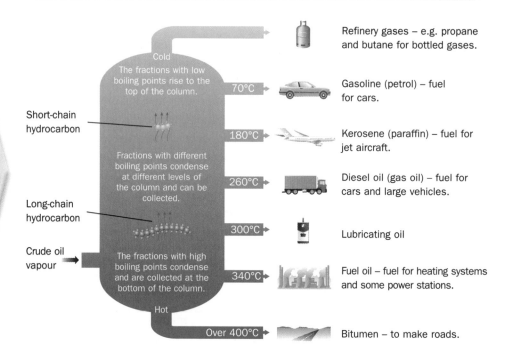

The forces of attraction between the hydrocarbon molecules are much weaker than the forces of attraction within the molecules. The larger the hydrocarbon molecule is, the stronger the forces of attraction between the molecules are, so more energy is required to overcome the force of attraction. Larger hydrocarbon molecules have higher boiling points.

Using different fractions of crude oil

OCR A	C2	✓
OCR B	C1	✓
EDEXCEL	C1	✓
WJEC	C1	✓

The different fractions obtained from crude oil have different uses.

* Liquid petroleum gas (LPG) contains propane and butane. These gases are used in domestic heating and cooking.
* Petrol is used as a fuel for some cars.
* Kerosene is used as a fuel for aeroplanes.
* Diesel oil is used as a fuel for some cars, lorries and trains.
* Fuel oil is used as a fuel for large ships and power stations.
* Bitumen is used to make roads and roofs.

Cracking

AQA	C1	✓
OCR B	C1	✓
EDEXCEL	C1	✓
WJEC	C1	✓

The large hydrocarbon molecules separated during the fractional distillation of crude oil are not very useful.

> **KEY POINT**
>
> However, these hydrocarbon molecules can be broken down into smaller, more useful and more valuable molecules by a process called **cracking**.

The cracking of long chain hydrocarbons is carried out on a large scale. First, the long hydrocarbon molecules are heated until they evaporate. The vapour is then passed over a hot aluminium oxide catalyst. In this example, decane is being cracked to produce octane and ethene.

$$\text{decane } C_{10}H_{22} \longrightarrow \text{octane } C_8H_{18} + \text{ethene } C_2H_4$$
(from the naphtha fraction)

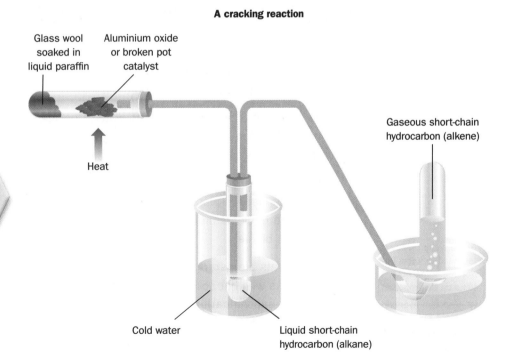

Make sure that when you balance equations for cracking you have the same number of each type of atom on both sides of the equation.

Octane is one of the hydrocarbon molecules in petrol. Ethene, a member of the alkene family of hydrocarbons, is also produced. Ethene is used to make a range of new compounds including plastics and industrial alcohol. As we only have a finite amount of crude oil left, scientists are working to find replacement fuels for the future.

A cracking reaction

Glass wool soaked in liquid paraffin

Aluminium oxide or broken pot catalyst

Gaseous short-chain hydrocarbon (alkene)

Heat

> Make sure you can sketch the apparatus for the cracking of liquid paraffin in the laboratory

Cold water

Liquid short-chain hydrocarbon (alkane)

Cracking is an example of a thermal decomposition reaction. Some of the products of cracking, for example, petrol and diesel, are very useful fuels.

7.3 Vegetable oils

LEARNING SUMMARY

After studying this section, you should be able to:

- Recognise that vegetable oils are extracted from the seeds of a variety of plants.
- Recall that vegetable oils can be processed to make biofuels and soap.
- Describe what an 'emulsion' is.
- Explain why vegetable oils may be hydrogenated to make margarine.

Using vegetable oils

AQA   C1   ✓

Vegetable oils are often removed by crushing up the plant material and collecting the oil. Other oils are collected using distillation. These processes remove water and other impurities to produce pure oil.

Fats have higher boiling points than water. Cooking food by frying is therefore much faster than cooking food in boiling water. In addition, frying foods produces interesting new flavours and increases the energy content of the food.

When vegetable oils are burned they release lots of energy. In fact, vegetable oils can be used in place of fossil fuels in the form of **biodiesel**. This is an alternative to diesel produced from crude oil. Fuels made from plant materials are called **biofuels**.

> To get a top grade, you need to know the word equation that sums up this reaction.
>
> fat + sodium hydroxide → soap + glycerol
>
> This is a hydrolysis reaction.

Oils and fats are **esters**. Soap can be produced by reacting vegetable oils or animal fats with hot sodium or potassium hydroxide solution. The process is known as **saponification** and also produces glycerol. Soaps are the sodium or potassium salts of carboxylic acids with long carbon chains.

Emulsions

AQA   C1   ✓
OCR B   C1   ✓

Oils do not dissolve in water. Salad dressing is an example of a type of everyday mixture called an **emulsion**. It is a mixture of two liquids: oil and water containing the vinegar. Salad dressing is made by shaking oil and vinegar so that they mix together. After a short while, however, the oil and vinegar separate out to form two distinct layers. If the salad dressing was placed in a separating funnel, the lower, denser layer could be run off leaving the less dense layer in the separating funnel. An emulsion is thicker than either of its separate parts. Emulsions have some special properties that make them very useful. Emulsions can improve a product's texture, appearance or ability to coat foodstuffs. Emulsions are widely used to make:

- ice creams
- mayonnaise
- cosmetics
- paints.

Milk is an oil-in-water emulsion. Butter is a water-in-fat emulsion.

Emulsifiers

AQA   C1   ✓
OCR B   C1   ✓

Emulsifiers are molecules with two very different ends. In a salad dressing, one end of the emulsifier molecule is attracted to the oil, while the other end is attracted to the water in the vinegar. The addition of emulsifier molecules keeps the two liquids mixed together.

Simple model of an emulsifier

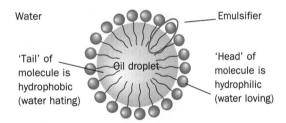

Water

Emulsifier

'Tail' of molecule is hydrophobic (water hating)

Oil droplet

'Head' of molecule is hydrophilic (water loving)

Hydrogenated vegetable oils

AQA   C1   ✓

> **KEY POINT**
>
> Vegetable oils are often liquids at room temperature because they contain C=C bonds. There are, however, advantages to using fats that are solid at room temperature.

They are easier to spread and can be used to make new products such as cakes and pastries.

Hydrogenation produces more saturated fat, which is harmful to health.

Vegetable oils can be made solid at room temperature by a process known as **hydrogenation**. The oils are heated to 60°C with hydrogen and a nickel catalyst. The hydrogen atoms add across double bonds to form fats that are solid at room temperature. Hydrogenated vegetable oils also have a longer shelf life.

7.4 Plastics

LEARNING SUMMARY

After studying this section, you should be able to:

- Understand the term polymer and recall some examples of polymers.
- Describe what happens in an addition polymerisation reaction.
- Write equations to represent polymerisation reactions.
- Explain the difference between thermoplastic and thermosetting materials.
- Relate the properties of plastics to their uses.

Polymerisation

AQA	C1	✓
OCR A	C2	✓
OCR B	C1	✓
EDEXCEL	C1	✓
WJEC	C1	✓

Plastics are **synthetic** (manufactured) **polymers**. **Natural polymers** include cotton, wood, leather, silk and wool. In polymers, lots of small molecules are joined together to make one big molecule.

The simplest **alkene**, ethene, can be formed by the cracking of large **hydrocarbon** molecules. If ethene is heated under pressure in the presence of a **catalyst**, many ethene molecules can join together to form a larger molecule called poly(ethene) or polythene. The diagram below shows how a large number of ethene molecules join together to form polythene.

$$ n \quad \begin{matrix} H & H \\ | & | \\ C = C \\ | & | \\ H & H \end{matrix} \Rightarrow \left(\begin{matrix} H & H \\ | & | \\ C - C \\ | & | \\ H & H \end{matrix} \right)_n $$

The 'n' at the start of the equation and the section of the polymer surrounded by brackets represents the number of molecules involved. The brackets are used because it would be impractical to write out the complete structure. The brackets surround a representative unit that is then repeated through the whole polymer. The small starting molecules, in this case the ethene molecules, are called **monomers**. The C=C bonds in the ethene molecules join together to form long chain molecules called **polymers**. So, a polymer is made from lots of monomer units; in fact, 'poly' means lots. This is an example of an **addition polymerisation** reaction. The ethene molecules have simply joined together.

Other polymers

OCR A   C2   ✓
OCR B   C1   ✓
EDEXCEL C1   ✓
WJEC   C1   ✓

Polymerisation reactions may involve other monomer units. The exact properties of the polymer formed depend upon:

- the monomers involved
- the conditions under which it was made
- the length of the polymer chains.

For example, low density polythene and high density polythene have very different properties and uses because they are produced using different catalysts and different conditions. A plastic's properties are also affected by the amount of **crystallinity** of its structure. The more crystalline a plastic is the more brittle it will be.

Addition polymerisation reactions

AQA   C1   ✓
OCR A   C2   ✓
OCR B   C1   ✓
EDEXCEL C1   ✓
WJEC   C1   ✓

Polymer	Description	Image
Polypropene	Made by an addition polymerisation reaction between many propene molecules.	n CH_3H C=C H H → (C-C)$_n$ with CH_3H
Polyvinyl chloride (PVC)	Made by an addition polymerisation reaction between many chloroethene molecules. Chloroethene used to be called vinyl chloride.	n Cl H C=C H H → (C-C)$_n$
Polytetra-fluoroethene (PTFE or Teflon)	Made by an addition polymerisation reaction between many tetrafluoroethene molecules.	n C=C → (C-C)$_n$ PTFE is known as 'Teflon'. Surfaces coated in Teflon have low friction. It is used to coat some frying pans and saucepans.

Thermoplastics and thermosetting plastics

| OCR A | C2 | ✓ |
| OCR B | C1 | ✓ |

Thermoplastics consist of long polymer chains with a few cross-links.

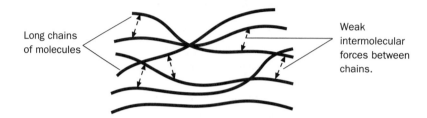

Long chains of molecules

Weak intermolecular forces between chains.

When heated, the material softens. It can then be reshaped. On cooling, the material becomes solid and stiff again because cross-links are made. Thermoplastics can be heated and reshaped many times. Polythene is a thermoplastic. Thermoplastics can be stretched easily.

Thermosetting plastics consist of long, heavily cross-linked polymer chains.

Long chains of molecules

Strong covalent bonds between chains.

When they are first made these thermosetting plastics are soft and can be shaped. Once they have set, however, they become solid and stiff. They do not soften again, even if they are heated to very high temperatures, and so they cannot be reshaped. Melamine is a thermosetting plastic. Thermosetting plastics are rigid and cannot be stretched.

New polymers

AQA	C1	✓
OCR A	C2	✓
WJEC	C1	✓

Scientists are developing new and exciting polymers that have a wide range of uses, for example:

- dental polymers
- wound dressings
- hydrogels
- shape memory alloys (SMA).

Uses of plastics

AQA	C1	✓
OCR A	C2	✓
OCR B	C1	✓
EDEXCEL	C1	✓
WJEC	C1	✓

Polymers have some very useful properties. They are:

- flexible
- good thermal and electrical insulators
- resistant to corrosion
- waterproof
- easy to mould and shape as they generally have low melting points.

The table shows some different plastics and their properties.

Plastic	Description
Polythene	Polythene is cheap and strong. It is used to make plastic bags and bottles. Polythene bags are cheaper than the paper bags they have widely replaced.
PVC	PVC is rigid and can be used for building materials such as drainpipes. PVC has replaced metal drainpipes because PVC is cheaper and lighter than metal. Chemicals called **plasticisers** can be added to PVC to make products such as Wellington boots and mackintoshes.
Polypropene	Polypropene is strong and has a high elasticity. It is used for crates and ropes.
Polystyrene	Polystyrene is cheap and can be moulded into different shapes. It is used for packaging and for plastic casings.

Nylon and polyester

OCR B　C1　✓

Nylon and polyester are condensation polymers that are used to make clothes. Nylon can be used to make cheap waterproof jackets. Nylon is lightweight, hard wearing, keeps UV light out and is waterproof, but it is not breathable so perspiration can make a nylon jacket quite uncomfortable to wear.

Gore-tex™

OCR B　C1　✓

More expensive Gore-tex™ jackets are breathable. Gore-tex™ consists of a thin membrane of PTFE, which is used to coat nylon fabrics. The membrane has lots of little holes. Liquid water is too big to go through these holes, so the fabric is waterproof. Water vapour is small enough to pass through the holes, so it is breathable.

PROGRESS CHECK

1. What type of reaction is involved in the formation of polythene?
2. What is the name given to the small units that join together to form a polymer?
3. Teflon is used to coat frying pans. This coating helps to prevent food from sticking to the pan during cooking. Teflon is made from the monomer tetrafluoroethene.
   a) Draw a tetrafluoroethene molecule.
   b) Is a tetrafluoroethene molecule saturated or unsaturated? Explain your answer.
   c) Draw the repeating unit for the polymer made from the addition polymerisation of tetrafluoroethene molecules.

PROGRESS CHECK

c)
$$\left(\begin{matrix} F & F \\ | & | \\ C - C \\ | & | \\ F & F \end{matrix}\right)_n$$

b) Unsaturated – there is a double bond between the two carbon atoms.

3. a) The diagram has two carbon atoms joined by a double bond. Each carbon atom is also joined by single bonds to two fluorine atoms.

2. Monomers.

1. Addition polymerisation.

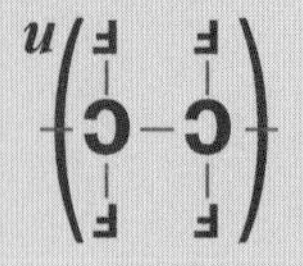

7.5 Ethanol

LEARNING SUMMARY

After studying this section, you should be able to:

- Recall some important uses of ethanol.
- Recall that ethanol may be produced by fermentation of glucose.
- Recall that ethanol may be produced by hydration of ethene.

Ethanol

AQA   C1   ✓

Ethanol, C_2H_5OH, is a member of the **alcohol** family of organic compounds. The diagram below shows the structure of ethanol. It is not a hydrocarbon because it contains an oxygen atom as well as carbon and hydrogen atoms.

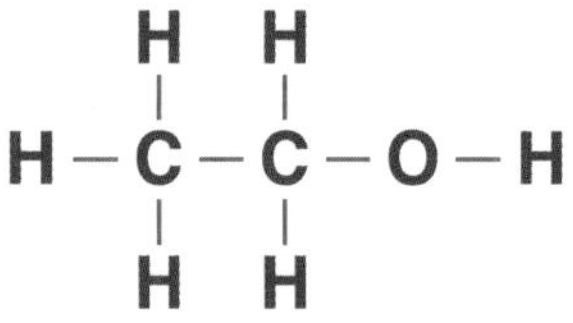

$$\begin{matrix} & H & H & \\ & | & | & \\ H - & C - & C - & O - H \\ & | & | & \\ & H & H & \end{matrix}$$

Ethanol can be produced by reacting ethene with steam:

ethene   +   steam   →   ethanol
C_2H_4 + H_2O → C_2H_5OH

It can also be produced by fermentation with yeast, using renewable sources, e.g. fruits, vegetables and cereals, as a source of glucose.

sugar   →   carbon dioxide   +   ethanol

Ethanol as a fuel

AQA   C1   ✓
EDEXCEL C1   ✓

In some countries, sugar made from sugar beet or sugar cane is made into alcohol. This alcohol can then be mixed with petrol to produce a fuel for vehicles, such as cars.

KEY POINT

Ethanol is a **renewable** energy resource that burns very cleanly, producing carbon dioxide and water vapour.

Alcohols, however, release less energy than petrol when they are burned. In order to produce enough alcohol for fuel, large areas of fertile land and a favourable climate are required to grow the plants needed. Producing fuels in this way is particularly attractive for countries that do not have large reserves of fossil fuels. However, if land is being used to grow crops to produce ethanol, this will reduce the amount of land available to grow food for people to eat.

The plants take in carbon from carbon dioxide during **photosynthesis** and then release the carbon as carbon dioxide when they are burned as fuels.

PROGRESS CHECK

1. What is the formula of ethanol?
2. Why is ethanol not a hydrocarbon?
3. Which crops can be used to produce sugar for making alcohol?
4. What is the catalyst used in fermentation?

1. C_2H_5OH.
2. It contains oxygen as well as hydrogen and carbon.
3. Sugar beet and sugar cane.
4. Yeast.

Sample GCSE questions

1   Polytetrafluoroethene, or PTFE, is a man-made polymer. It is produced from the monomer tetrafluoroethene:

$$
\begin{array}{ccc}
F & & F \\
| & & | \\
C & = & C \\
| & & | \\
F & & F
\end{array}
$$

(a)   (i)   What do you understand by the term 'polymer'?   **[2]**

A polymer is a long-chain molecule, made from many smaller molecules joined together.

(ii)   Write an equation to show the formation of PTFE from tetrafluoroethene.   **[2]**

$$
n \;
\begin{array}{ccc}
F & & F \\
| & & | \\
C & = & C \\
| & & | \\
F & & F
\end{array}
\;\longrightarrow\;
\left(
\begin{array}{ccc}
F & & F \\
| & & | \\
C & - & C \\
| & & | \\
F & & F
\end{array}
\right)_n
$$

> Remember that the double bond breaks when the polymer forms, so replace it with single bonds.

(iii)   What type of polymerisation does this represent?   **[1]**

Addition polymerisation

> This is the answer whenever the polymer is the only product.

(b)   One property of PTFE is that it has a very low coefficient of friction.

(i)   Give one example of a use for PTFE that relies on this property, explaining how it helps.   **[2]**

PTFE is used to coat non-stick pans, so that food doesn't stick to them when cooking.

(ii)   Is PTFE a thermoplastic or a thermosetting material? Explain how you can tell.   **[3]**

It must be thermosetting, otherwise it would soften and melt when heated. It is used on pans which are heated to high temperatures.

Exam practice questions

1 Look at the displayed formulae shown below.

```
     H   H                      H   H                      H   H
     |   |                      |   |                      |   |
 H — C — C — H              C = C                  H — C — C — O — H
     |   |                      |   |                      |   |
     H   H                      H   H                      H   H
```

Ethane   **Ethene**   **Ethanol**

(a) Which of the compounds above is an alcohol? [1]

....

(b) Which of the compounds above is unsaturated and would decolourise bromine water? [1]

....

(c) Which of the compounds above could be used to make a plastic through the process of polymerisation? [1]

....

2 Butane and butene are both hydrocarbons.

(a) What is the chemical formula of butane? .... [1]

(b) Which of the two hydrocarbons is a saturated hydrocarbon? .... [1]

(c) To which series of hydrocarbons does butane belong? .... [1]

(d) Describe a chemical test that would distinguish butane from butene. [2]

....

....

3 **(a)** Crude oil is a mixture of hydrocarbons.

Explain how fractional distillation separates the fractions in crude oil. [2]

....

....

(b) What is cracking and why is it used? [2]

....

....

(c) Explain why small hydrocarbon molecules have a lower boiling point than large hydrocarbon molecules. [2]

....

....

8 Metals and tests

The following topics are covered in this chapter:

- **Extraction of iron**
- **Iron and steel**
- **Aluminium**
- **Transition metals**
- **Copper**
- **Chemical tests**

8.1 Extraction of iron

LEARNING SUMMARY

After studying this section, you should be able to:

- Explain why displacement reactions occur.
- Understand the role of carbon in the extraction of iron from its ore.
- Understand the terms 'oxidation' and 'reduction'.

Methods of extracting metals

AQA	C1	✓
OCR B	C2	✓
EDEXCEL	C1	✓
WJEC	C1	✓

Metals are very useful materials but they are normally found combined with other elements in **compounds** in the Earth's crust. The more **reactive** a metal is, the harder it is to remove it from its compound.

Gold is so **unreactive** that it is found uncombined, but most other metals are found in compounds. Occasionally, rocks are found that contain metals in such high concentrations that it is economically worthwhile to extract the metal from the rock. Such rocks are called **ores**. The ores are **mined**. The metals can be **extracted** using **chemical reactions**. The exact method chosen depends on the reactivity of the metal and the purity of the metal required.

Displacement reactions

AQA	C1	✓
EDEXCEL	C1	✓
WJEC	C1	✓

In **displacement** reactions, a more reactive metal takes the place of a less reactive metal. Iron is more reactive than copper so if an iron nail is placed in a solution of blue copper(II) sulfate the nail changes colour from silver to pink-orange and the solution turns pale. There is also a slight temperature rise.

The more reactive metal, iron, displaces the less reactive metal, copper, from a solution of its compound.

iron + copper(II) sulfate → iron(II) sulfate + copper

The balanced symbol equation for this displacement reaction is:

Fe + CuSO$_4$ → FeSO$_4$ + Cu

The iron atoms are oxidised while the copper ions are reduced.

In a similar way, copper will displace silver from a solution of silver nitrate. The copper atoms are oxidised while the silver ions are reduced.

copper + silver nitrate → copper nitrate + silver
Cu + 2AgNO$_3$ → Cu(NO$_3$)$_2$ + 2Ag

In **competition** reactions, a metal is heated with the metal oxide of a less reactive metal. If iron is heated with copper(II) oxide the more reactive metal, iron, removes the oxygen from the less reactive metal, copper.

iron + copper(II) oxide → iron(II) oxide + copper
Fe + CuO → FeO + Cu

Extracting iron

AQA	C1	✓
EDEXCEL	C1	✓
WJEC	C1	✓

Iron is an **element**. Elements are substances that are made of only one type of atom. There are only about 100 different elements. Iron is an extremely important metal. It is extracted from iron ore in a **blast furnace**. Iron is less reactive than carbon. Iron can be extracted from iron oxide by reducing the metal oxide with carbon.

Oxidation and reduction in the extraction of iron

AQA	C1	✓
OCR A	C1	✓
WJEC	C1	✓

In many examples, oxygen is gained in **oxidation** reactions and oxygen is lost in **reduction** reactions. Oxidation and reduction always happen together. During the extraction of iron the carbon is first oxidised to carbon monoxide. The iron oxide is reduced to iron and the carbon monoxide is oxidised to carbon dioxide.

Corrosion is an example of an oxidation reaction. The less reactive a metal is the more slowly it corrodes.

PROGRESS CHECK

1. What happens in a displacement reaction?
2. What colour is copper(II) sulfate solution?
3. Give the word equation for the reaction between copper sulfate and iron.
4. Zinc is more reactive than copper. Write the word and symbol equations to sum up the reaction between zinc metal and copper(II) sulfate solution. Which metal is oxidised and which metal is reduced in this reaction?

1. A more reactive metal takes the place of a less reactive metal.
2. Blue.
3. iron + copper(II) sulfate → iron(II) sulfate + copper
4. zinc + copper(II) sulfate → zinc(II) sulfate + copper
Zn + CuSO$_4$ → ZnSO$_4$ + Cu
The zinc is oxidised and the copper is reduced.

8.2 Iron and steel

LEARNING SUMMARY

After studying this section, you should be able to:
- Describe the problems caused by the rusting of iron and steel.
- Compare the different ways that iron and steel can be protected against rusting.
- Explain how alloying can alter the properties of a metal.
- Understand the differences between cast iron, wrought iron and steel.
- Relate the properties of different steels to their uses.

Preventing iron from rusting

| OCR B | C2 | ✓ |
| EDEXCEL | C1 | ✓ |

Iron **corrodes**, or **rusts**, faster than most other **transition metals**.

> **KEY POINT**
>
> Rusting involves **oxidation**. It requires the presence of both oxygen and water and produces hydrated iron(III) oxide.

Rusting is accelerated by salt water and by acid rain. Iron can be prevented from rusting by completely removing it from contact with either oxygen or water.

iron + oxygen + water → hydrated iron(III) oxide

Oxidation and reduction reactions always involve **electrons**.

> **KEY POINT**
>
> In oxidation reactions electrons are always lost. In reduction reactions electrons are always gained.

In this example, the iron is oxidised and oxygen is reduced. The iron is the reducing agent and the oxygen is the oxidising agent.

Coating the iron

Painting or **coating** iron in plastic, oil or with tin plate can stop oxygen and water from reaching the metal. If the coating is damaged, however, the iron will start to rust.

Tin is less reactive than iron. If the tin is scratched, the iron will react by losing electrons, even faster than it would normally do, so the iron will rust more quickly.

Sacrificial protection

Sacrificial protection involves placing iron in contact with a more reactive metal like zinc or magnesium to prevent rusting. The iron is protected because the more reactive metal reacts by losing electrons, instead of the iron – which is why the method is called sacrificial protection. **Galvanising** protects iron by coating it in a layer of zinc, another sacrificial metal. The zinc layer stops oxygen and water from reaching the iron.

Alloying the metal

AQA	C1	✓
OCR B	C2	✓
EDEXCEL	C1	✓
WJEC	C1	✓

Alloys are mixtures containing one or more metal. They are made by mixing molten mixtures of metals together. Most **pure metals**, such as copper and aluminium, are too soft for many uses so molten mixtures of similar metals are combined to form alloys. Pure metals have layers because all the atoms are the same size and these atoms can pass over each other.

> **KEY POINT**
>
> In alloys the atoms are different sizes; this causes disruption of the layers so they cannot pass over each other. Alloys are much harder and so much more useful, such as brass, bronze, steel, solder and amalgam.

Cast iron and wrought iron

AQA	C1	✓
OCR B	C2	✓

The iron that is made in a blast furnace contains large amounts of the element carbon. If this iron is allowed to cool down and solidify, it forms **cast iron**. Cast iron contains about 96% pure iron and is used to make objects like drain covers. It is hard, strong and does not rust. Cast iron does have one notable disadvantage: it is brittle and can crack easily.

Wrought iron

Wrought iron is made by removing the impurities from cast iron. It is much softer than cast iron and is used to make objects like gates.

Wrought iron is softer and easier to shape than cast iron because of its structure. It is made from almost pure iron. The iron atoms form a very regular arrangement. The layers of iron atoms are able to slip easily over each other.

Wrought iron structure

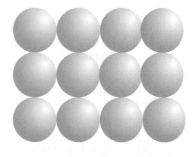

Steel

AQA	C1	✓
OCR B	C2	✓
EDEXCEL	C1	✓

Most of the iron made in the blast furnace is used to produce steel. Mixing iron with other metals and carbon to form alloys, such as stainless steel, will also protect the metal. To make steel:

- Any carbon impurities must first be removed from the iron, to produce pure iron.
- Other metals and carefully controlled amounts of the non-metal element carbon are added to the iron.

Steel is much harder than wrought iron because it consists of atoms of different elements. These atoms are different sizes and cannot pack together to form a regular structure. This irregular structure makes it very difficult for layers of atoms to slide over each other, which makes the steel very hard.

By carefully controlling the amount of carbon that is added to steel, scientists can produce a metal that has exactly the right properties for each particular job:

Steel structure

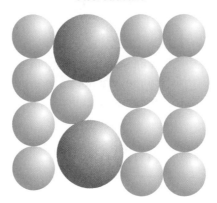

Low carbon steels are soft and easy to shape. Objects such as car bodies are made from low carbon steels.

- **Medium carbon steels** are harder, stronger and less easy to shape. Objects such as hammers are made from medium carbon steels.
- **High carbon steels** are hard, strong, brittle and hard to shape. Objects such as razor blades are made from high carbon steels.
- **Iron** can also be alloyed with other metals to form different types of steel.

Stainless steel is a very widely used alloy. It consists of 70% iron, 20% chromium and 10% nickel. Stainless steel is extremely resistant to corrosion.

PROGRESS CHECK

1 What must be present for iron to rust?
2 Give the chemical name for rust.
3 What are alloys?
4 A sample of pure silver was found to be too soft for making jewellery. Explain how the silver could be made more hard-wearing in terms of the atoms involved.

4. The silver should be alloyed with another metal to make it harder. Pure metals have layers because all the atoms are the same size and these layers can pass over each other. In alloys the atoms are different sizes; this causes disruption of the layers so they cannot pass over each other.
3. Alloys are mixtures containing one or more metal.
2. Hydrated iron(III) oxide.
1. Water and oxygen.

8.3 Aluminium

LEARNING SUMMARY

After studying this section, you should be able to:

- Recall the properties and uses of aluminium.
- Understand the use of electrolysis in extracting aluminium from its ore, bauxite.
- Understand the role of cryolite in the electrolysis.
- Describe what happens at each electrode in the electrolytic cell.
- Use the terms 'oxidation' and 'reduction' to categorise the discharging of ions.

Properties and uses of aluminium

AQA	C1	✓
EDEXCEL	C1	✓
WJEC	C1	✓

Although pure aluminium is quite **soft**, when it is alloyed with other metals it becomes much stronger. Aluminium alloys combine high strength with low density. This makes aluminium a very useful metal for producing objects like aeroplanes and mountain bikes. It is also a good electrical conductor.

Aluminium is a reactive metal and yet it is widely used to make drinks cans. Aluminium is much less reactive than its position in the reactivity series would suggest. This is because when aluminium objects are made their surfaces quickly react with oxygen to form a thin layer of **aluminium oxide**. This layer stops the aluminium metal from coming into contact with other chemicals and so prevents any further reaction. The layer of aluminium oxide means that it is quite safe to drink fizzy, acidic drinks from aluminium cans.

Aluminium reacts with oxygen to form aluminium oxide

Aluminium metal

Layer of aluminium oxide
The layer of aluminium oxide stops aluminium from reacting further.

The extraction of aluminium

AQA	C1	✓
EDEXCEL	C1	✓
WJEC	C1	✓

KEY POINT

Aluminium is more reactive than carbon and so it is extracted from its ore, bauxite, using **electrolysis**, even though this is a very expensive method.

For electrolysis to occur, the aluminium ions and oxide ions in bauxite must be able to move. This means that the bauxite has to be either heated until it melts or dissolved in something.

Bauxite has a very **high melting point** and heating the ore to this temperature is very expensive. Fortunately, another ore of aluminium, called **cryolite**, has a much lower melting point. First, the cryolite is heated up until it melts and then the bauxite is dissolved in the molten cryolite. Extracting aluminium from its ore requires a lot more **energy** than extracting iron from its ore.

Electrolysis of molten aluminium oxide

AQA C1 ✓
EDEXCEL C1 ✓
WJEC C1 ✓

Electrolysis of bauxite (aluminium oxide)

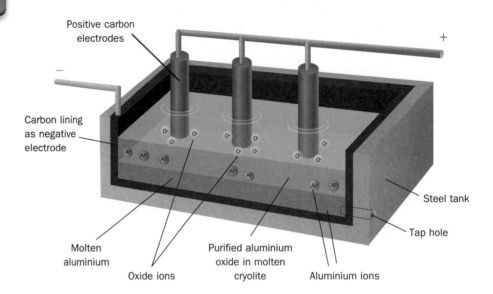

Positive carbon electrodes

Carbon lining as negative electrode

Steel tank

Tap hole

Molten aluminium

Oxide ions

Purified aluminium oxide in molten cryolite

Aluminium ions

Aluminium can now be extracted by electrolysis. By dissolving the aluminium oxide, both the aluminium, Al^{3+} and the oxide, O^{2-} ions can move. During electrolysis, the aluminium, Al^{3+} ions are attracted to the negative electrode (the cathode) where they pick up electrons to form aluminium Al atoms. The aluminium metal collects at the bottom of the cell where it can be gathered.

aluminium ions + electrons → aluminium atoms
$$Al^{3+} + 3e^- \rightarrow Al$$

The oxide, O^{2-} ions are attracted to the positive electrode (the anode) where they deposit electrons to form oxygen molecules.

oxide ions → oxygen molecules + electrons
$$2O^{2-} \rightarrow O_2 + 4e^-$$

The oxygen that forms at the positive electrode readily reacts with the carbon, graphite electrode to form carbon dioxide. The electrodes, therefore, must be replaced periodically. Extracting aluminium is expensive because lots of energy is required and because there are lots of stages in the process.

To get a top grade, make sure you can write equations for the reactions taking place at the electrodes.
$Al^{3+} + 3e^- \rightarrow Al$
$2O^{2-} - 4e^- \rightarrow O_2$

Oxidation and reduction in electrolysis

EDEXCEL C1 ✓
WJEC C1 ✓

In the electrolysis of aluminium oxide:

- Aluminium ions are reduced to aluminium atoms.
- Oxide ions are oxidised to oxygen molecules.

Reduction reactions happen when a species gains electrons. In this case, each aluminium ion gains three electrons to form an aluminium atom.

Oxidation reactions occur when a species loses electrons. In this case, two oxide ions both lose two electrons to form an oxygen molecule.

Reduction and oxidation reactions must always occur together and so are sometimes referred to as **redox** reactions.

Oxidation and reduction can be remembered using the mnemonic OIL RIG:
Oxidation Is Loss
Reduction Is Gain (of electrons).

PROGRESS CHECK

1. What is the formula of aluminium oxide?
2. What is the name of the method used to extract aluminium from its ore?
3. In the extraction of aluminum, why is bauxite dissolved in molten cryolite?

and, therefore, the energy needed.
3. Bauxite has a very high melting point and the addition of cryolite reduces this temperature
2. Electrolysis.
1. Al_2O_3.

8.4 Transition metals

LEARNING SUMMARY

After studying this section, you should be able to:

- Show where transition metals are found on the Periodic Table.
- Recall the properties of a typical transition metal.
- Relate the properties of transition metals to their uses.
- Describe the stages involved in the production of titanium.
- Relate the properties of titanium to specific uses.

Properties and reactions of transition metals

AQA   C1   ✓

Transition metals are found in the middle section of the periodic table. Copper, iron and nickel are examples of very useful transition metals.

KEY POINT

All transition metals have characteristic properties:

- High **melting points** (except for mercury, which is a liquid at room temperature).
- A high **density**.

Transition metals produce **coloured compounds**:

- Copper(II) compounds are blue or green.
- Iron(II) compounds are green.
- Iron(III) compounds are a 'foxy' red.

Transition metals are also strong, tough, good thermal and electrical conductors, malleable and hard wearing. All transition metals are much less reactive than group 1 metals. They react much less vigorously with oxygen and water. Many transition metals can form ions with different charges. This makes transition metals useful catalysts for many reactions.

Titanium

AQA   C1   ✓
WJEC   C1   ✓

Despite being very abundant in the Earth's crust, **titanium** is an expensive metal. This is because it is difficult to extract titanium from its ore. The main ore of titanium is **rutile**. Rutile contains the compound titanium oxide, TiO_2. Titanium is more reactive than carbon and so cannot be extracted simply by heating titanium oxide with carbon.

The extraction of titanium is quite a complicated process:

- First, the titanium oxide is converted to titanium chloride.
- Next, the titanium chloride is reacted with molten magnesium. Magnesium is more reactive than titanium and a chemical reaction takes place in which titanium is displaced.

  titanium chloride + magnesium → titanium + magnesium chloride

The **extraction** of titanium involves many steps and requires a lot of **energy**, so it is very **expensive**.

Titanium has some very special properties:

- It is very strong and hard when **alloyed** with other metals.
- It has a very **low density**.
- It is easy to shape.
- It has a very high melting point.
- It is very resistant to **corrosion**.

Titanium appears to be **unreactive** because the surface of titanium objects quickly reacts with oxygen to form a layer of titanium oxide. This layer prevents any further reaction taking place.

Titanium's properties mean that this metal is very useful. Titanium alloys are used to make:

- replacement hip and elbow joints
- aircraft
- rockets and missiles.

Other useful metals

AQA   C1   ✓
EDEXCEL C1   ✓
WJEC   C1   ✓

Copper has some very special properties:

- It is a good **thermal** and **electrical conductor**.
- It is easy to shape.
- It is very **unreactive** – even with water.
- It has an attractive colour and lustre.
- It is very resistant to **corrosion**.

Copper's properties mean that it is a very useful metal. Copper is used to make water pipes and tanks, saucepans, and electrical wires.

Iron made in the **blast furnace is strong but brittle**. Iron is often made into steel. **Steel** is strong and cheap and is used in vast quantities, but it is also heavy and may rust. Iron and steel are useful structural materials. They are used to make buildings, bridges, ships, cars and trains. Iron is used as a **catalyst** in the **Haber process**.

Gold is used to make jewellery and electrical components. Gold is a highly valued metal that has an attractive colour and lustre. It is also a good thermal conductor and, because of its low reactivity, is very resistant to corrosion. Pure gold is too soft for many uses so it is usually mixed with other metals to form alloys. The **carat scale** and the **fineness scale** are both used to show the amount of pure gold in the alloy; in both cases, the higher the number the greater the proportion of gold.

> Make sure you can suggest some uses for these different metals

Nickel is used as a **catalyst** in the manufacture of margarine.

Common metal alloys

| AQA | C1 | ✓ |
| OCR B | C2 | ✓ |

Common alloys include:

- Amalgams which are mainly mercury.
- Brass which is made from copper and zinc.
- Bronze which is made from copper and tin.
- Solder which is made from lead and tin.
- Steel which is mainly iron.

PROGRESS CHECK

1. In which section of the periodic table are the transition metals found?
2. Why is copper used for electrical wiring and for water pipes?
3. In which process is iron used as a catalyst?
4. Why are many transition metal compounds useful catalysts?

4. Many transition metals can form ions with different charges.
3. The Haber process.
2. It is a good electrical conductor that can be shaped.
1. The middle section.

8.5 Copper

LEARNING SUMMARY

After studying this section, you should be able to:

- Describe how copper may be extracted from copper carbonate and from copper oxide.
- Understood the terms 'bioleaching' and 'phytomining' in copper extraction.
- Explain the purification of copper by electrolysis.
- Write equations for the reactions occurring at the electrodes in copper purification.
- Explain why copper is often alloyed with other metals to improve its properties.

Extraction of copper

| AQA | C1 | ✓ |
| OCR B | C2 | ✓ |

Copper is an unreactive metal that has several ores. It has been known since ancient times, so the richest supplies of ores have been exhausted. Copper is now extracted from rocks that do not contain large amounts of the metal. This means that a lot of rock has to be **quarried** in order to extract enough copper which can cause significant damage to the local area.

Copper sometimes is found uncombined (or native) in nature. The mineral malachite contains copper carbonate, $CuCO_3$. When it is heated, the copper carbonate breaks down to form copper oxide and carbon dioxide.

copper carbonate → copper oxide + carbon dioxide

$$CuCO_3 \rightarrow CuO + CO_2$$

The copper oxide produced reacts with carbon to form copper and carbon dioxide.

copper oxide + carbon → copper + carbon dioxide

$$2CuO + C \rightarrow 2Cu + CO_2$$

Extracting copper from low-grade ores

| AQA | C1 | ✓ |

Scientists are developing ways to exploit copper from **low-grade ores**, which contain copper at lower concentrations than would normally be economically worthwhile to use. The idea is to leach copper out of the ores to form a solution then extract the copper from the solution using electrolysis or by displacement with scrap iron.

Metals can be extracted from low-grade ores using plants. As the plant grows, it takes up the metal, which accumulates in the plant's biomass. When the plant is harvested the biomass can be burned to produce a bio-ore. This process, called **phytomining**, allows scientists to exploit ores that had previously been uneconomic to use.

Bioleaching is the process of extracting metals from their ores using **bacteria**. Advantages of bioleaching include:

* It is a simpler and cheaper process compared to traditional smelting methods.
* It causes less damage to the landscape than traditional methods.

Disadvantages of bioleaching include:

* It is a very slow process.
* There is a risk of pollution if toxic chemicals are allowed to escape into the environment.

Phytomining allows scientists to recover toxic metals from waste dumps and to reclaim **contaminated** areas of land. The recovered metals, such as nickel and cobalt, can be used for new purposes. The land can also be converted to new uses, such as agriculture or for building new homes.

KEY POINT

Recycling copper is better for the environment because fewer raw materials are needed. As less energy is required, the copper is cheaper to buy.

However, people have to be persuaded to recycle their waste metals rather than putting them into landfill sites. Sorting waste metals can also be very labour intensive and expensive.

Purification of copper

| AQA | C1 | ✓ |
| OCR B | C2 | ✓ |

Copper must be purified before it can be used for some applications, such as high-specification wiring. Copper is purified using electrolysis.

Electrolysis of copper

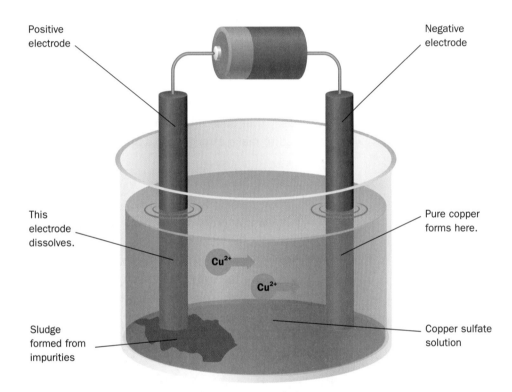

- During the electrolysis of copper, the impure copper metal is used as the positive electrode where the copper atoms give up electrons to form copper ions.
- As the positive electrode dissolves away, any impurities fall to the bottom of the cell to form sludge.
- Copper ions in the solution are attracted towards the negative electrode where the copper ions gain electrons to form copper atoms.
- The positive electrode gets smaller while the negative electrode gets bigger. In addition, the negative electrode is covered in very pure copper.

153

Electrode reactions during copper purification

| AQA | C1 | ✓ |
| OCR B | C2 | ✓ |

The reaction at the positive electrode:

copper atoms → copper ions + electrons
$$Cu \rightarrow Cu^{2+} + 2e^-$$

The reaction at the negative electrode:

Copper ions + electrons → Copper atoms
$$Cu^{2+} + 2e^- \rightarrow Cu$$

To get a top grade, you should be able to write word and symbol equations for the reactions that take place at the electrodes.

Copper alloys

| OCR B | C2 | ✓ |
| WJEC | C1 | ✓ |

Pure copper is too soft for many uses. In pure copper the atoms are all the same size and so they form a regular arrangement. Copper is soft because the layers of atoms can pass easily over each other. Copper is often mixed with other metals to form **alloys**.

Bronze is made by mixing copper and tin. It is much harder than either copper or tin and consists of different sized atoms, so the atoms cannot pack together to form a regular structure. Bronze is hard because the layers of atoms cannot pass easily over each other. The invention of bronze was a major advance: it was used to make stronger tools and weapons.

PROGRESS CHECK

1. What method is used to purify copper?
2. If you wanted to coat a metal object with copper, which electrode should you attach it to?
3. Copper can be purified by electrolysis.
   a) Give the symbol equation for the reaction that takes place at the positive electrode during the purification of copper.
   b) Give the symbol equation for the reaction that takes place at the negative electrode during the purification of copper.

1. Electrolysis.
2. The negative electrode.
3. a) $Cu \rightarrow Cu^{2+} + 2e^-$.
   b) $Cu^{2+} + 2e^- \rightarrow Cu$.

8.6 Chemical tests

LEARNING SUMMARY

After studying this section, you should be able to:

- Recall the gas tests for carbon dioxide, hydrogen, chlorine, oxygen and ammonia.
- Describe how to identify metal carbonates.

Gas tests

OCR B   C1, C2   ✓
EDEXCEL C1   ✓
WJEC   C1   ✓

Chemists use these tests to identify the following common gases:

Carbon dioxide: The gas is bubbled through limewater. The limewater turns cloudy. Carbonates react with acids to produce carbon dioxide.

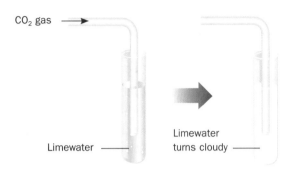

Hydrogen: A lighted splint is placed nearby. The hydrogen burns with a squeaky pop. The flame goes out.

Chlorine: Place damp litmus paper in the gas. The litmus paper is bleached.

> Make sure you are familiar with the tests for common gases – you will need to state the reagents used and the results in the exam.

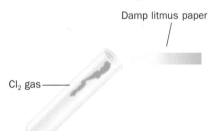

Oxygen: A glowing splint is placed in the gas. The splint relights.

Ammonia: Place damp red litmus paper in the gas. The damp red litmus paper turns blue.

Identifying carbonates

OCR A	C3	✓
OCR B	C2	✓
EDEXCEL	C1	✓
WJEC	C1	✓

Metal **carbonates** react with dilute hydrochloric acid to form a salt, water and carbon dioxide gas. To prove the gas produced is carbon dioxide, place a drop of limewater (calcium hydroxide $Ca(OH)_2$ solution) on a glass rod. If carbon dioxide is present the limewater turns cloudy.

When copper(II) carbonate is heated it decomposes to form copper(II) oxide and carbon dioxide. This can be identified by a distinctive colour change: copper carbonate is green and copper oxide is black.

PROGRESS CHECK

1 What are the tests for carbon dioxide, hydrogen, chlorine and oxygen?
2 What colour is copper carbonate?
3 What gas is given off when metal carbonates react with hydrchloric acid?

1. When carbon dioxide is bubbled through limewater it turns the limewater cloudy.
Hydrogen burns with a squeaky pop.
Chlorine bleaches damp litmus paper.
Oxygen relights a glowing splint.
2. Green.
3. Carbon dioxide.

Sample GCSE questions

1. Aluminium is extracted from its ore, bauxite, using electrolysis.

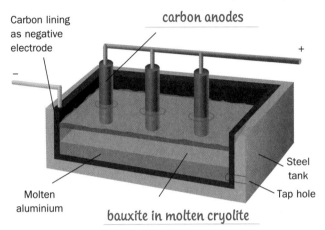

Carbon lining as negative electrode

carbon anodes

+

−

Steel tank

Tap hole

Molten aluminium

bauxite in molten cryolite

(a) (i) Add the two labels that are missing from the diagram. **[2]**

(ii) Why is it not possible to reduce the aluminium oxide in bauxite using carbon? **[2]**

Aluminium is more reactive than carbon. Carbon cannot displace aluminium from a compound.

(b) Aluminium is a more reactive element than iron, but it does not corrode as much.

(i) Explain why aluminium is more resistant to corrosion than iron. **[2]**

An oxide layer forms on the surface which protects the metal.

(ii) Apart from resistance to corrosion, why might it be an advantage to make a boat from aluminium instead of steel? **[3]**

Aluminium has a lower density than steel, so it will make the boat lighter. The boat will require less energy to move through the water.

Notice that there are three marks, so the question obviously expects either more than one answer or a fully explained answer.

Exam practice questions

1 The main ore of iron is haematite: its formula is Fe_2O_3. Iron may be extracted from haematite in a blast furnace.

(a) What is an 'ore'? [2]

....

....

(b) Which element displaces iron from its oxide in the blast furnace? [1]

....

2 Explain why the method used to extract aluminium from its oxide is different from that used to extract iron from its oxide. [4]

....

....

....

....

3 (a) Steel is an alloy composed mainly of iron. Explain why steel is more useful for making support cables in bridges than iron. [2]

....

....

(b) Name the metal that is mixed with lead to make solder. [1]

....

(c) Give two properties that make solder useful for welding metal gas pipes together. [2]

....

4 Flame tests are used in the chemical analysis of salts.

(a) What can be identified by carrying out a flame test? [1]

....

(b) If a salt produces a yellow flame, what does that show? [1]

....

(c) Why might it be easy to confuse copper salts with barium salts? [1]

....

(d) Why must the wire be cleaned before each flame test? [2]

....

....

9 Acids, bases and salts

The following topics are covered in this chapter:

- Acids and bases
- Making salts
- Limestone
- Metal carbonate reactions
- The electrolysis of sodium chloride

9.1 Acids and bases

LEARNING SUMMARY

After studying this section, you should be able to:

- Explain the difference between a strong acid and a weak acid.
- Relate the strength of an acid to its uses.
- Explain the difference between a strong alkali and weak alkali.
- Use the pH scale as a measure of acidity or alkalinity.
- Recognise the property that makes indicators useful.

Strong acids

OCR B	C2	✓
EDEXCEL	C1	✓
WJEC	C1	✓

Acids and **bases** are chemical **opposites**. Some bases dissolve in water and are called **alkalis**.

Acidic solutions have a **pH** less than 7. **Acidic compounds** can be solids like citric acid or tartaric acid, liquids like sulfuric acid, nitric acid or ethanoic acid or gases like hydrogen chloride.

Some acids are described as **strong**. Examples of strong acids include hydrochloric acid, which is produced in the stomach and helps break down food and kills bacteria, sulfuric acid and nitric acid.

Strong acids are completely **ionised** in water. When hydrochloric acid is placed in water, every hydrogen chloride molecule splits up to form hydrogen ions and chloride ions.

$$HCl \rightarrow H^+ + Cl^-$$

Weak acids

OCR B	C2	✓
WJEC	C1	✓

Other acids are described as **weak acids**. Examples of weak acids include ethanoic acid, citric acid and carbonic acid.

Weak acids do not completely ionise in water. When ethanoic acid is placed in water, only a small fraction of the ethanoic acid molecules split up to form hydrogen ions and ethanoate ions.

> **Acids are proton donors. Bases are proton acceptors.**

$$CH_3COOH \rightleftharpoons H^+ + CH_3COO^-$$

Notice that this reaction is **reversible**. Ethanoic acid reacts more slowly with metals, alkalis and carbonates than a comparative amount of a strong acid like hydrochloric acid would do. This is because ethanoic acid produces fewer H^+ ions and so there are fewer collisions between reactant particles and H^+ ions.

A sample of a weak acid, like ethanoic acid, has a lower conductivity than a sample of a strong acid, like hydrochloric acid, because hydrochloric acid is fully **dissociated** (that is, split up) in water and produces more H^+ ions to carry charge.

However, both acids would produce the same volume of carbon dioxide if they were reacted with calcium carbonate or magnesium carbonate.

Weak acids, such as vinegar, are widely used as descalers since they remove limescale without damaging the surface of the object being cleaned.

Concentrated sulfuric acid is a dehydrating agent and can be used to remove water from sugar and from hydrated copper sulfate.

Weak and strong alkalis

OCR A	C3	✓
OCR B	C2	✓
WJEC	C1	✓

Traditional sources of alkalis included stale urine and burned wood. With **industrialisation**, the demand for alkalis grew, so shortages of alkalis soon developed.

Alkalis were used to **neutralise** acid soils, to produce the chemicals needed to bind dyes to cloth, to convert fats and oils into soap and to manufacture glass. Early methods of manufacturing alkalis from limestone and salt produced a lot of **pollution**, including the acid gas hydrogen chloride and waste heaps that slowly released the toxic and unpleasant smelling gas hydrogen sulfide. **Oxidation** of hydrogen chloride forms chlorine gas.

Alkaline solutions have a pH more than 7.

> **KEY POINT**
>
> Some alkalis are described as **strong alkalis**. Examples of strong alkalis include sodium hydroxide and potassium hydroxide.

> **Hydroxide ions have the formula OH⁻. Remember to add the negative charge. Strong alkalis have a high pH and are fully ionised.**

Strong alkalis are completely ionised in water. When sodium hydroxide is placed in water, it splits up to form sodium ions and hydroxide ions.

$$NaOH \rightarrow Na^+ + OH^-$$

> **KEY POINT**
>
> Other alkalis are described as weak. Ammonia is an example of a **weak alkali**.

Weak alkalis do not completely ionise in water. Ammonia produces hydroxide, OH^-, ions when it reacts with water.

ammonia + water ⇌ ammonium ion + hydroxide ion

$$NH_3 + H_2O \rightleftharpoons NH_4^+ \qquad + OH^-$$

Ammonium salts are useful **fertilisers**.

The pH scale

The pH scale can be used to distinguish between weak and strong acids and alkalis. The pH scale measures the concentration of hydrogen ions. Neutral solutions have a pH of 7. Acidic solutions have a pH of less than 7.

The strongest acids have a pH of 1. Dilute solutions of weak acids have higher pH values than dilute solutions of strong acids. Many foods, such as lemons, contain acids. These foods taste sour. If water is added to an acid it becomes more dilute and less corrosive. Alkaline solutions have a pH of more than 7. The strongest alkalis have a pH of 14. Many cleaning materials contain alkalis. If water is added to an alkali it becomes more dilute and less corrosive.

The pH scale

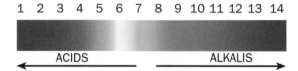

1 2 3 4 5 6 7 8 9 10 11 12 13 14

← ACIDS   ALKALIS →

Indicators

Indicators can be used to show the pH of a solution. Indicators work by changing colour. They can show when exactly the right amount of acid and alkali have been added together. Red litmus turns blue in alkaline conditions while blue litmus turns red in acidic conditions.

PROGRESS CHECK

1. Which ions are found in acidic solutions?
2. Which ions are found in alkaline solutions?
3. Name three strong acids and explain why they are described as 'strong'.
4. A 1 g sample of calcium carbonate was placed in 50 cm^3 of 1.0 mol dm^{-3} ethanoic acid. An identical sample of calcium carbonate was then placed in 50 cm^3 of 1.0 mol dm^{-3} hydrochloric acid.
   a) In what ways would the reactions be the same?
   b) In what ways would the reactions be different?

4. a) Both reactions would produce carbon dioxide/bubbles would be seen/the same volume of gas would be made in both experiments.
   b) The reaction involving hydrochloric acid would be faster because it is a strong acid while ethanoic acid is a weak acid.
3. Hydrochloric acid, sulfuric acid and nitric acid. They are completely ionised in water.
2. OH⁻ ions.
1. H⁺ ions.

9.2 Making salts

After studying this section, you should be able to:

- Explain neutralisation, using the ionic equation for the formation of water.
- Predict what type of salt will be produced when using a given acid.
- Recall that metal salts are made from metals or from metal oxides with acids.

Neutralisation reactions

OCR A	C3	✓
OCR B	C2	✓
EDEXCEL	C1	✓
WJEC	C1	✓

The reaction between an acid and a base is called **neutralisation**.

- Acidic solutions contain hydrogen, H^+ ions.
- Alkaline solutions contain hydroxide, OH^- ions.

The reaction between an acid and an alkali can be shown in a word equation:

acid + alkali → salt + water

The ionic equation for all neutralisation reactions is:

$H^+(aq) + OH^-(aq) \rightarrow H_2O(l)$

The type of salt that is produced during the reaction depends on the acid and the alkali used. Indigestion medicines contain chemicals that react with, and neutralise, excess stomach acid.

Naming salts

OCR B	C2	✓
EDEXCEL	C1	✓
WJEC	C1	✓

Neutralising hydrochloric acid will produce **chloride salts**.

hydrochloric acid + sodium hydroxide → sodium chloride + water

Neutralising nitric acid will produce **nitrate salts**.

nitric acid + potassium hydroxide → potassium nitrate + water

Neutralising sulfuric acid will produce **sulfate** salts.

sulfuric acid + sodium hydroxide → sodium sulfate + water

Ammonia reacts with water to form a weak alkali. Ammonia solution can be neutralised with acids to form **ammonium salts**.

Making salts from metal oxides

OCR B	C2	✓
EDEXCEL	C1	✓

Metal oxides are also bases. They can be reacted with acids to make salts and water:

metal oxide   + acid   → salt   + water

copper(II) oxide + hydrochloric acid → copper(II) chloride + water
Cu   + 2HCl   → CuCl₂   + H₂O

zinc oxide + sulfuric acid → zinc sulfate + water
ZnO   + H₂SO₄   → ZnSO₄   + H₂O

9.3 Limestone

LEARNING SUMMARY

After studying this section, you should be able to:

- Understand the classification of rocks into three types: sedimentary, igneous and metamorphic.
- Recall that limestone is calcium carbonate and explain how it was formed.
- Write an equation for the thermal decomposition of calcium carbonate.
- Write an equation for the reaction between calcium oxide and water.
- Recall the many useful products that are made from limestone.

Types of rock

OCR A	C3	✓
OCR B	C2	✓
EDEXCEL	C1	✓

Rocks can be classified into three groups: **sedimentary**, **metamorphic** and **igneous**.

- **Limestone** and **chalk** are **sedimentary rocks**. These rocks sometimes contain **fossils** and are relatively soft and easy to erode. Sedimentary rocks are formed when layers of sediment are compacted over millions of years. The presence of shell fragments in fossils indicate that the rocks formed in a **marine environment**.
- **Marble** is an example of a **metamorphic rock**. Marble is made when limestone or chalk are subjected to high pressures and temperatures.
- **Granite** is an example of an **igneous rock**. Igneous rocks are harder than metamorphic rocks which, in turn, are harder than sedimentary rocks. They are formed when **magma** (liquid rock below the Earth's surface) or **lava** (liquid rock above the Earth's surface) cool down and solidify. The faster the crystals in the rocks form the smaller the crystal will be.

Natural geological processes, such as **sedimentation** and **evaporation**, lead to the formation of valuable resources such as salt, limestone and coal.

Limestone

AQA	C1	✓
OCR B	C2	✓
EDEXCEL	C1	✓

The materials used in everyday life, such as metals, ceramics and polymers, are chemicals or mixtures of chemicals. Some materials, such as cotton, paper, silk and wool, are made from living things.

Raw materials from the Earth's crust can be made into useful new synthetic materials. Chemical industries developed in the north-west of England because important resources including salt, limestone and coal could be found nearby.

> **KEY POINT**
>
> When limestone (calcium carbonate) is heated, it breaks down to form quicklime (calcium oxide) and carbon dioxide.

calcium carbonate → calcium oxide + carbon dioxide

$$CaCO_3(s) \rightarrow CaO(s) + CO_2(g)$$

This is an example of a thermal decomposition reaction.

> **KEY POINT**
>
> Quicklime (calcium oxide) can be reacted with water to form slaked lime (calcium hydroxide). A solution of slaked lime is known as limewater.

calcium oxide + water → calcium hydroxide

$$CaO(s) + H_2O(l) \rightarrow Ca(OH)_2(s)$$

Calcium carbonate, calcium oxide and calcium hydroxide are all bases and so can be used to neutralise acidic lakes and soils.

Limewater is used to test for the presence of the gas carbon dioxide. Carbon dioxide turns limewater cloudy.

calcium hydroxide + carbon dioxide → calcium carbonate + water

$$Ca(OH)_2(aq) + CO_2(g) \rightarrow CaCO_3(s) + H_2O(l)$$

When limestone is heated, the mass decreases because the gas carbon dioxide is produced.

Limestone quarry

The thermal decomposition of limestone is an example of a reaction that takes in heat. This is called an endothermic reaction. The formula $CaCO_3$ shows us the type and ratio of atoms present. Here, the calcium, carbon and oxygen atoms are present in the ratio 1 : 1 : 3. Calcium oxide is an example of a compound that is held together by ionic bonds. Ionic bonding involves the transfer of electrons. This forms ions with opposite charges, which then attract each other.

Uses of limestone

AQA	C1	✓
OCR B	C2	✓
EDEXCEL	C1	✓

Limestone is used to make iron and steel and to build roads. It can also be used to make a range of building materials.

- **Cement** is produced by roasting powdered clay with powdered limestone in a rotating kiln. If water is added, and the mixture is allowed to set, it forms the hard, stone-like material cement. Clay can also be used to make bricks.
- When water is mixed with cement and sand, and then allowed to set, **mortar** is made.
- **Concrete** is made by mixing cement, sand and aggregate (rock chippings) with water. When water is added to cement it **hydrates** and binds together all the particles to form a material that is as hard as rock. Concrete is tough and cheap; it is widely used in building, for example, bridges.
- **Reinforced concrete** is a useful **composite material**. It is made by setting concrete around steel supports. This material combines the hardness of concrete with the flexibility of steel.
- **Glass** can be made by heating up a mixture of limestone (calcium carbonate), sand (silicon dioxide) and soda (sodium carbonate) until the mixture melts.

PROGRESS CHECK

1. What is the main chemical in limestone?
2. What type of rock is limestone?
3. What type of rock is marble?
4. What type of rock is granite?
5. When calcium carbonate is heated fiercely a chemical reaction takes place.
   a) Write a balanced symbol equation for this reaction.
   b) Why does the sample of calcium carbonate have a lower mass after heating?

1. Calcium carbonate.
2. Sedimentary rock.
3. Metamorphic rock.
4. Igneous rock.
5. a) $CaCO_3(s) \rightarrow CaO(s) + CO_2(g)$
   b) The gas carbon dioxide is given off, which has mass.

9.4 Metal carbonate reactions

LEARNING SUMMARY

After studying this section, you should be able to:

- Understand what is happening when a metal carbonate undergoes thermal decomposition.
- Write balanced equations for thermal decomposition reactions of metal carbonates.
- Write balanced equations for metal carbonate reactions with acids.
- Predict the salt produced when a metal carbonate reacts with a given acid.
- Describe the procedure for making a soluble salt from the reaction between a metal carbonate and acid.

Thermal decomposition reactions

AQA	C1	✓
OCR B	C2	✓
EDEXCEL	C1	✓

When calcium carbonate is heated fiercely it decomposes to form calcium oxide and carbon dioxide. The general equation for the reaction is:

metal carbonate → metal oxide + carbon dioxide

Other metal carbonates, including the carbonates of copper, iron, manganese, calcium, magnesium, and zinc, decompose in a similar way when they are heated. When copper carbonate is heated it breaks down to give copper oxide and carbon dioxide. Copper(II) carbonate is green while copper(II) oxide is black. The colour change shows a new substance has been made.

Be able to give the symbol equation for this reaction.

$CuCO_3 \rightarrow CuO + CO_2$

copper(II) carbonate → copper(II) oxide + carbon dioxide

Group 1 carbonates and naming compounds

| AQA | C1 | ✓ |
| EDEXCEL | C1 | ✓ |

Not all metal carbonates of group 1 metals will decompose at the temperatures that can be reached using a Bunsen burner.

If two elements join together in a chemical reaction, the name of the compound is given by the two elements that have joined together, for example:

sodium + chlorine → sodium chloride

Heating baking powder

| OCR B | C1 | ✓ |

When metal hydrogencarbonate compounds are heated, they undergo thermal decomposition reactions to form metal carbonates, carbon dioxide and water.

The main chemical compound in baking powder is sodium hydrogencarbonate, $NaHCO_3$. When heated fiercely it reacts to form sodium carbonate, carbon dioxide and water. It is the carbon dioxide produced by the reaction that makes cakes rise.

Be able to recall the equation that sums up this reaction.

$2NaHCO_3 \rightarrow Na_2CO_3 + CO_2 + H_2O$

sodium hydrogencarbonate → sodium carbonate + carbon dioxide + water

Making salts from metal carbonates

OCR B	C2	✓
EDEXCEL	C1	✓
WJEC	C1	✓

Acids can be neutralised by metal carbonates to form salts. Most metal carbonates are insoluble, so they are bases, but they are not alkalis. When acids are neutralised by metal carbonates, a salt, water and carbon dioxide are produced. This means that rocks, such as limestone, that contain metal carbonate compounds are damaged by acid rain. The general equation for the reaction is:

metal carbonate + acid → salt + water + carbon dioxide

A gas (carbon dioxide) is made so bubbles will be seen. The name of the salt produced depends on the acid and the metal carbonate used.

- Hydrochloric acid makes chloride salts.
- Sulfuric acid makes sulfate salts.
- Nitric acid makes nitrate salts.
- Ethanoic acid is neutralised to form ethanoate salts.
- Phosphoric acid is neutralised to form phosphate salts.

The reactions between acids and metal carbonates are exothermic.

Examples of carbonate reactions

OCR B	C2	✓
EDEXCEL	C1	✓
WJEC	C1	✓

zinc carbonate + sulfuric acid → zinc sulfate + water + carbon dioxide

$$ZnCO_3 + H_2SO_4 \rightarrow ZnSO_4 + H_2O + CO_2$$

copper(II) carbonate + hydrochloric acid → copper(II) chloride + water + carbon dioxide

$$CuCO_3 + 2HCl \rightarrow CuCl_2 + H_2O + CO_2$$

Make sure you can apply this idea to other examples.

The diagram below shows how copper chloride salt is made.

Making copper chloride

The steps involved in the production of copper chloride are as follows:

1 Copper carbonate is added to hydrochloric acid until all the acid is used up. Solid remains.
2 Any unreacted copper carbonate is filtered off.
3 The solution of copper(II) chloride and water is poured into an evaporating basin.
4 The basin is heated gently until the first crystals of copper chloride start to appear.
5 The solution is then left in a warm place for a few days to allow the remaining copper chloride to crystallise.

9.5 The electrolysis of sodium chloride

LEARNING SUMMARY

After studying this section, you should be able to:

- Recall some important uses of sodium chloride.
- Explain the electrolysis of sodium chloride to produce hydrogen, chlorine and sodium hydroxide.
- Write equations for the reactions that occur at the electrodes.
- Recall the main uses of the products of electrolysing sodium chloride solution.

Sodium chloride

OCR A C3 ✓
OCR B C2 ✓

Sodium chloride (**common salt**) is an important resource. It is an **ionic compound** formed from the **combination** of a group 1 metal (sodium) and a group 7 non-metal (chlorine). Sodium chloride is dissolved in large quantities in **seawater**.

Salt can be obtained by **mining** or from allowing seawater to **evaporate**; the method used depends on how the salt is to be used and how pure it needs to be. **Quarrying** salt can have a dramatic impact on the environment. **Rock salt** (unpurified salt) is often used on icy roads. The salt lowers the freezing point of water from 0°C to about −5°C. Sprinkling rock salt on roads means that any water present will not freeze to form ice unless the temperature is very low.

Salt and diet

OCR A C3 ✓
OCR B C2 ✓

Salt is also used in cooking, both to **flavour** food and as a **preservative**. However, eating too much salt can increase blood pressure and the chance of heart disease and stroke occurring. **Food packaging** may contain information on the sodium levels in a food.

Sodium ions may come from several sources, including sodium chloride salt. Government bodies, such as the Department for Health, produce guidelines to inform the public about the effects of different foods. A solution of sodium chloride in water is called **brine**.

Electrolysis of sodium chloride solution

OCR A	C3	✓
OCR B	C2	✓
EDEXCEL	C1	✓

The **electrolysis** of concentrated sodium chloride solution is an important industrial process and produces three useful products (hydrogen, chlorine and sodium hydroxide). The electrodes are made of inert materials so they do not react with the useful products made during the electrolysis reaction.

- During electrolysis, pairs of hydrogen ions, H^+ ions, are attracted to the negative electrode where they pick up electrons to form hydrogen molecules, H_2.

  Hydrogen ions + Electrons → Hydrogen molecules
  $$2H^+ + 2e^- \rightarrow H_2$$

- Pairs of chloride ions, Cl^- ions, are attracted to the positive electrode where they deposit electrons to form chlorine molecules.

  Chloride ions → Chlorine molecules + Electrons
  $$2Cl^- \rightarrow Cl_2 + 2e^-$$

- A solution of sodium hydroxide, NaOH is also produced.

Each of these products (hydrogen, chlorine and sodium hydroxide) can be used to make other useful materials. When there is a mixture of ions, such as Cl^- and OH^- and Na^+ and H^+ as in this case, the products that are formed depends on the **reactivity** of the elements involved. Electrolysis can also be used to **electroplate** objects. This can protect surfaces from **corrosion** and make them more attractive. Copper and silver plating are both produced by electrolysis.

In the electrolysis of a concentration of sodium chloride solution:

- Hydrogen ions are **reduced** to hydrogen molecules; the hydrogen ions both gain an electron to form a hydrogen molecule.
- Chloride ions are **oxidised** to chlorine molecules; the two chloride ions both lose an electron to form a chlorine molecule.

> **KEY POINT**
>
> Reduction and oxidation reactions must always occur together, so they are sometimes referred to as **redox** reactions.

Chlorine is used:

- to make **bleach**
- to sterilise water
- to produce hydrochloric acid
- in the production of PVC.

Hydrogen is used in the manufacture of margarine.

Sodium hydroxide is an alkali used in paper making and in the manufacture of many products including soaps and detergents, and rayon and acetate fibres.

PROGRESS CHECK

1 What groups do sodium and chlorine belong to?
2 Where is sodium chloride found?
3 How are **a)** chlorine, **b)** hydrogen and **c)** sodium hydroxide used?

c) In soap, detergents, paper, rayon, acetate.
b) In the manufacture of margarine.
3. a) In bleach, to sterilise water, production of hydrochloric acid and PVC.
2. In seawater and in underground deposits.
1. Groups 1 and 7.

Sample GCSE questions

1   Limestone is a valuable natural resource.

(a)   Draw a line to match the following calcium compounds obtained from limestone with the correct chemical name. **[2]**

Limestone		Calcium oxide
Quicklime		Calcium hydroxide
Slaked lime		Calcium carbonate

Exam questions on limestone are common, so make sure you learn the chemical names for the calcium compounds and their applications.

(b)   State the type of reaction that takes place to obtain calcium oxide from calcium carbonate. **[1]**

Thermal decomposition

(c)   Limewater can be used to test for the presence of a specific gas.

    (i)   State the name of the gas. **[1]**

    Carbon dioxide

    (ii)   Describe how limewater is used to test for the gas. **[2]**

    The gas is bubbled through limewater using a delivery tube. The limewater will turn cloudy if the gas is carbon dioxide.

The test for carbon dioxide is relevant to a lot of topics. It is a common test, so make sure you know it.

(d)   'When it comes to the environment, quarrying limestone is a controversial subject'.

Explain this statement, including arguments for and against quarrying limestone.

The quality of written communication will be assessed in your answer. **[6]**

Quarrying limestone is a controversial subject because the process of quarrying has a negative impact on the environment, but some of the calcium compounds obtained from limestone can be used to positive effect.

Quarrying involves large pits being dug out of the ground, which destroys natural habitats. The machinery used to extract and transport the limestone is powered by fossil fuels and therefore produces pollutant gases.

However, the calcium compounds obtained from limestone are all bases and they can be used to neutralise acidic lakes and soils, improving conditions for plants and aquatic life.

You will only gain full marks if your answer is clear, accurate and easy to follow, so make sure you structure it in a logical way. Deal with the positives and negatives separately, rather than jumping around, and include a summary – this could be in the opening or closing part of your answer.

Exam practice questions

1 Hydrochloric acid is a strong acid and ethanoic acid is a weak acid.

(a) State which acid is fully ionised when in solution. .... **[1]**

(b) State which ion is produced by both acids when in solution. .... **[1]**

(c) Which acid would react more rapidly with magnesium ribbon if the concentration was the same? **[1]**

....

(d) Explain why ethanoic acid is better than hydrochloric acid for descaling a kettle. **[2]**

....

....

2 Sulfuric acid reacts with magnesium metal, giving off a gas.

(a) Which gas is produced in this reaction? .... **[1]**

(b) How does the pH of the acid change as it reacts? .... **[1]**

(c) What compound is produced in this reaction? .... **[1]**

(d) Give the names of two other substances that would react with sulfuric acid to produce the same compound. **[2]**

....

3 Limestone is an important raw material that is quarried in many parts of the UK.

(a) What is the name of the main chemical present in limestone? **[1]**

....

(b) Describe how limestone is turned into cement. **[2]**

....

....

(c) Describe four factors that should be taken into consideration when quarrying for limestone. Your answer must include at least one each of the environmental, economic and social effects. **[4]**

....

....

....

....

....

Energy

The following topics are covered in this chapter:

- **The electricity supply**
- **Generating electricity**
- **Renewable sources of energy**
- **Electrical energy and power**
- **Electricity matters**
- **Particles and heat transfer**

10.1 The electricity supply

LEARNING SUMMARY

After studying this section, you should be able to:

- Explain what is meant by sustainable energy.
- Explain the difference between a primary energy source and a secondary energy source.
- Calculate the efficiency of electrical appliances and power stations.
- Draw Sankey diagrams to show energy transfers.

Energy resources

AQA	P1	✓
OCR A	P3	✓
OCR B	P1	✓
EDEXCEL	P1	✓
WJEC	P1	✓

People in modern societies use a lot of **energy resources**. Energy resources we use directly are called **primary energy resources**. Examples include diesel, petrol and solar energy. **Electricity** is a **secondary energy resource**. It has to be made from a primary resource. We use a lot of electricity because:

- It's easy to transmit long distances.
- It can be used to do lots of different jobs.
- There is no pollution at the point where it is used.

> **KEY POINT**
>
> A **sustainable energy** supply is one that meets our needs without leaving problems for future generations, for example, without using up all the resources, causing air pollution or climate change.

Efficiency

AQA	P1	✓
OCR A	P3	✓
OCR B	P1, P2	✓
EDEXCEL	P1	✓
WJEC	P1	✓

Whenever energy is transferred from a primary resource to electricity, some of it is wasted as heat in the process. No power station is **100% efficient**. In a coal-fired power station, for example, for every 100 J of energy stored in the coal that is burned, only 40 J is transferred to the electricity. Energy is a conserved quantity, which means that the total amount of energy remains the same. The 60 J of energy that is not transferred to the electricity is wasted and ends up as heat in the surrounding environment. This will cause a slight temperature increase in the surroundings.

KEY POINT

The efficiency of an energy transfer is the fraction, or percentage, of the energy input that is transferred to useful energy output.

$$\text{Efficiency} = \frac{\text{useful energy output}}{\text{total energy input}}$$

Or as a percentage:

$$\text{Efficiency} = \frac{\text{useful energy output}}{\text{total energy input}} \times 100\%$$

Draw two Sankey diagrams in your notes, one for a process that has more wasted energy than useful energy and one with more useful energy than wasted energy. Label the input energy, which is 100%, and the useful energy and wasted energy. When you look at them, they will remind you of all the information summarised by a Sankey diagram.

Energy transfers taking place in a process can be shown on a **Sankey energy flow diagram**.

Energy transformed in a coal-fired power station.

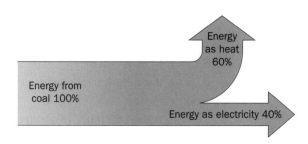

Energy as heat 60%

Energy from coal 100%

Energy as electricity 40%

The width of the arrows is proportional to the amount of energy represented by the arrow.

Improving efficiency

AQA	P1	✓
OCR A	P3	✓
OCR B	P1, P2	✓
EDEXCEL	P1	✓
WJEC	P1	✓

The European Union (EU) has banned the sale of 100 W filament lamps because about 90% of the input energy is wasted as heat. Their efficiency is only 10% because only 10% of the output is useful light. Replacement lamps like compact fluorescent lamps (CFLs) are more efficient. For example, a CFL that uses 18 J of energy each second emits 10 J of light.

Its efficiency $= \dfrac{10}{18} \times 100 = 56\%$

A standard 100 W filament lamp   **A fluorescent lightbulb**

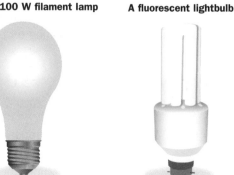

To get an A* you should be able to compare the efficiency of different processes and explain that it is important to develop more efficient ways of generating electricity to save energy resources.

Gas-fired power stations are more **efficient** than coal-fired power stations. More of the chemical energy stored in the gas is transferred to the electricity. Gas-fired power stations are about 50% efficient, whereas coal-fired power stations are about 40% efficient.

Solar energy

AQA	P1	✓
OCR A	P3	✓
OCR B	P2	✓
WJEC	P1	✓

There are two ways of using solar energy:

● **Passive solar heating** uses radiation from the Sun to heat water. Solar panels may contain water that is heated by radiation from the Sun. This water may then be used to heat buildings or provide domestic hot water.

● **Solar cells**, or **photocells**, transfer energy from sunlight into electricity.

Solar cells

| OCR B | P2 | ✓ |
| WJEC | P1 | ✓ |

Solar cells contain crystals of **silicon**. Light gives the silicon atoms energy and knocks **electrons** loose from the atoms. The electrons flow as an **electric current**. The current (which is D.C, see page 184) is increased by increasing:

● The surface area that the light falls on.
● The light intensity.

PROGRESS CHECK

1. Electricity is a secondary energy resource. Explain what this means.
2. A power station burns natural gas. Every second 755 MJ of electricity is generated from 1300 MJ of energy from the gas.
   a) Draw a Sankey diagram for the process.
   b) Calculate the efficiency of the power station.
3. An electric light uses 60 J of electrical energy every second and produces 8 J of light energy each second. Calculate its efficiency.
4. A power station burns coal and converts 3500 kJ of chemical energy to electrical energy every second. 2010 kJ of energy is wasted as heat in the power station and 300 kJ is wasted in the overhead cables every second.
   a) Draw a Sankey diagram.
   b) Calculate the efficiency of the power station in delivering useful electricity to your home.
5. Explain why it is more efficient to use a primary energy resource to heat your home than to use an electric heater.

5. When the primary energy resource is used to generate electricity, energy is wasted as heat in the power station. If the primary resource is burned in your home all the heat is useful.
   b) (1190 ÷ 3500) × 100 = 34%
4. a) 3500 kJ = 100% on left; useful = 1190 kJ = 34%; two wasted arrows; heat in power station = 2010 kJ = 57%; overhead cables = 300 kJ = 9%
3. 13%
   b) (755 ÷ 1300) × 100 =58%
2. a) Arrow 100% = 1300 MJ on left; useful energy = 755 MJ; wasted energy = 545 MJ
1. It has to be made from another, primary, energy source

10.2 Generating electricity

After studying this section, you should be able to:

● Draw a flow diagram for a power station.
● Explain the steps in generating electricity in power stations.
● Explain the process of electromagnetic induction.
● List the fuels that are used in power stations.

Power stations

AQA	P1	✓
OCR A	P3	✓
OCR B	P2	✓
EDEXCEL	P1	✓
WJEC	P1	✓

Turning a **generator** produces electricity. To turn the generators we connect them to **turbines**. We use different energy resources to turn the turbines. Wind and water flow can turn turbines directly. Steam is often used, produced by heating water. The heating is done by burning fuels or using other heat sources. The diagram shows the parts of a coal-fired power station. In a modern **gas-fired** power station the hot exhaust gases from the burners are used to turn the turbines and then to heat water to steam which turns the turbines.

Learn to label the different parts of a power station and practise by drawing a flow diagram.
1 Furnace (or nuclear reactor)
2 Boiler
3 Turbine
4 Generator
5 Transformer

A coal-fired power station.

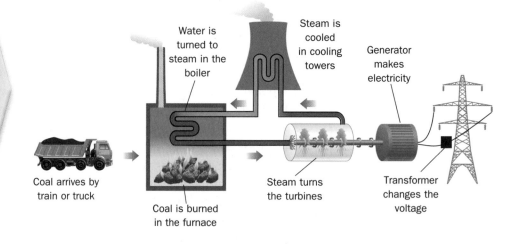

Coal arrives by train or truck

Water is turned to steam in the boiler

Coal is burned in the furnace

Steam is cooled in cooling towers

Steam turns the turbines

Generator makes electricity

Transformer changes the voltage

The main fuels

AQA	P1	✓
OCR A	P3	✓
OCR B	P2	✓
EDEXCEL	P1	✓
WJEC	P1	✓

Electricity can be generated in large power stations from different fuels:

● **Fossil fuels** such as **coal**, **natural gas** and **oil**. Fossil fuels were formed over 300 million years ago. They take millions of years to form so that they will eventually run out. All the fossil fuels produce carbon dioxide when burned. Carbon dioxide absorbs infrared radiation and warms the atmosphere. The extra carbon dioxide from burning fossil fuels may be the cause of global warming and could cause climate change.

For AQA you need to know about carbon capture technology – ways of safely storing the carbon dioxide.

● In a **nuclear** reaction a large amount of energy is released from a small amount of **plutonium** or **uranium** by fission (see page 185). One advantage is that no carbon dioxide is formed.
● **Biofuels** such as **wood**, **sugar**, **straw** and **manure**. Biofuels are materials from recently living plants and animals. Carbon dioxide is removed from the

atmosphere when plants grow and then released when fuels are burned or fermented. As long as more plants are grown there is no net change. So biofuels are carbon neutral.

Lifecycle assessments

| OCR A | P3 | ✓ |
| WJEC | P1 | ✓ |

When we decide which fuels to use in power stations we have to take lots of factors into account:

- The cost of the fuel.
- The availability of the fuel – will it run out or will it be difficult to obtain?
- The start-up time – how long it will take to commission (plan and build)?
- The cost of building the power station.
- How much it will cost to decommission (take apart at the end of its life) and to dispose of waste materials.
- The maintenance costs.
- The pollution and waste, for example whether carbon dioxide is emitted.
- The risk of accidents.

Make sure you can compare advantages and disadvantages of the different fuels on page 176 and the renewables in the next section.

Generators

OCR A	P3	✓
OCR B	P2	✓
EDEXCEL	P1	✓

KEY POINT

A voltage is **induced** across a coil of wire by moving a magnet into or out of a coil. Moving the coil instead of the magnet would have the same effect.

This process is called **electromagnetic induction**.

A voltage is induced.

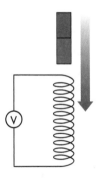

This effect is used in **dynamos** and **generators**. There are several ways to increase the voltage:

- Use stronger magnets.
- Use more turns of wire in the coil.
- Move the magnet (or the coil) faster.
- Place an iron core inside the electromagnetic coil.

A generator in a power station uses an electromagnet to produce a magnetic field. The electromagnet rotates inside coils of wire so that the electromagnet coils are in a changing magnetic field and a voltage is induced.

The bigger the voltage, the bigger the current, so to supply a large current the generator will use more primary fuel each second.

Electromagnetic induction

OCR A   P3   ✓
OCR B   P2   ✓
EDEXCEL P1   ✓

A voltage is only induced when there is movement of the magnet or coil. The direction of the voltage is reversed when the movement is reversed, or when the poles of the magnet are swapped.

PROGRESS CHECK

1. What is the difference between the way the energy is produced from the source in a coal-fired power station and a nuclear power station?
2. What is the energy source in a nuclear power station?
3. Which of these are biofuels: chicken manure, coal, natural gas, uranium or willow?
4. Give two advantages and two disadvantages of a biofuel power station.

1. Coal is burned but uranium/plutonium is split in a nuclear reaction (fission).
2. Uranium or plutonium.
3. Chicken manure and willow.
4. Examples of advantages: carbon dioxide released is matched by carbon dioxide taken up during life of fuel, so there is no net change. A way of using up waste products like manure, or methane.
Disadvantages: large amount of land required to grow some crops – maybe conflict with food crops or wildlife. Supply needs to be planned – e.g. willow planted.

10.3 Renewable sources of energy

LEARNING SUMMARY

After studying this section, you should be able to:

- Explain what a renewable source of energy is.
- List the renewable energy sources.
- Give advantages and disadvantages of renewable energy sources.
- Compare renewable and non-renewable energy sources.

Renewable resources

AQA   P1   ✓
OCR A   P3   ✓
OCR B   P2   ✓
EDEXCEL   P1   ✓
WJEC   P1   ✓

KEY POINT

Renewable sources of energy are those that are being made today and so will not be used up. Most renewable resources make use of the Sun's energy.

The Sun evaporates water and causes the rain that fills the rivers. The Sun also causes convection currents that produce winds, which produce waves. **Geothermal** heat and tidal energy do not originate from the Sun's energy. Geothermal heat originates from inside the Earth and the tides are caused by the Moon.

These are the renewable resources:

To remember all the renewables make up a mnemonic that contains the first letters of each. For example: <u>H</u>igh <u>W</u>inds <u>S</u>ometimes <u>W</u>ave <u>B</u>ig <u>G</u>reen <u>T</u>rees.

- **Hydroelectric Power (HEP)** is electricity generated using fast flowing water to turn the turbines. Dams are built to form reservoirs of water in high locations. The water is channeled down pipes to the power station gaining kinetic energy.
- **Wind turbines** use the energy of the wind to turn the turbines. Wind farms are collections of wind turbines.
- **Solar cells** are not used to turn turbines. Instead they produce electricity inside the cell.
- **Wave generators** use the movement of waves to generate electricity.
- **Biofuels**, or **biomass** fuels (see page 176), can be burned, or they can be used to produce methane gas or alcohol.
- **Geothermal energy** is used in power stations in places where the Earth's crust is thin and the heat is close to the surface. Geothermal power stations can use this heat.
- **Tides** change the height of the water in some areas so much that it is worth using it to generate electricity.

Advantages and disadvantages of renewable resources

AQA   P1   ✓

Source	Advantages	Disadvantages
HEP	No waste or air pollution. No fuel cost. Can generate a lot of electricity in mountainous areas.	Rainfall or snow is not constant. Building dams and flooding valleys changes the environment. Homes, farmland and natural habitats are lost forever.
Wind	No polluting waste gases. The wind is free, so the cost of electricity is low.	The wind does not always blow. Some people consider wind turbines noisy and an eyesore, and they take up a lot of space for the amount of electricity generated.
Solar cells	No air pollution. No fuel cost. No moving parts so they do not need much maintenance. They have a long life. They can be used in remote locations.	Cannot produce power at night or in bad weather.

Source	Advantages	Disadvantages
Wave generators	No air pollution. No fuel cost. Lots of available energy.	Waves are destructive, so it has been difficult to develop the technology.
Biofuels	A way of disposing of waste. In the case of waste and manure, the pollution would be produced anyway. Carbon neutral.	Power stations need a steady supply. They produce pollution – carbon dioxide, other gases and ashes.
Geothermal	No air pollution. No fuel cost.	Earthquakes and volcanic action may damage the power station.
Tides	The tide does not depend on the weather.	The habitats of many birds and other animals may be destroyed.

Make sure you can explain why it is important to have a reliable supply of electricity and why this means it is best to have a mixture of ways of generating electricity and not have to rely on one method.

PROGRESS CHECK

1. Explain how a hydroelectric power station works.
2. Choose two renewable energy sources that are suitable for use in the UK. Give your reasons for choosing them.
3. Choose two renewable energy sources that are not suitable for use in the UK. Give your reasons for deciding they are not suitable.
4. Jenny says that it would be best to generate all our electricity from wind farms and wave generators.
   a) List some advantages of wind farms and wave generators.
   b) Explain some reasons why Jenny's idea is not a good one.
5. Explain which energy source is most suitable for:
   a) Providing an electric light for a rural bus stop.
   b) Providing energy to mine and process aluminium ore in a mountainous region.

1. Rain or snow fills lakes or reservoirs high up on mountains. This water falls through fast rivers or pipes gaining kinetic energy. It is used to turn the turbines at the hydroelectric power station, which turn the generators to generate electricity.
2. Examples of suitable choices:
Wind turbines: Offshore windfarms can make use of the high winds around the coast.
Wave generators: Once suitable technology has been developed we have lots of sites where ocean waves can be exploited by wave generators.
Solar cells: Newer technology means that solar cells can produce useful amounts of energy in the UK.
3. Examples of unsuitable choices:
Hydroelectric power because there are no high mountains, so we only have very small amounts of HEP.
Tidal energy: There are no large tidal changes. The Severn estuary would be the best site, but is an important site for wildlife.
4. a) No carbon dioxide emitted. Renewable-fuel will not run out. Some good sites round the coast.
b) Winds and waves very variable. Often little wind when there is very cold weather. Lots of space required to generate a small amount of electricity. Lots of overhead power lines needed to connect them all to the grid. Some people consider wind turbines an eyesore and they can be noisy. It is best to have a mix of energy generation methods to avoid a complete loss of production, for example if there is a very damaging storm.
5. a) A solar panel would not need connecting to the grid and can charge batteries during the day for use at night. A light does not require much energy.
b) This requires a lot of electricity. An HEP station could be built because the area is mountainous, and it would generate a large amount.

10.4 Electrical energy and power

LEARNING SUMMARY

After studying this section, you should be able to:

- Calculate electric power and energy.
- Use joules and kilowatt hours as units of energy.
- Calculate the cost of using electrical appliances.
- Use the equation $P = I \times V$ to calculate power, current or voltage.

Energy and power

AQA	P1	✓
OCR A	P3	✓
OCR B	P2	✓
EDEXCEL	P1	✓
WJEC	P1	✓

We use electrical appliances at home to transfer energy from the mains supply to:

- heating
- light
- movement and sound.

In two hours an electric lamp uses twice as much energy as it uses in one hour.

> **KEY POINT**
>
> The **power** of an electrical appliance tells us how much electrical energy it transfers in a second.
>
> Power, P is measured in **watts** (W) where 1 W = 1 J/s.

Appliances used for heating have a much higher rating than those used to produce light or sound.

Power ratings of electrical appliances.

2 kW   1 kW   800 W

The amount of energy transferred in the mains appliance depends on the power rating of the appliance and the length of time for which it is switched on.

Energy transferred is worked out by:

Energy = power × time
$E = P \times t$
Energy, E is measured in:

- **joules** (J) when the power is in watts and the time, t, is in seconds.
- **kilowatt hours** (kWh) when the power is in kilowatts and the time, t, is in hours.

Example: A 300 W electric pump is switched on for 1 minute. The energy used is:
$E = 300 \text{ W} \times 60 \text{ s}$
$E = 18\ 000 \text{ J}$

The power used by an electrical appliance is the rate at which it transfers electrical energy. A 100 W light bulb uses more electrical energy than a 60 W light bulb every second. It transfers energy at a faster rate.

Paying for electricity

AQA	P1	✓
OCR A	P3	✓
OCR B	P2	✓
EDEXCEL	P1	✓
WJEC	P1	✓

The units on an electricity bill, and measured by an electricity meter, are kilowatt hours. The cost of a unit of electricity varies. The electricity bill is calculated by working out the number of units used and multiplying by the cost of a unit.

> Remember that the kilowatt hour is a unit of energy – not power. Power is measured in watts or kilowatts.

cost of electrical energy used = power in kW × time in hours × cost of one unit

or

cost = number of kW h used × cost of one unit

Example: The 800 W toaster in the diagram on the previous page is used for half an hour and the cost of a unit is 12p:
1 kW = 1000 W
Cost = 0.8 kW × 0.5 hours × 12 p/kW h
Cost = 4.8 p = 5 p to nearest 1p

> The unit is kilowatts multiplied by hours = kWh.
>
> A common mistake is to say kilowatts per hour kW/h.

Power tells you how quickly energy is being used. A 3 kW fire uses the same energy in 1 hour as a 1 kW fire does in 3 hours. The energy is power × time

3kW fire: 3kW × 1h = 3kWh

1kW fire: 1kW × 3h = 3kWh

Power, current and voltage

OCR A	P3	✓
OCR B	P2	✓
EDEXCEL	P1	✓
WJEC	P1	✓

The mains voltage in the UK is 230 V. Electrical power depends on the current and the voltage:

> **KEY POINT**
>
> **Power = current × voltage**
> **$P = I \times V$**
>
> Power is measured in watts (W), current, I, in **amps** (A) and voltage, V, in **volts** (V).

A torch with a 3.0 V battery has a current of 0.3 A. Its power is:

$P = 3.0 \times 0.3 = 0.9$ W

Calculating the current

OCR A	P3	✓
OCR B	P2	✓
EDEXCEL	P1	✓
WJEC	P1	✓

To calculate the current in a 2 kW kettle re-arrange the equation to give:

$$I = \frac{P}{V}$$

$$\frac{2000 \text{ W}}{230 \text{ V}} = 8.7 \text{ A}$$

Be careful with time when doing calculations. Change minutes to seconds if you are using energy in joules and to hours if the energy is in kilowatt hours.

PROGRESS CHECK

1. What unit is power measured in?
2. What is the power of a 230 V lamp with a current of 0.05 A?
3. Referring to the figure on page 181 how much energy in kWh does the kettle in the diagram use in six minutes?
4. Referring to the figure on page 181 how much energy in joules does the toaster in the diagram use in one minute?
5. What is the current in a 1 kW microwave oven?
6. A unit costs 12p. How much does it cost to use a 1kW microwave oven for 15 minutes?

1. Watts (W)
2. 11.5 W
3. 2kW x 0.1 h = 0.2 kWh
4. 800 W x 60s = 48 000 J
5. 1000W/230V = 4.3 A
6. units = 1kW x 0.25h = 0.25 kWh cost = 0.25 x 12p = 3p

10.5 Electricity matters

LEARNING SUMMARY

After studying this section, you should be able to:

- Describe the National Grid.
- Explain how transformers are used to reduce power loss.
- Describe how nuclear power stations work.
- Give advantages and disadvantages of nuclear fuel compared to fossil fuel.

The National Grid

AQA	P1	✓
OCR A	P3	✓
OCR B	P2	✓
EDEXCEL	P1	✓
WJEC	P1	✓

In the UK the **National Grid** is a network that connects all the generators of electricity, like power stations, to all the users, for example homes and workplaces.

> **KEY POINT**
>
> Mains electricity is an **alternating current (a.c.)** which means that the **current** keeps changing direction. Current from batteries is **direct current (d.c.)** meaning it always flows in the same direction.

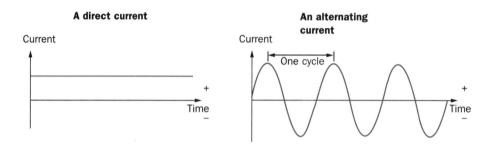

The National Grid.

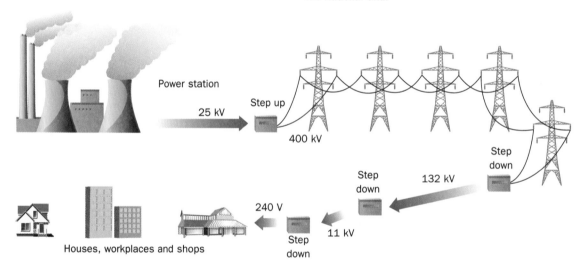

Advantages of having a National Grid are:

- Power stations can be built where the fuel reserves are, or near the sea or rivers for cooling.
- Pollution can be kept away from cities.
- Power can be diverted to where it is needed, if there is high demand or a breakdown.

A disadvantage of the National Grid is that power is wasted as heat energy in the power lines.

For OCR A you need to be able to use all the information in this chapter to discuss energy choices in the home, national and global contexts.

Transformers

AQA	P1	✓
OCR A	P3	✓
OCR B	P2	✓
EDEXCEL	P1	✓
WJEC	P1	✓

A **transformer** changes the size of an **alternating voltage**. Transformers will not work with a constant voltage. One of the reasons we have an a.c. mains supply is that the voltage is alternating and can be changed using transformers. This means it can be distributed more efficiently by using high voltages, for example 400 kV (1 kV = 1000 V).

Step-up transformers increase voltage and **step-down transformers** decrease voltage.

The voltage is stepped-up at the power station, transmitted at high voltage to reduce power losses, and stepped down at the local sub-station.

Reducing power loss in cables

AQA	P1	✓
OCR A	P3	✓
OCR B	P2	✓
EDEXCEL	P1	✓
WJEC	P1	✓

Example: To supply 100 kW of power we can use:

High voltage and small current: P = 100 kW = 1 A × 100 kV
Low voltage and large current: P = 100 kW = 100 A × 1 kV

The heating effect in the cables depends on the current. By making the current as small as possible the energy wasted as heat in the cables is reduced. The current can be small if the voltage is high. There are many hundreds of miles of overhead power cables so this saves a lot of energy.

Nuclear power stations

AQA	P1	✓
OCR A	P3	✓
OCR B	P2	✓
WJEC	P1	✓

> **KEY POINT**
>
> Nuclear power stations are like fossil fuel power stations, but instead of burning fuel they use a nuclear reaction, **nuclear fission**, to transfer energy as heat. Nuclear fuels are **uranium** and **plutonium**, which are radioactive.

Uranium is mined. Plutonium is formed in nuclear reactors. A disadvantage is that **radioactive waste** is produced that remains dangerous to living things for millions of years.

Radioactive materials emit **ionising radiation**. This is dangerous to living things.

The nuclear option

AQA	P1	✓
OCR B	P2	✓
WJEC	P1	✓

Advantages of nuclear power stations include:

- No carbon dioxide is formed in the nuclear reaction.
- A small amount of fuel releases a large amount of energy.
- The fuel is not expensive, so the running costs of nuclear power stations are not high.

Disadvantages include:

- There is the risk of an accidental emission of radioactive material while the power station is operating. This could happen due to human error, for example at Chernobyl, or to natural disasters, like earthquakes, for example at Fukushima in Japan.
- Both the power station and the fuel are targets for terrorists.
- The risks to living things from radioactive materials mean that there are high maintenance costs and high decommissioning costs. Radioactive waste must be stored safely for thousands of years.

PROGRESS CHECK

1. What is the difference between a.c. and d.c. electricity?
2. What is the National Grid?
3. Give two similarities and two differences between a nuclear power station and a coal-fired power station.
4. Why is radioactive waste dangerous?
5. What device is used inside a mobile phone charger to convert the 230 V supply to 12 V?
6. Why does the National Grid transmit electricity at 400 kV?

1. a.c. is alternating current – reverses direction d.c. is direct current – steady current.
2. The distribution network of cables and overhead power lines that links power stations with users of electricity.
3. Any two similarities, e.g. both have generators, turbines, boilers, both heat water to steam. Any two differences, e.g. nuclear: small amount of nuclear fuel (uranium/plutonium) coal: large amount of coal
Nuclear: no CO_2 but produces radioactive waste Coal: CO_2, lot of waste but not radioactive
Nuclear: nuclear reaction/fission releases a lot of energy Coal: burning/combustion of coal, less energy released.
4. It emits ionising radiation which can kill or damage living cells or cause them to turn cancerous.
5. A step-down transformer.
6. Transmitting at a high voltage means that a much smaller current can be used, for the same amount of power. This means that there is less heat lost in the cables, which saves a lot of energy, as there are hundreds of km of cables.

10.6 Particles and heat transfer

LEARNING SUMMARY

After studying this section, you should be able to:

- Calculate energy or temperatures using specific heat capacity.
- Explain the ways in which heat is transferred.
- Describe how buildings can be insulated.
- Explain and use the terms payback time and U-value.

Specific heat capacity

| AQA | P1 | ✓ |
| OCR B | P1 | ✓ |

When the temperature of an object increases it has gained energy. The amount of energy depends on:

- the temperature change, θ
- the mass of the object, m
- the specific heat capacity, c.

The **specific heat capacity** is different for different materials. It is the energy needed to increase the temperature of 1 kg of the material by 1°C and is measured in J/kg °C.

Energy = mass × specific heat capacity × temperature change
$$E = m \times c \times \theta$$

This is how to measure the specific heat capacity of a metal block:

- Measure the temperature and the mass of the block, m, at the beginning.
- Use an electric heater to raise the temperature of the metal block. Energy supplied, E = power × time.
- Measure the temperature of the block at the end of the heating time and calculate the increase in temperature θ.
- Calculate the specific heat capacity of the metal,

$$c = \frac{E}{m \times \theta}$$

Heat transfer

AQA	P1	✓
OCR B	P1	✓
EDEXCEL	P1	✓
WJEC	P1	✓

Heat can be transferred by conduction, convection and radiation. It is only transferred from hotter things to cooler things. The bigger the temperature difference between a hot object and cold surroundings the faster the hot object will cool. In a hot solid, particles vibrate more. They collide with the particles next to them and set them vibrating. The kinetic energy is transferred from particle to particle. Metals are the best conductors. Solids are better than liquids. Gases are very poor conductors. They are insulators.

For OCR B the hot object is called the 'source' and the cold object is called the 'sink'.

Conduction in a solid. Energy is transferred from molecule to molecule.

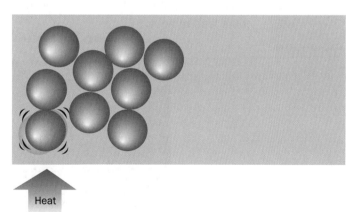

Heat

In a hot fluid (gas or liquid) the particles have more kinetic energy so they move more. They spread out and the fluid becomes less dense. The hot fluid rises above the denser cold fluid forming a **convection current**.

Convection currents.

All objects emit and absorb **infrared radiation**. The higher the temperature the more they emit. When objects absorb this energy their temperature increases. Radiation will travel through a vacuum – it does not need a medium (material) to pass through.

- Dark and matt surfaces are good absorbers and emitters of infrared radiation.
- Light and shiny surfaces are poor absorbers and emitters of infrared radiation.
- Light and shiny surfaces are good reflectors of infrared radiation.

The role of electrons in heat transfer

AQA P1 ✓
OCR B P1 ✓

Metals are made of a lattice of positive ions with 'free' electrons that can move through the lattice. This makes them good **conductors** of heat because they have 'free' electrons to carry the energy. Because electrons are negatively charged this also makes metals good conductors of electricity.

Heat is transferred to, or from, an object at a rate that depends on:

- Its surface area and volume.
- The material it is made from.
- What the surface is like.
- The temperature difference between the object and its surroundings.

The bigger the temperature difference, the faster the object will heat up or cool down.

Insulation

AQA P1 ✓
OCR B P1 ✓
EDEXCEL P1 ✓
WJEC P1 ✓

When we insulate our homes we reduce the heat lost, we use less fuel and it costs less to heat.

Energy flow from an uninsulated house.

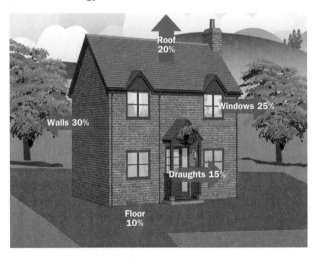

Still air is a good insulator, so materials with air trapped in them are often used.

- In cavity walls the air gap between the walls stops conduction.
- Cavity wall insulation works by filling the cavity with foam or mineral wool.
- Loft insulation uses layers of fibreglass or mineral wool.
- Reflective foil on walls reflects infrared radiation.
- Draught-proofing stops hot air leaving and cold air entering the house.

> **Convection can occur in the cavities in cavity walls – cavity wall insulation stops this.**

All these improvements cost money to buy and install, but they save money on fuel costs. You can work out the **payback time**, which is the time it takes before the money spent on improvements is balanced by the fuel savings, and you begin to save money.

> **KEY POINT**
>
> $$\text{payback time (in years)} = \frac{\text{cost of insulation}}{\text{cost of fuel saved each year}}$$

If the price of the fuel increases, the payback time will be less.

U-values
AQA   P1   ✓

The materials used in constructing a building, like glass, brick, wood and concrete, are given a **U-value** to indicate how good they are at insulating. The lower the U-value the better the insulator.

> **PROGRESS CHECK**
>
> 1. How much energy is needed to raise the temperature of 1 kg of water by 2°C? (water, $c = 4200$ J/kg°C)
> 2. Draw and label convection currents in a beaker of water heated by a Bunsen burner.
> 3. A new boiler costs £2000. It saves £100 on fuel costs each year. What is the payback time?
> 4. 4400 J of energy raises the temperature of 0.5 kg of aluminium from 15°C to 25°C. Calculate the specific heat capacity of aluminium.
> 5. How does cavity wall insulation work?
>
> 5. Traps the air in an insulating foam so that conduction and convection are stopped.
> 4. 4400 J = 0.5kg × c × 10 °C; c = 4400 J ÷ (0.5 kg × 10 °C) = 880 J/kg°C
> 3. £2000 ÷ £100 per year = 20 years
> 2. Diagram similar to convection current in house shown on page 188. Hot water rises, cold water sinks.
> 1. $E = 1$ kg × 4200 J/kg°C × 2°C = 8400 J

Sample GCSE questions

1 A coal-fired power station generates electricity.

(a) Complete the boxes to describe the processes in a coal fired power station. **[5]**

Furnace		Boiler		Turbine		Generator		Transformer
burns the coal	→	Heats water	→	turned by steam and rotates the generator	→	generates electricity	→	changes the voltage

(b) A coal fired power station uses 1500 MW of power from coal to produce 555 MW.

Calculate the efficiency of the power station. **[1]**

$$\text{efficiency} = \frac{555}{1500} \times 100\% = 37\%$$

← Always show your working

(c) Energy is wasted in the power station and also in the transmission lines. Complete this Sankey diagram to show

- where the energy is wasted in the power station each second
- how much energy reaches the customers each second. **[2]**

155J heat

40J

1500J energy in coal

510 J of electrical energy reaches consumers

550J electrical energy generated

795 J of heat in water in cooling towers

(d) An 3kW electric fire is switched on for 4 hours every evening for 2 weeks. A unit of electricity costs 12p.

Calculate the bill for using the fire. **[3]**

3kW x (4 hours x 7 x 2) = 168 kWh
cost = 168 kWh x 12p per kWh = £20.16

(e) The National Grid has hundreds of miles of power lines. Explain how the energy lost in heating these overhead power lines is reduced. *The quality of your written communication will be assessed in this answer.* **[6]**

Transformers (1 point) are used to change the voltage (1 point). Step-up transformers increase voltage (1 point) at the power station (1 point) to very high voltages (1 point). The power is transmitted at high voltage (1 point). Step-down transformers decrease voltage at the substation (1 point).

← Marks will be awarded depending on the number of relevant points included in the answer and the spelling, punctuation and grammar. In this question there are 12 relevant points so 10 or 12 with good spelling punctuation and grammar will gain full marks.

Sample GCSE questions

Power = voltage x current (1 point) , so using high voltage means a low current (1 point) can be used for the same power (1 point). Low current means less energy is wasted (1 point) as heat in the power lines (1 point).

[Total = 17]

2   A public enquiry has been set up to decide whether to build a nuclear power station or a coal-fired power station.

The coal-fired power station would release a gas that most scientists think may contribute to climate change.

(a)   What is the name of the gas?   **[1]**

carbon dioxide

(b)   Explain how the gas may contribute to climate change.   **[2]**

absorbs infrared radiation and warms the atmosphere

(c)   Choose A, B, C or D. Tick the correct answer.
The fuel that is used in some nuclear reactors is:
A Caesium   **C** Uranium ✓
B Radium   **D** Vanadium   **[1]**

(d)   Some local people are consulted about their views.

Andy

In an earthquake or an accident there could be a release of radioactive material.

Bella

Climate change is a much more serious threat to life on Earth than ionising radiation from nuclear waste.

Chloe

A nuclear power station can produce more electricity than a coal-fired power station.

Dan

Radioactive waste has to be kept safe for hundreds of years.

(i)   Who is talking about a risk of nuclear power?   Andy and Dan

(ii)   Who is talking about a risk of coal-fired power?   Bella

(iii)   Who is talking about a benefit of nuclear power?   Chloe   **[3]**

(e)   To decide which power station to build a 'Life Cycle Assessment' is made. State three factors considered in a 'Life Cycle Assessment'.   **[3]**

It takes into account all the energy costs of building (1 mark), running (1 mark), and decommissioning (1 mark) the power station.

[Total = 10]

Exam practice questions

1 This table shows some electrical power ratings for wind generators.

Model	Maximum power rating of one turbine (kW)	Wind turbine recommended for:
A	0.025	Battery charger
B	0.5	Electricity for a caravan
C	5	Domestic electricity for a house
D	25	Electricity for a school
E	500	One for a wind farm
F	1500	One for an offshore wind farm

(a) What will affect the amount of power that a wind turbine can generate? [1]

....

(b) What model is recommended for a house? [1]

....

(c) A house has an average power use of 0.5 kW. Describe how the actual power used might be

    (i) higher than average [1]

....

    (ii) lower than average. [1]

....

    (ii) Suggest two reasons why model B is not recommended for this house. [2]

....

....

(d) Wind turbines are often used to recharge banks of batteries. Why is this a good idea? [1]

....

(e) A power station generates 750 MW of electrical power. How many wind turbines would be needed to replace it with

    (i) an offshore wind farm? [1]

....

    (ii) an onshore wind farm? [1]

....

(f) What is meant by 'the payback time?' [1]

....

[Total = 10]

Exam practice questions

2   The electrical power used by an appliance is   **[1]**

   A   the efficiency per second.   ☐
   B   the electric current per second.   ☐
   C   the energy per second.   ☐
   D   the voltage per second.   ☐

3   A 100 W light bulb uses 100 W of electrical power to produce 8 W of light energy.

   (a)   Calculate the efficiency of the light bulb.   **[2]**

   ....

   ....

   (b)   Explain what happens to the rest of the electrical energy supplied to the light bulb.   **[1]**

   ....

   (c)   An energy saving lamp has an efficiency of 40% and gives the same output power of 8 W.
           What electrical power does it use?   **[2]**

   ....

   ....

   (d)   A student uses a desk lamp for 3 hours a day. How many kilowatt hours of electricity
           does the lamp use in a week if it is fitted with a 100 W light bulb?   **[2]**

   ....

   ....

   ....

                                                                                          [Total = 7]

4   A public enquiry has been set up to decide whether to build a new gas-fired power station or a
       nuclear power station. Describe the advantages and disadvantages of a nuclear power station
       compared to a gas-fired power station. *The quality of written communication will be assessed in
       your answer.*

   ....

   ....

   ....

   ....

   ....

                                                                                          [Total = 6]

11 Waves

The following topics are covered in this chapter:

- **Describing waves**
- **Wave behaviour**
- **Seismic waves and the Earth**

11.1 Describing waves

LEARNING SUMMARY

After studying this section, you should be able to:

- Explain the difference between longitudinal and transverse waves.
- Give examples of longitudinal and transverse waves.
- Describe waves, using words like frequency, wavelength and amplitude.
- Calculate the speed of waves, their frequency or wavelength.

Transverse and longitudinal waves

AQA	P1	✓
OCR A	P1	✓
OCR B	P1	✓
EDEXCEL	P1	✓
WJEC	P1	✓

A **wave** is a **vibration** or disturbance transmitted through a material (a medium) or through space. Waves transfer energy and information from one place to another, but they do not transfer material.

A **transverse wave** has vibrations at right angles (perpendicular) to the direction of travel. The wave has **crests** and **troughs**. Examples include water waves, waves on strings or rope, light and other electromagnetic waves.

A transverse wave.

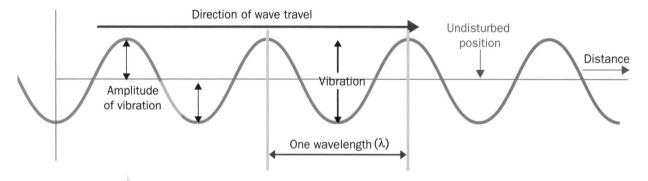

A **longitudinal wave** has vibrations parallel to the direction of wave travel. It has **compressions** and between these are stretched parts called **rarefactions**. Examples include sound waves, **ultrasound** waves, which are sound waves with frequency greater than 20 kHz, and waves along a spring. Infrasound waves are waves with a frequency lower than 20 Hz.

Ultrasound is used for sonar, animal communication and fetal scanning. Infrasound is used for animal communication and detecting disturbances like animal movement and meteors.

194

A longitudinal wave.

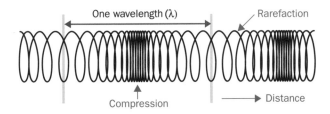

Wave travel and properties

AQA	P1	✓
OCR A	P1	✓
OCR B	P1	✓
EDEXCEL	P1	✓
WJEC	P1	✓

Longitudinal waves travel through solids, liquids and gases, but they cannot travel through a vacuum.

Transverse **electromagnetic waves** can travel through a vacuum. They are oscillations of a magnetic and electric field.

There are two types of **seismic waves** (see page 200) called **P-waves** and **S-waves**:

- **P-waves** are longitudinal waves that travel through solid or liquid rock. They travel faster than S-waves.
- **S-waves** are transverse waves that can only travel through solid materials in the Earth

> A common mistake is to mark the amplitude from the top of a peak to the bottom of a trough – this is twice the amplitude.

Amplitude is the maximum displacement (change in position) from the undisturbed position.

Wavelength (λ) is the distance in metres from any point on the wave to where it repeats.

Frequency is the number of waves that pass in one second. This depends on how fast the source of the waves is vibrating. The frequency is usually expressed in hertz (Hz) where one Hz is one cycle (wave) per second.

Example: Four waves pass a point in one second. The frequency = 4 Hz.

Example: A wave takes two seconds to pass a point. The frequency = 0.5 Hz.

> Use words like the ones below to explain what you mean, so the examiner can award you the marks.
>
> - Oscillation for side to side, up and down, or back and forth movements.
> - Perpendicular for at right angles.
> - Parallel for in the same direction.

Wave speed depends on the medium that the wave is travelling through.

distance wave travels = wave speed × time ($d = v \times t$)

Example: A water wave travels at 5 cm/s.
In 4 s it travels d = 5 cm/s × 4s = 20 cm.

KEY POINT

The **wave equation** relates the wavelength and frequency to the wave speed. For all waves:

wave speed (v) = frequency (f) × wavelength (λ) *(v = f λ, where f is in Hz, λ is in m, v is in m/s).*

Example: Water waves with wavelength λ = 10 cm and frequency f = 4Hz have a speed v = 10 cm × 4 Hz = 40 cm/s.

Waves with different frequency and wavelength.

A wave on a rope   A higher frequency wave

Using the wave equation

AQA	P1	✓
OCR A	P1	✓
OCR B	P1	✓
EDEXCEL	P1	✓
WJEC	P1	✓

The wavelength of light is very small and the wave speed and frequency are very high.

Example: Light travels at 300 000 000 m/s = 3×10^8 m/s.

Wave speed $v = 3 \times 10^8$ m/s.

Green light has wavelength, λ = 520 nm = 5.2×10^{-7} m

(1 nm is 1 nanometre = 1×10^{-9} m).

To calculate the frequency, *f*, of the light waves, re-arrange the wave equation:

$$f = \frac{v}{\lambda}$$

$$f = \frac{3 \times 10^8 \text{ m/s}}{5.2 \times 10^{-7} \text{m}} = 5.8 \times 10^{14} \text{ Hz}$$

Sound waves

AQA	P1	✓
EDEXCEL	P1	✓

For sound and ultrasound waves:

- The **pitch** of the sound is the frequency of the vibrations.
- The **loudness** of the sound depends on the amplitude of the vibrations.

Sound travels much faster in solids than in liquids and faster in liquids than in gases.

> **PROGRESS CHECK**
>
> 1. Draw a transverse wave.
> 2. Mark on the wave the amplitude and the wavelength.
> 3. How is a longitudinal wave different to a transverse wave?
> 4. A sound wave has frequency 256 Hz and wavelength 1.30 m. Calculate the speed of the sound.
> 5. Water waves pass a marker at a rate of one every four seconds. What is their frequency?
> 6. What is the frequency of radio waves with a wavelength of 3 m?

11.2 Wave behaviour

LEARNING SUMMARY

After studying this section, you should be able to:

- Describe reflection and the images formed by a plane mirror.
- Describe and explain refraction.
- Describe and explain diffraction.
- Draw ray diagrams and wave diagrams.

Reflection

AQA P1 ✓
EDEXCEL P1 ✓

All waves can be reflected, but this does not prove they are waves because particles also show these effects. According to the **law of reflection**, the angle of incidence equals the angle of reflection. This can be shown on a wave diagram or a ray diagram.

Reflection.

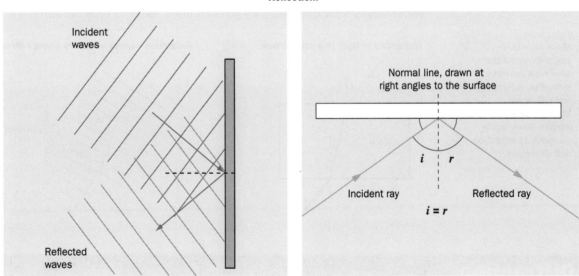

Echoes are reflections of sound waves from hard surfaces.

The image in a mirror

AQA   P1   ✓

The **image** in a plane (flat) mirror is the same distance behind the mirror as the object is in front. It is a virtual image. The image is also upright and laterally inverted (left becomes right).

The image in a plane mirror.

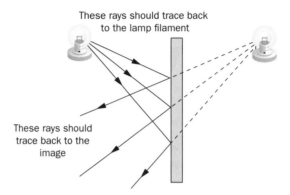

These rays should trace back to the lamp filament

These rays should trace back to the image

Remember that the angles of incidence, reflection and refraction are all measured to the normal, not to the surface. Draw the normal at right angles to the surface.

Refraction

AQA   P1   ✓
OCR B   P1   ✓
EDEXCEL P1   ✓

When waves enter a different **medium** they change **speed**. The wavelength changes, but the frequency stays the same. They change direction unless they are travelling along the normal to the boundary. This is called **refraction**.

As light waves enter a **denser medium** they slow down and bend towards the normal. As light waves enter a **less dense medium** they speed up and bend away from the normal.

Water waves slow down as they go from deep water to shallow water.

Make sure that you understand the difference between reflection, refraction and diffraction. Students often muddle these words – especially refraction and diffraction.

Refraction of light in a glass block.

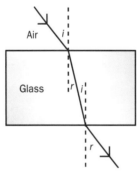

Air

Glass

Refraction causes waves to change direction

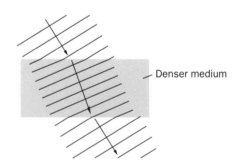

Denser medium

Diffraction

AQA   P1   ✓
OCR B   P1   ✓

Diffraction is the spreading out of a wave when it passes through a gap. The effect is most noticeable when the gap is the same size as the wavelength. Particles cannot be diffracted, so diffraction is good evidence for the existence of a wave.

Diffraction.

a)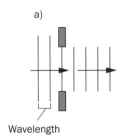

Wavelength

b)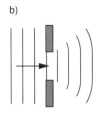

c)

It is important to compare the size of the gap with the wavelength when you are explaining whether diffraction will occur and when the effect will be biggest.

Diffraction effects

AQA   P1   ✓

The wavelength of sound waves is about a metre, so when sound waves are diffracted through doorways people can hear round corners.

Water waves are sometimes diffracted by harbour entrances.

The wavelength of light is about half of a millionth of a metre – so small that diffraction effects are only noticeable when light waves pass through gaps of about a hair's width. Larger gaps have shadows with sharp edges. This is one reason why it took so long for scientists to realise that light can behave as a wave.

PROGRESS CHECK

1 If the angle of incidence is 30°, what is the angle of reflection?
2 A ray goes from air to glass with an angle of incidence of 30°. Is the angle of refraction bigger, smaller or the same?
3 Draw a ray diagram to show light at an angle to the normal crossing a boundary from a) air to glass and b) from water to air.
4 Draw a ray diagram to show how two mirrors can be used to see round a corner.
5 Sketch a diagram of:
   a) Water waves with wavelength 1 cm passing through a 1 cm gap.
   b) Light waves with wavelength 5×10^{-7} m passing through a 1 mm gap.
   c) The same light waves passing through a 1 micrometre gap $(1 \times 10^{-6}$ m).

5. a) like diagram c) top of page 199
   b) like diagram a) top of page 199
   c) like diagram b) top of page 199

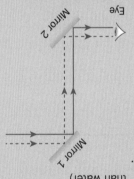

4.

3. As diagram on page 198 a) top boundary b) bottom boundary (air is less dense than water)
2. smaller
1. 30°

199

11.3 Seismic waves and the Earth

After studying this section, you should be able to:

- Explain the difference between S-waves and P-waves.
- Interpret a seismograph.
- Explain how S-waves and P-waves can give scientists information about the structure of the Earth.
- Describe the structure of the Earth and plate tectonics.

Seismic waves

OCR A	P1	✓
OCR B	P1	✓
EDEXCEL	P1	✓

Seismic waves are caused by earthquakes or large explosions, such as quarrying operations or atomic bomb tests. P-waves and S-waves both travel *through* the Earth and are detected at monitoring stations all around the Earth by instruments called **seismometers**. They record the waves arriving on a **seismograph**.

P-waves travel faster through the Earth than other seismic waves, so they are the first to be detected after an earthquake.

S-waves are detected after P-waves.

The time delay between the arrival of the P-wave and S-waves is greater at stations further from the earthquake, so the distance to the earthquake centre can be calculated. Using information from several stations the position of the earthquake is worked out.

> For Edexcel you need to explain that it is difficult for scientists to predict earthquakes because there is little advance warning and the time scales are very long – 'sometime during the next 50 years'.

A seismograph

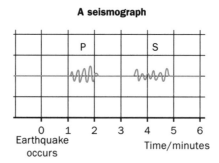

The structure of the Earth's crust can be investigated by setting up monitoring equipment at different points and setting off a controlled explosion. The waves are then recorded arriving at the monitoring points. Analysing this data gives information about the rock structure. The speed of the waves is different in different materials and waves will be reflected and refracted at boundaries between different types of rock.

Information from waves

OCR A	P1	✓
OCR B	P1	✓
EDEXCEL	P1	✓

Data from all the monitoring stations after earthquakes shows a **shadow zone** on the opposite side of the Earth to the earthquake where no S-waves are detected. This can be explained by the Earth having a liquid core, because S-waves don't travel through liquids.

The diagram below shows the paths of P-waves and S-waves through the Earth following an earthquake. The waves are reflected and refracted at the boundaries.

> Think of P-waves as primary waves and S-waves as secondary waves. After an earthquake, P-waves arrive first and S-waves arrive second. P-waves have a faster speed.

P and S waves travel through the Earth.

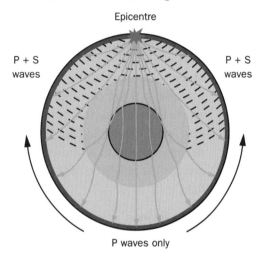

The rock cycle

OCR A	P1	✓

The Earth must be older than the oldest rocks, which scientists believe are about four thousand million years old. Rock processes seen today can explain changes that happened in the past. Rocks are worn down by erosion. Sediments are deposited in layers by rivers and seas and form new rocks. All the continents would be worn flat if new mountains were not being formed.

The structure of the Earth

OCR A	P1	✓
EDEXCEL	P1	✓

The Earth is made up of a **core**, a **mantle** and a **crust**.

The Earth's structure.

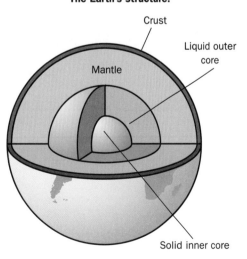

The theory of continental drift was first suggested by Alfred Wegener in 1912, based on the way the continents appeared to fit together like a jigsaw, and matching fossils and rock layers on different continents. Due to lack of evidence, it was not until 1967 that the theory of plate tectonics was accepted.

The Earth's crust consists of a number of moving sections called **tectonic plates**. The mantle behaves like a very thick liquid. The plates move because of convection currents in the mantle.

Plate tectonics

OCR A	P1	✓
EDEXCEL	P1	✓

Magma flows out of the mid-ocean ridges forming new rock, so the sea floor spreads by a few centimetres a year and this causes the continents to move apart. Evidence for this is found in the new rocks at the mid-ocean ridge. The new rocks are rich in iron. Every few thousand years the Earth's magnetic field reverses direction. As the rocks solidify they are magnetised in the direction of the Earth's magnetic field, so the rocks contain a magnetic record of the Earth's field.

At boundaries, where two plates collide, rocks are pushed up forming new mountain ranges or when plates slide past each other this can sometimes cause earthquakes. At boundaries where magma comes to the surface there are volcanoes. This is why earthquakes, mountains and volcanoes are generally found along the edges of the tectonic plates.

PROGRESS CHECK

1. Which arrives first after an earthquake, P-waves or S-waves?
2. What is a seismometer?
3. What does the theory of plate tectonics suggest about the surface of the Earth?
4. How can the distance to an earthquake be worked out from seismometer readings?
5. Are **a)** P-waves and **b)** S-waves transverse or longitudinal?
6. How do scientists know there is a liquid part of the Earth's core?

6. Because there is an S-wave shadow zone, S-waves cannot travel through liquids.
5. a) P waves are longitudinal   b) S-waves are transverse.
4. The time delay between P-waves and S-waves arriving depends on how far away the earthquake is.
3. It's made up of a number of plates floating on the mantle.
2. An instrument for detecting seismic waves from e.g. earthquakes.
1. P-waves

Sample GCSE questions

1 This diagram shows a water wave travelling across the surface of a pond.

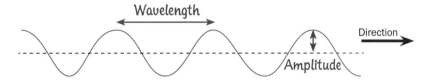

Wavelength

Direction

Amplitude

(a) What is the name of this type of wave? **[1]**

transverse

(b) Mark on the wave **(i)** the amplitude **(ii)** the wavelength **[2]**

(c) Two wave crests pass a post in the water every second.
What is the frequency of the wave? **[1]**

2 Hz

(d) The wavelength of the wave is 30 cm.
Calculate the speed of the waves **[2]**

v = 2 Hz x 30 cm
v = 60 cm/s
Wave speed = 60 cm/s **[Total = 6]**

See diagram. The amplitude can be from the centre of the wave to the top of a crest or to the bottom of a trough. A wavelength is one complete wave. The starting point can be at any point on the wave, so choose an easy one, for example crest to crest.

Don't forget the units, there are no marks for '2'

Show your working. There is one mark for '2 x 30' even if your final answer is incorrectly calculated.

2 This chart is a seismograph recorded some distance away from an earthquake. It shows the arrival of P-waves and S-waves.

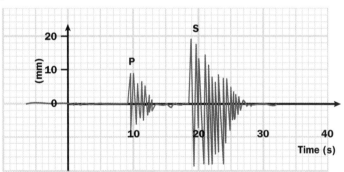

(a) Why do the P-waves arrive before the S waves? **[1]**

The P-waves travel faster

(b) Describe the difference in amplitude of the waves shown on the seismograph. **[1]**

The S-waves have larger amplitude

(c) Give one other major difference between P-waves and S-waves. **[1]**

P are longitudinal, S are transverse

(d) What is the time delay between the arrival of the P-waves and the arrival of the S-waves? **[1]**

12 s

[Total = 4]

Or P travel through liquids S do not. Remember that it is not enough to say just 'P waves travel through liquids' or 'P waves are longitudinal'.

Not 12 but 12 s or 12 seconds (accept any answers between 10–12 s)

Exam practice questions

1 These waves are travelling across a ripple tank. The wave generator moves up and down with a frequency of 4 Hz.

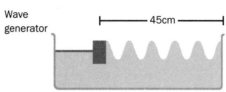

(a) What is the wavelength of the waves?

....

....

Wavelength = ... cm   **[2]**

(b) Calculate the speed of the waves. Write down the equation you use and show how you calculated your answer.

....

....

Wave speed = ... cm/s   **[2]**

(c) What will happen to the speed of the waves when the depth of the water is increased?   **[1]**

....

[Total = 5]

2 This diagram shows the water waves with wavelength 10 m entering a harbour.

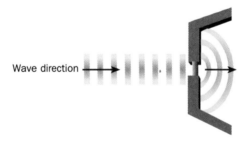

(a) What is this effect called?   **[1]**

....

(b) On another day there are smaller waves with wavelength 2 m. Describe how the waves in the harbour will be different. A diagram may help you. *The quality of your written communication will be assessed in this answer.*   **[6]**

....

....

....

[Total = 7]

12 Electromagnetic waves

The following topics are covered in this chapter:

- **The electromagnetic spectrum**
- **Light, radio waves and microwaves**
- **Wireless communication**
- **Infrared**
- **The ionising radiations**
- **The atmosphere**

12.1 The electromagnetic spectrum

LEARNING SUMMARY

After studying this section, you should be able to:

- List the types of radiation in the electromagnetic spectrum in order of wavelength, frequency and energy.
- Recognise typical wavelengths for each type of radiation.
- Understand and use the term intensity.
- Calculate energy or intensity of radiation.

The electromagnetic spectrum

AQA	P1	✓
OCR A	P2	✓
OCR B	P1	✓
EDEXCEL	P1	✓
WJEC	P1	✓

The spectrum of electromagnetic waves is continuous from the longest wavelengths (**radio waves**) through to the shortest wavelengths (**gamma rays.**)

The spectrum goes from radio waves to gamma rays. To remember what comes in between:

- Remember the colours of visible light using the mnemonic ROY G BIV.
- Next remember infrared is under red and ultraviolet is above violet in energy.
- Then remember waves (radio and micro) are below infrared and rays (X and gamma) are above ultraviolet.

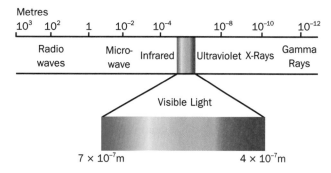

The electromagnetic spectrum

Metres

| 10^3 | 10^2 | 1 | 10^{-2} | 10^{-4} | 10^{-8} | 10^{-10} | 10^{-12} |

Radio waves | Micro-wave | Infrared | Ultraviolet | X-Rays | Gamma Rays

Visible Light

7×10^{-7}m 4×10^{-7}m

All electromagnetic waves are transverse waves that can travel through a vacuum. They all travel through empty space at a speed of 300 000 000 m/s. Radio waves have the longest wavelength, lowest frequency and lowest energy. Gamma rays have the shortest wavelength, highest frequency and highest energy. The wavelengths are related to the frequencies using the wave equation (see page 196).

Wavelength ranges

AQA	P1	✓
OCR A	P2	✓
OCR B	P1	✓
EDEXCEL	P1	✓
WJEC	P1	✓

The wavelength of visible light is about half a thousandth of a millimetre, which is so small that it is not obvious that it is a wave. Sometimes light behaves as a stream of particles.

There are not fixed boundaries between the different types of electromagnetic waves. The diagram on page 205 shows the typical values of wavelength for each type of wave. Gamma rays are always shown as shorter wavelength than X-rays, but the ranges overlap. The real difference is that gamma rays come from radioactive materials and X-rays are produced in an X-ray tube.

Remember these typical wavelengths:

- 1 km = radio
- 1 cm = microwave
- 0.1 mm = infrared
- 10^{-10} m = X-ray

Energy and intensity

OCR A	P2	✓

Radiation spreads out from the source.

spotlight

A1

larger area
less intensity

A2

> **KEY POINT**
>
> When electromagnetic radiation strikes a surface, the **intensity** of the radiation is the amount of energy arriving at a square metre of the surface each second.

Radiation is emitted from a source and travels towards a destination. On this journey the radiation spreads out, so the further away a detector is from the source the less energy is detected. The intensity of the radiation can be increased by moving closer to the source.

Intensity can also be increased by increasing the radiation from the source.

The identical spotlights on the same area double the intensity.

 Spotlight   Spotlight

Double intensity

A

Radiation is **transmitted** from the source to the detector. Some materials **absorb** some types of electromagnetic radiation. The further the radiation travels through an absorbent material the lower its intensity will be when it reaches the end of its journey. More of the radiation energy is absorbed by the material and it heats up.

On some journeys, electromagnetic radiation is **reflected** at a boundary between two different materials.

When the energy of the radiation is absorbed by the detector it may:

- Have a heating effect.
- Produce small electric currents in aerials (if microwaves or radio waves).
- Make chemical reactions more likely, for example light causes photosynthesis in plants.
- Ionise atoms (if ultraviolet, X-ray or gamma).

Comparing intensities

OCR A   P2   ✓

To compare the **intensity** of radiation we measure the amount of energy falling on one square metre of the surface in each second. The energy absorbed by the surface or detector can be calculated by:

Energy (J) = intensity (W/m^2) × time (s)

Electromagnetic radiation sometimes behaves as waves, and sometimes as packets of energy called **photons**. A gamma ray photon has the most energy. The energy of the photons increases with the frequency of the radiation. The energy arriving at a surface is the number of photons multiplied by the energy of the photon.

Blue light has more energy than red light.

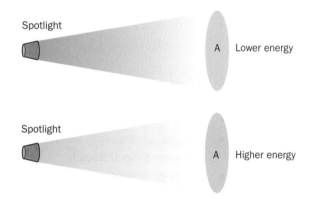

Spotlight

A   Lower energy

Spotlight

A   Higher energy

PROGRESS CHECK

1. State two properties that all electromagnetic waves have in common.
2. State one difference between infrared and ultraviolet rays.
3. An electromagnetic wave has a wavelength of 10^{-6} m (0.001 mm). What type of electromagnetic radiation is it?
4. Which radiations have an ionising effect?
5. Microwaves from Source A have a frequency of 3 GHz and from Source B have a frequency of 30 GHz.
   a) Which microwaves have the most energy?
   b) Calculate the wavelength of the microwaves from A and B.

1. Two from: transverse; travel at 3×10^8 m/s in a vacuum; can travel through a vacuum; are oscillations of a magnetic and electric field.
2. Infrared have lower frequency or longer wavelength, or lower energy than ultraviolet. Or ultraviolet are ionising, infrared are not.
3. Infrared
4. Ultraviolet, X-rays, gamma rays
5. a) B have the most energy (higher frequency so higher energy)
   b) A = $3 \times 10^8 \div 3 \times 10^9 = 0.1$ m or 10 cm; B = $3 \times 10^8 \div 30 \times 10^9 = 0.01$ m or 1 cm

12.2 Light, radio waves and microwaves

LEARNING SUMMARY	After studying this section, you should be able to:
	• Explain some properties and uses of visible light.
	• Explain how the eye is similar to a camera.
	• Explain some properties of radio waves and microwaves.
	• Describe differences between radio waves and microwaves.
	• Explain uses of microwaves and radio waves.

Visible light

AQA	P1	✓
OCR A	P2	✓
OCR B	P1	✓
EDEXCEL	P1	✓

When electromagnetic radiation from the Sun arrives at the Earth's atmosphere, some of it is reflected, some is transmitted to the Earth's surface and some is absorbed by the atmosphere. The types of electromagnetic radiation that arrive at the Earth's surface are:

- high energy infrared
- visible light
- low energy ultraviolet.

Some of the ways visible light is used include:

- When images are formed on the retina at the back of the eye.
- When images are formed on the light sensitive film in a camera.
- In digital photography when images are formed on the light sensitive screen and stored electronically.
- During photosynthesis when plants use light as an energy source.

Making images

EDEXCEL	P1	✓

How an image is formed

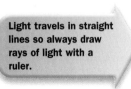

Light travels in straight lines so always draw rays of light with a ruler.

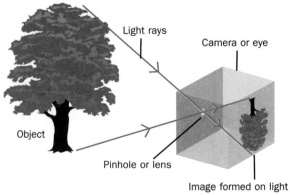

Light rays

Camera or eye

Object

Pinhole or lens

Image formed on light sensitive surface

The eye is similar to a camera. In both, light rays pass through a small hole and produce a small upside down image. A lens can be used to gather and focus more light. The image is formed on a light sensitive surface in the following ways:

- On photographic film a chemical reaction occurs which changes the colour of the film.
- On the cells of the retina a chemical reaction causes electric signals to travel along the **optic nerve** to the brain.
- On the screen inside a digital camera electronic signals are sent to the memory. The amount of information to store the picture is measured in **bytes**.

> The more bytes the higher the quality of the image or sound.

Radio waves and microwaves

AQA	P1	✓
OCR A	P2	✓
OCR B	P1	✓
EDEXCEL	P1	✓

Here are some important properties of radio waves and microwaves:

- They are reflected by metal surfaces.
- They heat materials if they can make particles in the material vibrate.
- The amount of heating depends on the power of the radiation and the time that the material is exposed to the radiation.

Radio waves are produced when an alternating current flows in an aerial. They spread out and travel through the atmosphere. Another aerial is used as a detector. The radio waves produce an alternating current in it, with a frequency that matches that of the waves.

Transmitting and receiving radio waves.

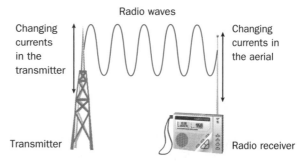

> Make a table of materials that reflect, absorb and transmit light, radio waves and microwaves. This will help you to remember the similarities and the differences.

Microwaves are transmitted through glass and plastics. They are absorbed by water, though how well depends on the frequency (energy) of the microwaves. Microwave ovens use a microwave frequency which is strongly absorbed by water molecules, causing them to vibrate, increasing their **kinetic energy**. This heats materials containing water, for example food. The microwaves penetrate about 1 cm into the food. Conduction and convection processes spread the heat through the food.

Microwave oven radiation will heat up our body cells and is very dangerous at high intensity because it will burn body tissue. The radiation is kept inside the oven by the reflecting metal case and metal grid in the door.

A microwave oven.

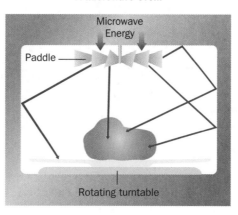

The atmosphere

AQA	P1	✓
OCR A	P2	✓
OCR B	P1	✓
EDEXCEL	P1	✓

Radio waves are transmitted through the **atmosphere** without being absorbed. Medium wavelength radio waves are reflected from the **ionosphere**, which is a layer of charged particles in the upper atmosphere.

Most microwaves are transmitted through the atmosphere, but some wavelengths are absorbed or scattered by dust and water vapour in the atmosphere and also by water droplets in rain and clouds. They pass through the ionosphere without being reflected.

How radio waves and microwaves travel.

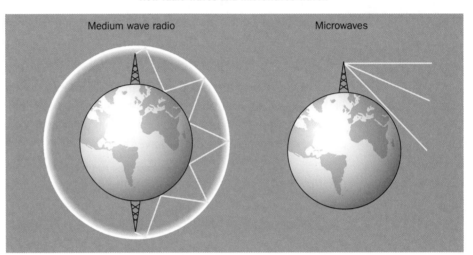

Medium wave radio   Microwaves

PROGRESS CHECK

1. Give two differences between an object you look at and the image formed on your retina.
2. What material would you use for a cooking container for use in a microwave oven? Explain your choice.
3. An 850 W microwave oven heats food for 10 seconds. How much energy in joules heats the food?
4. Why are the microwaves used in microwave ovens especially dangerous to the human body?
5. How is the eye similar to a digital camera?
6. How could microwaves that are absorbed by water droplets be used in weather forecasting?

1. The image is smaller and upside down compared to the object.
2. Glass or plastic because they do not absorb microwaves.
3. 850 W × 10 s = 8500 J
4. They are absorbed by water molecules and heat them up. The human body contains a lot of water, or human cells contain water.
5. They both have a lens, small hole for light to enter, form an image on a light sensitive surface, electric signals are produced that go to the memory/brain.
6. If they are sent through the atmosphere between a transmitter and a receiver, the amount received will depend on whether it is raining, this could be used to track rainfall.

12.3 Wireless communication

LEARNING SUMMARY

After studying this section, you should be able to:

- Explain how the atmosphere, the ionsphere and diffraction affect radio waves and microwaves.
- Describe how microwaves and radio waves are used in communicating.
- Discuss, using data and evidence, whether mobile phones are safe.
- Explain the differences between analogue and digital signals.

Radio waves

AQA	P1	✓
OCR A	P2	✓
OCR B	P1	✓
EDEXCEL	P1	✓

Radio waves are suitable for **broadcasting** radio and television programmes to large numbers of people. Anyone with a receiver can tune it to the radio frequency to pick up the signal. When radio stations use similar transmission frequencies the waves sometimes **interfere** with each other. Medium wavelength radio waves are reflected from the ionosphere so they can be used for long distance communication, but not for communicating with satellites above the ionosphere.

Microwaves

AQA	P1	✓
OCR A	P2	✓
OCR B	P1	✓
EDEXCEL	P1	✓
WJEC	P1	✓

The transmitter and receiver for transmitting microwaves must be in line of sight (one can be seen from the other). Transmitters are positioned high up, often on tall masts. They must be close together so that hills, or the curvature of the Earth, cannot block the beam. Signals can be sent to and from **satellites**, because microwaves can pass through the **atmosphere** and through the **ionosphere**. The satellites can relay signals around the Earth which may be for television programmes, telephone conversations or monitoring the Earth, for example weather forecasting.

Satellite communication

Make sure you can compare the use of microwaves and radio waves and that you know the differences in how they behave, and how they are used. In 'compare' answers refer to both, for example microwaves will pass through the ionosphere, but medium wave radio waves do not.

Satellites in a **geosynchronous orbit** take 24 hours to orbit the Earth. The Earth rotates once in 24 hours, so these satellites stay fixed above the same point on the Earth's surface. They are then in the right position to send and receive microwave signals.

Diffraction

AQA	P1	✓
OCR A	P2	✓
OCR B	P1	✓
EDEXCEL	P1	✓

Diffraction is the spreading of a beam through gaps and around corners (see page 198). The maximum effect occurs when the gap has a similar size to the wavelength.

Radio waves of about 5 m are diffracted by large buildings. Radio waves of 1 km are diffracted around hills and through valleys, so they are able to reach most areas and are suitable for broadcasting. Microwave beams of a few centimetres are not spread round corners or around hills. This is why the transmitters and receivers must be in line of sight. When microwaves are transmitted from a satellite dish the wavelength must be small compared to the dish diameter to reduce diffraction. This means that, compared to radio waves, microwaves can be sent as a thin beam.

Diffraction of microwaves and radio waves

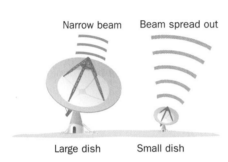
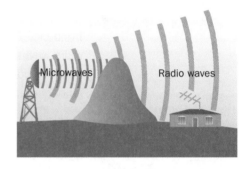

Analogue and digital signals

| OCR A | P2 | ✓ |
| OCR B | P1 | ✓ |

A common mistake is to think that we can hear radio waves. We cannot hear any electromagnetic radiation. The radio waves are the carrier used to carry a signal that is converted into a sound wave by the receiver.

Radio waves, microwaves, infrared and visible light are all used to carry information, which can be sound, pictures or other data. The information is called the **signal**. It is added to an electromagnetic wave called the **carrier wave** so that it can be transmitted. When the wave is received the carrier wave is removed and the signal is reconstructed. There are two types of signal, **analogue** and **digital**.

> **KEY POINT**
>
> An analogue signal changes in frequency and amplitude continually in a way that matches changes in the voice or music being transmitted. A digital signal has just two values – represented as 0 and 1 (or on and off).

In digital transmissions, the signal is converted into a code of 0 and 1 values. The signal is added to the carrier wave and transmitted. After the signal is received it is decoded to recover the original signal.

Analogue and digital signals.

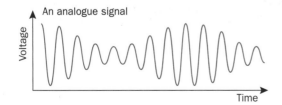
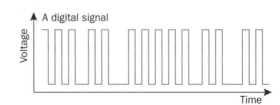

Both analogue and digital signals can pick up unwanted signals that distort the original signal. These unwanted signals are called **noise**. Digital signals give a better quality reception because the noise is more easily removed. They can be cleaned up in a process known as **regeneration**. The 0 or 1 values can be restored because each pulse must be a 0 or a 1. Analogue signals can be **amplified**, but the noise is amplified too.

Wireless and mobile phones

AQA	P1	✓
OCR A	P2	✓
OCR B	P1	✓
EDEXCEL	P1	✓
WJEC	P1	✓

Wireless communication uses microwaves and radio waves to transmit information. The advantages of this are:

- No wires are needed to connect laptops to the internet, or for mobile phones or radio.
- Phone calls and e-mail are available 24 hours a day.
- Communication with wireless technology is portable and convenient.

Wireless communications.

> An advantage of digital signals is that they can be stored and processed by computers.

> Remember that the danger of microwaves and other electromagnetic radiation at the low energy end of the spectrum depends on its intensity. Do not confuse this with the danger of the ionising radiations at the high energy end of the spectrum.

Mobile phones use microwave signals. The signals from the transmitting phones are reflected by metal surfaces and walls, and travel through the air to communicate with the nearest transmitter mast. There is a network of transmitter masts to relay the signals on to the nearest mast to the receiving phone.

It is unclear whether there are any long-term effects of using mobile phones. There may also be a risk to residents living close to mobile phone masts. Most people consider the risks and benefits, and decide that the benefit of using a mobile phone outweighs the risk.

Wireless and mobile phones

AQA	P1	✓
OCR A	P2	✓
OCR B	P1	✓
EDEXCEL	P1	✓
WJEC	P1	✓

We have only limited data about the possible dangers of mobile phones. The transmitter is held close to the user's head, so the microwaves must have a small heating effect on the brain. There is no evidence that this is dangerous. However, there has not yet been enough time to determine if there is a long-term risk. We need to collect and analyse data for an average lifetime of about 80 years before we can say whether there is any evidence of a long-term risk.

The Health Protection Agency (HPA) is made up of independent scientists, who look at the evidence of the effects of radiation on health. So far studies have not found that mobile phone users have suffered any serious ill effects. Their advice is to limit the use of handsets held close to the head, especially for young children in case there are long-term effects.

> This is an example of 'How Science Works'. It applies to all areas of physics.

Scientists do lots of studies to see if the results are **repeatable**. We can have more confidence in a study if the results been **replicated** by the scientists themselves and **reproduced** by other scientists.

Correlation between factors

AQA	P1	✓
OCR A	P2	✓
OCR B	P1	✓
EDEXCEL	P1	✓
WJEC	P1	✓

A good study uses a **large sample** of thousands of people. The sample will be matched, so that scientists compare the same type of people who use mobile phones with people who don't, to see if this is a **factor** that increases the risk. For example, they might compare women, children, or men who smoke. If they find a **correlation**, they will look to see if this is due to a different **cause**. A correlation is a link between two factors.

Correlation.

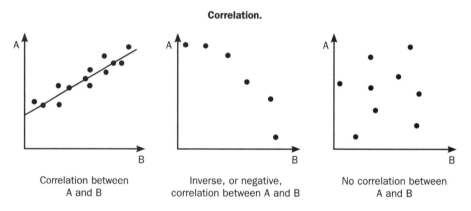

| Correlation between A and B | Inverse, or negative, correlation between A and B | No correlation between A and B |

If there is a correlation it does not always mean that one factor causes the other. For example, there is a correlation between increased sales of ice cream and an increase in hay fever, but this does not mean that eating ice cream causes hay fever. Both increase in hot sunny weather. It is important to scientists to find a **mechanism** that explains why a factor causes an **outcome**. For example, the mechanism by which radioactive materials cause cancer is the radiation ionising atoms and damaging body cells.

> Remember the ice cream example so that you can use it to explain why correlation is not the same as cause.

It is very difficult to control other factors in a study of people using mobile phones because there are so many things people do differently. Laboratory investigations should be designed to control all the factors.

Example: In an experiment to see how the distance microwaves travel in glass affects their absorption, you would make sure that these factors are kept constant:

- The intensity of microwaves from the source.
- The detector.
- The distance the microwaves travel in air before and after the glass.
- The type of glass.

PROGRESS CHECK

1. What type of electromagnetic waves are used to a) broadcast TV and b) for satellite TV?

2. Why are there often lots of microwave transmitters on the top of hills?

3. What is the difference between an analogue signal and a digital signal?

4. In communication signals, what is noise?

5. Give one advantage of wireless technology.

6. Give an example of a benefit and a risk of using a mobile phone.

7. Sketch a graph showing how ice cream sales and hay fever might be related.

8. What affect do microwaves have that might be a mechanism for causing damage to the body?

9. Why are satellite dishes larger than the wavelength of microwaves they transmit?

10. Television pictures from analogue signals often have white speckles on the picture, but digital pictures do not.
    a) What is this effect called?
    b) Why does it only happen to analogue pictures?

11. Why do scientists think that young children should use hand held mobile phones as little as possible?

12. In the example experiment on page 214, to see how distance affects absorption of microwaves:
    a) What is the factor and what is the outcome?
    b) Describe a correlation you might expect to find.
    c) What would be the effect of **not** controlling each factor?

1. a) radio waves b) microwaves
2. Need to be in 'line of sight' of the next one.
3. An analogue signal is continuously changing but digital has just two values (a labelled diagram to show this is acceptable).
4. Unwanted signals that are picked up and added to the signal.
5. We can receive phone calls and email 24 hours a day/No wires are needed to connect laptops to the internet, or for mobile phones or radio/Communication with wireless technology is portable and convenient.
6. Benefit: staying in contact with family/friends or emergency use. Risk: possible unknown long term health risk, or risk of distraction when crossing road/driving.
7. Graph showing a positive correlation – as hayfever increases sales of ice cream increase, or as sales of ice cream increase, hayfever increases.
8. A small heating effect, (or vibrate molecules).
9. So that diffraction does not make the beam spread out.
10. a) noise b) because digital signals can be cleaned up / the 0 and 1 values can be restored/ the noise/signals that produce the white specks can be removed.
11. Because they will be using them a lot over their lifetime and it is too early to be sure there are no long term effects.
12. a) factor = distance travelled in glass. Outcome = microwaves absorbed (fall in intensity detected)
    b) greater the distance the more microwaves absorbed (or lower intensity detected)
    c) They would all affect the intensity of microwaves received by the detector, so it would not be possible to tell what effect changing the distance in glass would have.

12.4 Infrared

LEARNING SUMMARY

After studying this section, you should be able to:

- Explain properties and uses of infrared radiation.
- Describe how optical fibres are used in communications.
- Explain how optical fibres work.

Uses of infrared

AQA	P1	✓
OCR A	P2	✓
OCR B	P1	✓
EDEXCEL	P1	✓
WJEC	P1	✓

A thermogram of an elephant.

> For Edexcel you need to know that infrared radiation was discovered by Herschel.

Our skin detects **infrared** radiation and we feel **heat**. All objects emit electromagnetic radiation. The amount depends on their temperature. Hot objects glow red and very hot objects glow white hot, because they emit light as well as infrared. The hotter the object, the more electromagnetic radiation it emits and the higher the maximum frequencies. Warm objects, like radiators and human bodies, emit infrared. Night-vision goggles, cameras and thermograms use false colour so that we can 'see' the radiation.

Infrared emission, absorption and reflection depends on the surface. When infrared is absorbed the particles in the surface vibrate and gain kinetic energy. This is why infrared radiation is used for cooking. The surface of food gets hot and then the inside is heated by convection and conduction. We must be careful that intense infrared radiation does not have this effect on our skin and cause burning. Some cooking appliances, like grills and toasters, emit red light as well as infrared.

Infrared radiation is used in **remote controls** for televisions and other electronic appliances. If you look at the beam from a remote control through a digital camera (which shows up infrared signals that our eyes cannot see) you can see the flashing infrared emitting diode sending the **digital signal**. These signals cannot pass through solid objects, but sometimes reflect off walls and ceilings to operate the television.

Infrared sensors

OCR A	P2	✓
OCR B	P1	✓
EDEXCEL	P1	✓

> Remember that infrared comes between microwaves and red light. Make sure you can explain the differences between them, especially their properties and uses.

Infrared sensors detect human body heat, so they are used in security systems. An infrared beam can be used as part of a burglar alarm. The burglar cannot see the beam and steps into it. This blocks the radiation reaching the sensor and triggers the alarm.

Night vision goggles and cameras work by detecting the infrared radiation emitted by objects at different temperatures. The different intensities of infrared are changed to different intensities of visible light, or often to different colours to help us see the objects even more clearly. Warm objects, like humans, other animals and cars, can be easily picked out.

Communications

AQA	P1	✓
OCR A	P2	✓
OCR B	P1	✓
EDEXCEL	P1	✓
WJEC	P1	✓

> **KEY POINT**
>
> Infrared radiation and light are both transmitted along glass optical fibres by **total internal reflection**.

Total internal reflection can only happen when light is refracted at a boundary with a less dense medium, for example travelling from glass to air.

The **critical angle** is the angle of incidence for which the angle of refraction is 90°. For the glass-air boundary this is about 42°.

- When the angle of incidence is less than the critical angle the light is refracted.
- When the angle of incidence is greater than the critical angle total internal reflection occurs.

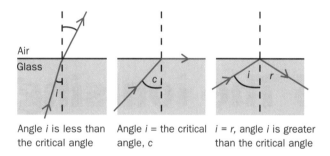

Angle i is less than the critical angle   Angle i = the critical angle, c $i = r$, angle i is greater than the critical angle

Light travels along optical fibres.

The fibres are made with a core that has a different refractive index to the outer cladding. Radiation is reflected at the boundary as shown in the diagram.

Digital signals can be sent for long distances using **optical fibres** because glass is transparent to visible light and infrared. When the signal needs boosting, digital signals are easily regenerated. A stream of data can be transmitted very quickly. Both infrared and red light **lasers** are used as radiation sources for fibre optic communications. Lasers produce a very narrow beam of intense radiation of one colour.

Fibre optic communications

AQA	P1	✓
OCR A	P2	✓
OCR B	P1	✓
EDEXCEL	P1	✓
WJEC	P1	✓

Advantages of fibre optic communication include:

- Infrared signals in fibre optic cables experience **less interference** (they pick up less noise) than microwaves passing through the atmosphere.
- It is possible to use **multiplexing**, which is when signals are divided into sections and sent alternately so that many different signals can be sent along one fibre at the same time.

Draw a diagram of a signal from a mobile phone travelling through a fibre optic link and a microwave link that includes a satellite. Label the diagram and it will help you to revise all the parts of microwave communication.

Lasers produce a beam with low **divergence** (does not spread out) in which all the waves have the same **frequency** and are **in phase** (in step) with each other. Lasers are also used in a compact disc (CD) player. CDs store information digitally as a series of pits and bumps (0s and 1s) on the shiny surface. A laser beam is reflected differently from the pits and bumps and a detector is used to 'read' the different reflections, reproducing the 0s and 1s of the signal.

PROGRESS CHECK

1. How do we detect infrared radiation?
2. How does a toaster cook a slice of bread?
3. Explain why the elephant's ear in the picture on page 216 is a different colour to the rest of the body.
4. Explain how the signal from a TV remote control would be different for selecting two different channels.
5. How is light from a laser different to light from a light bulb?
6. Give an advantage of using infrared radiation and fibre-optic cable over using a microwave link.

1. Our skin feels it as heat.
2. The infrared radiation from the wire is absorbed by the molecules on the surface of the bread which gets hot. Convection and conduction then carry this heat through the rest of the bread.
3. It is cooler so the infrared radiation has a lower frequency.
4. It is a digital code of 0s and 1s so the pattern of 0s and 1s would be different.
5. It is a thin beam (not divergent). It is one frequency e.g. one colour red – the light bulb is lots of frequencies. The waves are all in phase – in step – they are not from the light bulb.
6. Less interference. Signals can be multiplexed, many sent at once.

12.5 The ionising radiations

LEARNING SUMMARY

After studying this section, you should be able to:

- State which types of radiation are ionising.
- Explain why ionising radiations are dangerous.
- Describe radioactive emissions.
- Discuss benefits and risks of using ionising radiations.

Ionising radiation

OCR A	P2	✓
OCR B	P2	✓
EDEXCEL	P1	✓
WJEC	P1	✓
CCEA	P1	✓

Gamma rays, **X-rays** and high energy **ultraviolet radiation** are high energy radiations which can **ionise** atoms they hit. Atoms are ionised when electrons are removed and this makes them more likely to take part in chemical reactions. If the atom is inside a living cell this can be harmful.

KEY POINT

Ionising radiation can damage or kill living cells. If the DNA in a cell is damaged it may mutate. This can cause cells to grow out of control which means that they have become cancer cells.

Whether radiation is dangerous sometimes depends on whether a person is contaminated or irradiated. Make sure you can explain the difference.

KEY POINT

There are two types of danger from all these radioactive materials:

- **Irradiation** is being exposed to radiation from a source outside the body.
- **Contamination** is swallowing, breathing in, or getting radioactive material on your skin.

A short period of irradiation is not as dangerous as being contaminated because, once contaminated, a person is continually being irradiated.

Some materials are **radioactive**. This means they randomly emit ionising radiation from the nucleus of unstable atoms. There are three types:

- Gamma rays which are electromagnetic waves.
- **Alpha particles** which are helium nuclei. They are positively charged.
- **Beta particles** which are high energy electrons from the nucleus. They are negatively charged.

Uses of ionising radiation:

- Gamma rays are used for sterilizing medical equipment and killing cancer cells.
- Alpha emitters are used in smoke detectors
- Beta emitters are used as tracers.

X-rays

OCR A	P2	✓
EDEXCEL	P1	✓
WJEC	P1	✓

X-rays have high energy and pass through the body tissues. They are stopped by denser materials such as the bones and pieces of metal. They are used to image the body.

The figure shows X-rays directed towards the patient with a photographic plate placed behind. The plate darkens where the X-rays strike it and there are white shadows where the bones absorbed the X-rays.

Making an X-ray image.

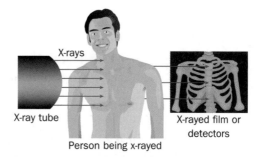

X-rays

X-ray tube

Person being x-rayed

X-rayed film or detectors

X-rays are also used for security scans of passengers' luggage. Metal items and batteries block the X-rays and show up as shadows on the screen.

Benefits and risks

OCR A	P2	✓
OCR B	P1, P2	✓
WJEC	P1	✓

There are benefits to using ionising radiation, but these must be weighed against the risks. To protect people dense materials, like lead screens and concrete, are used to absorb the radiation and act as barriers. Radiation workers, such as radiographers and workers at nuclear power stations, are monitored to make sure they are not exposed to high levels of radiation. They wear protective clothes.

A patient should not receive too many X-rays. They are used when the benefit (for example, finding a broken bone) is greater than the risk. In the 1950s all pregnant women were X-rayed to check on the development and position of the baby. This caused a few cancers among children. The benefits were not greater than the risks and routine X-rays were stopped.

Radiation workers do not benefit from a dose of radiation and would be at risk from high exposure every day. This is why radiographers leave the room when a patient is X-rayed.

People tend to overestimate the risks from unfamiliar things compared to familiar things (for example they may think flying is more risky than cycling). Because ionising radiation can't be seen, people tend to think it is more dangerous than it is.

Ultraviolet radiation

OCR A	P2	✓
OCR B	P1	✓
EDEXCEL	P1	✓
WJEC	P1	✓

The lower energy ultraviolet radiation that reaches the Earth's surface can cause:

- premature skin aging
- suntans
- sunburn
- skin cancer
- damage to the eyes.

> For Edexcel you need to know that Ritter discovered ultraviolet radiation.

The number of cases of skin cancer has increased in recent years as people spend more time in the Sun. Dark skins absorb more ultraviolet radiation than light skins, which are more easily damaged. To reduce the risk people should stay out of the Sun during the hottest part of the day and cover up with a hat and clothes. They should use a high protection factor sunscreen. Ultraviolet blocking sunglasses are recommended to protect the lens of the eye from damage.

> In a question about advantages and disadvantages, or about benefits and risks, you must give both to get full marks. A list of benefits cannot be awarded a mark for stating a risk.

There are benefits of spending time in the Sun, for example our skin makes vitamin D which reduces the risk of other cancers, so benefits must be weighed against risks.

Ultraviolet radiation is used to detect forged bank notes because genuine bank notes have some features that **fluoresce** in ultraviolet radiation.

PROGRESS CHECK

1. What does it mean if radiation is ionising?
2. What is the difference between being contaminated or irradiated by radioactive material?
3. Why are babies no longer routinely X-rayed in the womb?
4. Which type of electromagnetic radiation tans the skin?
5. How does leaving the room when an X-ray is taken protect a radiographer?
6. Give a benefit and a risk of sunbathing.

6. Ultraviolet causes skin to make vitamin D, but also causes skin cancer.
5. Walls absorb X-rays, so they will not be exposed.
4. Ultraviolet.
3. Because the ionising radiation is damaging and the benefit does not outweigh the risk.
Irradiation is when the rays from radioactive material reach your body.
2. Contaminated is when you swallow/breathe-in/get covered by radioactive material.
1. It removes electrons from atoms making them more likely to take part in chemical reactions.

12.6 The atmosphere

After studying this section, you should be able to:

- Explain the atmospheric greenhouse effect.
- Explain the factors affecting carbon dioxide in the atmosphere.
- Discuss global warning and climatic change.
- Explain the role of the ozone layer and ultraviolet radiation.
- Explain how the ozone hole formed, and action to reduce it.

Absorption of radiation

AQA	P1	✓
OCR A	P2	✓
OCR B	P2	✓
EDEXCEL	P1	✓
WJEC	P1	✓

The Earth is surrounded by an atmosphere made up of different gases. It allows some frequencies of electromagnetic radiation from the Sun to pass through (see page 208).

KEY POINT

The Earth emits infrared radiation at lower frequencies. These frequencies are absorbed by some gases in the atmosphere such as **carbon dioxide**, **water vapour** and **methane**. This keeps the Earth warm and it is called the atmospheric **greenhouse effect**. Without it the Earth would be much colder – too cold for some species to survive.

The atmospheric greenhouse effect

Less global warming

More global warming

More infrared absorbed

Infrared from Earth

Radiation from Sun

Less infrared from Earth

Radiation from Sun

Atmosphere containing more carbon dioxide

Earth

Earth

If the power radiated away = the power absorbed the temperature will stay the same.

The greenhouse effect and global warming

OCR A	P2	✓
OCR B	P2	✓
WJEC	P1	✓

High energy infrared and visible radiation from the Sun passes through the glass into a greenhouse. Low energy infrared radiation from inside the greenhouse cannot escape through the glass. This keeps the greenhouse warm and is called the greenhouse effect.

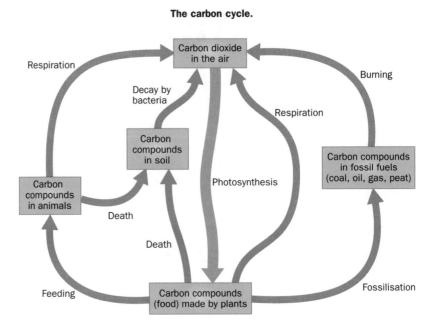

The carbon cycle.

Scientists agree that **global warming** is happening. The Earth is getting warmer.

In the last 200 years the amount of carbon dioxide in the atmosphere has steadily increased. Reasons include:

- Burning **fossil fuels**.
- Clearing forests so that fewer trees are using carbon dioxide for **photosynthesis**.

> **For OCR B you need to know that volcanic ash in the atmosphere can cause global cooling.**

Computer climate models show that human activities are increasing greenhouse gases and causing global warming, but some scientists do not agree. They do not agree about how much change is likely and what effect it will have. It could result in:

- Extreme weather conditions in some regions, such as droughts, heavy storms, flooding, very high or very low temperatures, more hurricanes, higher or less snowfall.
- Rising sea levels due to melting ice and expansion of water in oceans which may flood low lying land.
- Some regions no longer able to grow food crops, such as areas bordering deserts.

Ultraviolet in the atmosphere

OCR A   P2   ✓
OCR B   P1   ✓

Some ultraviolet radiation from the Sun reaches the surface of the Earth but, fortunately for living things, the highest energy ultraviolet radiation is stopped by the **ozone layer**. This is a layer of ozone gas in the upper atmosphere that absorbs ultraviolet radiation and chemical changes occur. Without this layer, higher frequency ultraviolet would cause more sunburn, skin cancer and cataracts.

In 1985 an ozone hole was discovered above the Antarctic. Scientists had been looking for a reduction in the ozone layer, but did not expect to find a large hole that formed so quickly. The measurements were repeated with new equipment. They were replicated by the scientists who discovered the hole and reproduced by other scientists. Where the ozone layer has been depleted, living organisms, especially animals, suffer more harmful effects from ultraviolet radiation.

The hole in the ozone layer.

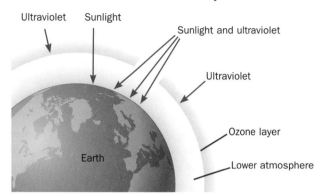

A common mistake is to muddle up the effect of the ozone layer on ultraviolet and the effect of infrared on the greenhouse effect. Make sure you understand the difference.

The ozone hole

| OCR A | P2 | ✓ |
| OCR B | P1 | ✓ |

The explanation that scientists had for the ozone hole was that using gases called **CFC gases** in aerosol cans (as the propellant to force the contents of the can out of the nozzle) and as the refrigerant in refrigerators and freezers, caused the concentration of CFC gas in the atmosphere to increase. This pollution reacted with the ozone in the springtime and reduced the amount in the ozone layer. Scientists predicted that the ozone hole would grow. This prediction was correct.

International agreements, like the Montreal Protocol in 1987, have stopped the use of CFCs and other ozone depleting gases. This is a good example of the world's governments working together. The ban is having an effect and the hole is getting smaller, but the CFCs are very stable so it will be at least 50 years before the hole disappears.

PROGRESS CHECK

1. Which gases in the atmosphere contribute to global warming?
2. Why is there more carbon dioxide in the atmosphere today than there was 100 years ago?
3. Which gas absorbs ultraviolet radiation and protects living things?
4. What effect did scientists discover in the 1980s that could increase cases of skin cancer in parts of the world?
5. Most scientists agree that the climate is changing. What do some disagree about?
6. Which gases cause the hole in the ozone layer and what has been done about this problem?

6. CFCs. They have been banned by governments all over the world.
5. Whether human activities are responsible.
4. The hole in the ozone layer.
3. Ozone.
2. Because of burning fossil fuels and clearing forests.
1. Carbon dioxide, water vapour and methane.

Sample GCSE questions

1. This diagram shows how the signal is sent from one mobile phone to another using the nearest mobile phone mast to each phone to receive and resend the signal.

Caller   Receiver

(a)   What type of electromagnetic radiation do mobile phones use to send and receive signals?   **[1]**

Microwaves

A mobile phone uses waves with a frequency of 900 MHz.   ← **MHz = Megahertz = 1 million or 10^6 Hz**

(b)   The wavelength of these waves in metres is calculated from

A $(3 \times 10^8) \times (900 \times 10^6)$ **C** $(300 \times 10^3) \times 900$
B $(3 \times 10^8) \div (900 \times 10^6)$ **D** $(300 \times 10^3) \div 900$

B   **[1]**

The mobile phone masts are placed on the top of hills and tall buildings, so that they are in line of sight of each other.

(c)   Explain what 'in line of sight' means and why the masts have to be positioned in this way.   **[2]**

Line of sight means that you can draw a straight line from one to the next without it being blocked by anything, so you would be able to see from one to the next. This is needed so that the microwaves will reach the receiving mast because they travel as a thin beam and do not spread out like radio waves.

Mobile phones are held close to the head and there have been concerns that this could be dangerous.

(d)   The effect of this radiation on the brain is:

A a small heating effect   **C** a small ionising effect
B a small illuminating effect   **D** no effect

A   **[1]**

Scientific studies have been carried out, and more are being conducted, to find out whether mobile phone users are more at risk of developing cancer.

(e)   Describe how scientists set up and carry out a well designed study to see if mobile phone users are more at risk of developing a brain

Sample GCSE questions

tumour. *The quality of your written communication will be assessed in this answer.* **[6]**

Scientists will set up two large (1 point) matched (1 point) samples. One will be people who use a mobile phone, and one will be people who do not (1 point) . Other factors like age, sex and other habits like smoking will be kept the same (1 point) (matched) in both groups. The larger the samples and the closer the matching the more confidence we have in the results (1 point). They will follow the groups over at least 10 years, (1 point) monitoring their mobile phone use and seeing how many people develop brain tumours in each group (1 point). If the group using phones develops more brain tumours (1 point) they will have found that mobile phones are a risk factor in developing a brain tumour.(1 point)

Scientists have not found evidence of a health risk but they still advise that young children should limit their use of mobile phones held close to their head.

(f) Explain why they give this advice. **[2]**

Mobile phones have not yet been in use for a complete lifetime of 70 or 80 years, so there has not been time to collect evidence of long term risks. Children will be using phones for many years to come.

[Total = 13]

2 To switch her TV on and off, and to change channel, Kate uses a remote control. This sends out a beam of infrared radiation. Infrared radiation is a type of electromagnetic radiation.

(a) Give two properties of electromagnetic radiation. **[2]**

1. Travels in a vacuum

2. Transverse waves

This diagram shows Kate using the remote control. She discovers that she can operate the TV by pointing the remote control at the ceiling.

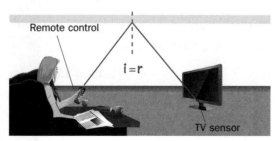

(b) On the diagram, complete the path taken by the infrared radiation to operate the TV. **[2]**

Marks will be awarded depending on the number of relevant points included in the answer and the spelling, punctuation and grammar. In this question there are 9 relevant points so 8 or 9 points with good spelling punctuation and grammar will gain full marks.

For the last point an alternative is to say that children's skulls are thinner so the exposure would be higher.

There are other properties which are also correct, for example, travel at 3×10^8 m/s in a vacuum, are oscillations of an electric and magnetic field.

Straight line from remote to ceiling, straight line from ceiling to TV, angle of incidence = angle of reflection. Use a ruler. There will be a tolerance allowed for the angle, but write that i = r in case your drawing is not accurate enough.

Sample GCSE questions

To operate the TV the remote control transmits a digital signal.

(c) What is the difference between an analogue signal and a digital signal? **[2]**

A digital signal has two values, often represented as 0 and 1. An analogue signal is continuously varying.

You can answer by referring to a labelled diagram as on page 212.

Infrared radiation is also used to transmit phone signals, but not through the atmosphere.

(d) What are used, together with infrared radiation, to transmit phone signals? **[1]**

optical fibres

The atmosphere absorbs infrared radiation and this helps to keep the Earth warm.

(e) What is this effect called? **[1]**

The atmospheric greenhouse effect.

(f) There has been a large change in the amount of a gas that absorbs infrared radiation in the atmosphere over the last one hundred years.

(i) What is this gas called? **[1]**

Carbon dioxide

(ii) Explain why the amount of this gas has changed and what effect this may have on the Earth. *The quality of your written communication will be assessed in this answer.* **[6]**

Plants take carbon dioxide from the atmosphere by photosynthesis (1 point). So trees reduce the amount and fossil fuels contain a lot of carbon (1 point). In the last one hundred years there has been a lot of deforestation (1 point) and burning of fossil fuels (1 point), so the amount of carbon dioxide in the atmosphere has increased (1 point). This increase causes global warming (1 point) and so human activity may be responsible (1 point) for the global warming effect which is causing the climate of the Earth to change (1 point).

Marks will be awarded depending on the number of relevant points included in the answer and the spelling, punctuation and grammar. In this question there are 8 relevant points so 6 to 8 points with good spelling punctuation and grammar will gain full marks.

[Total = 15]

Exam practice questions

1 List these electromagnetic waves in order of increasing energy. **[2]**

infrared   **radio waves**   **ultraviolet**   **visible light**

....

2 Explain why microwaves are suitable for satellite TV signals but radio waves are not. **[1]**

....

3 Describe how the eye is similar to the digital camera. **[3]**

....

....

4 Describe how microwaves that are absorbed by water droplets can be used in weather forecasting. **[2]**

....

....

5 How does light travel along optical fibres? **[1]**

A by diffraction

B by dispersion

C by refraction

D by total internal reflection

☐

6 Compare cooking with a microwave oven and a grill by giving one similarity and one difference. **[2]**

....

....

7 In a village all the residents can receive long wave radio broadcasts but not mobile phone signals. A scientist says this is a diffraction effect. Explain what the scientist means, and how it accounts for the difference. **[3]**

....

....

....

Exam practice questions

8 In the 1980s scientists discovered a hole in the ozone layer. Explain how this was caused, its effects, and what has been done to reduce it. *The quality of your written communication will be assessed in this answer.* **[6]**

....

....

....

....

....

....

9 This is a list of statements about electromagnetic radiation. Write **T** for the **true** statements and **F** for the **false** statements. **[6]**

(a) Gamma rays have higher energy photons than microwaves. ....

(b) High energy ultraviolet radiation is ionizing. ....

(c) The intensity of the radiation does not depend on the energy of the photons. ....

(d) Microwaves are reflected by glass. ....

(e) Infrared radiation and light travel along glass fibres by being diffracted. ....

(f) X-rays pass through soft tissues but are absorbed by bone. ....

13 Beyond the Earth

The following topics are covered in this chapter:

- The Solar System
- Space exploration
- A sense of scale
- Stars
- Galaxies and red shift
- Expanding Universe and the Big Bang

13.1 The Solar System

LEARNING SUMMARY

After studying this section, you should be able to:

- Describe the objects in the Solar System.
- Explain how gravity keeps planets in elliptical orbits.
- Compare the geocentric and heliocentric models of the Solar System.
- Describe NEOs and evidence for them colliding with Earth.

The Solar System

OCR A	P1	✓
OCR B	P2	✓
EDEXCEL	P1	✓
WJEC	P1	✓

The **Solar System** was formed over a very long time from clouds of gases and dust in space, about **five thousand million years ago**.

The **planets** orbit the **Sun**, which is the star at the centre of the Solar System. There are eight planets and Pluto, which is a dwarf planet. Some planets are orbited by one or more **moons**.

An object which orbits another is called a **satellite**. Our **Moon** is a natural satellite of the **Earth**.

Asteroids are rocks, up to about 1 km in diameter, that orbit the Sun. These

> To remember the order of the planets and Pluto (Mercury, Venus, Earth, Mars, Jupiter, Saturn, Uranus, Neptune and Pluto) use a mnemonic like:
>
> <u>M</u>y <u>V</u>ery <u>E</u>asy <u>M</u>ethod <u>J</u>ust <u>S</u>peeds <u>U</u>p <u>N</u>aming <u>P</u>lanets

Sun
Mercury
Venus
Earth
Mars
Jupiter
Saturn
Uranus
Neptune
*Pluto

have been around since the formation of the Solar System. Most of these are between Mars and Jupiter.

Jupiter is the largest planet and there is a large gravitational force towards it. This has prevented the formation of a planet between Mars and Jupiter, in the asteroid belt.

There are many **comets**. Some take less than a hundred years to orbit the Sun, while others take millions of years. They are made of ice and dust. Most have a nucleus of less than about 10 km, but this vapourises and becomes a cloud thousands of miles across when the comet is close to the Sun. Comets spend most of their time far from the Sun – much further away than the dwarf planet Pluto.

Meteors, or shooting stars, are caused by dust and small rocks, usually from a comet. When the Earth passes through this debris the rocks fall through the atmosphere. They heat up and glow. Any pieces that land on the Earth are called **meteorites**.

> Do not confuse asteroids, meteors, comets and meteorites.

Near Earth Objects (NEOs) are **comets** and **asteroids** in an orbit that brings them close to the Earth. Some of them could one day collide with Earth. The **craters** on the Moon are evidence of collisions in the past. Craters on the Earth have been mostly eroded away, but layers of unusual elements in rocks and sudden changes in fossil numbers between adjacent layers of rock are evidence of collisions in the past.

> NEOs are difficult to observe because they are small and dark.

Surveys by **telescopes** try to observe and record the paths (trajectories) of all NEOs. They can be monitored from Earth or by satellite. We can make sure that we have advance warning of a collision. The idea of deflecting a NEO using explosions is being considered. At present scientists are collecting information about the composition and structure of NEOs. The possibility of destroying one is still only in the planning stage.

Gravity and orbits

OCR B   P2   ✓

The **force of gravity** is an attractive force between the Sun and a planet. It keeps the planet moving in **orbit** around the Sun. For an object to move in a circle there must be a force on it towards the centre of the circle. This force is called the **centripetal force**. If an object moves closer to the Sun the gravitational force on it will increase and it will speed up.

Comets have very **elliptical orbits**. They are kept in orbit by the gravitational force of attraction to the Sun, but their distance from the Sun changes as shown in the diagram. The force on the comet is largest close to the Sun, where the distance is smallest. The speed of the comet is much greater close to the Sun.

A comet's orbit.

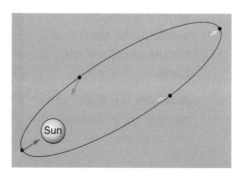

Models of the Solar System

EDEXCEL P1 ✓

In Ancient Greece scientists thought that the Earth was stationary and that the Sun, Moon and planets moved around the Earth. This is known as the **geocentric** model. As scientists made more accurate and detailed observations of the Solar System they noticed that the planets moved in complicated patterns. A simpler explanation was that all the planets, including Earth, orbited the Sun. This is called the **heliocentric** model.

The geocentric model of the Earth at the centre of the Universe, developed by Ptolemy, is also called the **Ptolemaic model. Copernicus** was the first person to write down a suggested heliocentric model of the Solar System. Galileo used a new telescope to observe moons orbiting Jupiter which added to the evidence that everything did not have to orbit the Earth. This new evidence was not accepted for many years because it did not agree with religious beliefs at the time.

PROGRESS CHECK

1. Which is the largest planet?
2. What is the difference between an asteroid and a comet?
3. Describe the heliocentric model of the Solar System.
4. What is the nearest star to Earth?
5. What force keeps a comet moving around the Sun?
6. What are the main differences between the orbit of a comet and the orbit of the Earth?

1. Jupiter.
2. An asteroid is a rock that orbits the Sun between Mars and Jupiter. A comet is a rock and ice that orbits the Sun in a very elliptical orbit, spending most of the time further away from the Sun than Pluto.
3. The Sun is at the centre of the Solar System. The planets orbit the Sun and moons orbit the planets.
4. The Sun.
5. Gravity.
6. The orbit of a comet is very elliptical going close to the Sun and further away than Pluto. The orbit of the Earth is almost circular and it stays roughly the same distance from the Sun.

13.2 Space exploration

LEARNING SUMMARY

After studying this section, you should be able to:
- Describe and compare ways of finding out about the Solar System.
- Explain advantages and disadvantages of manned and unmanned space missions.
- Explain how scientists think the Moon was formed.

Exploring the Solar System

OCR B   P2   ✓
EDEXCEL P1   ✓

Methods of finding out about the Solar System and what is beyond it are:

- To use telescopes.
- To send unmanned space probes.
- To send manned spacecraft.

> Remember if you are asked to compare telescopes on Earth and in orbit, or manned and unmanned space missions, that you must compare the two. Saying that telescopes in orbit are expensive will gain no marks. You must say that telescopes in orbit are more expensive than Earth based telescopes.

Beyond the Solar System, using a telescope is the only way to study the Universe, because of the huge distances and time needed to travel them. Telescopes are also useful for study of the Solar System. They can be positioned on Earth where they are easier to maintain and repair, but where they must look through the **atmosphere**. Some telescopes are positioned high up on mountain tops to get above the clouds, dust and pollution, and away from city lights. Telescopes in orbit avoid these problems and have a much clearer view of the stars. Launching a telescope into orbit is more expensive than building one on Earth. There are telescopes designed to use all types of **electromagnetic waves**, including **radio telescopes**, which observe radio waves from space. As X-rays do not pass through the atmosphere, **X-ray telescopes** are always placed in orbit.

Hubble space telescope

A radio telescope

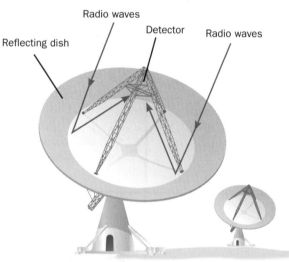

Radio waves

Detector   Radio waves

Reflecting dish

Unmanned missions

OCR B   P2   ✓
EDEXCEL P1   ✓

Many unmanned space probes have been launched. NASA spacecraft and Mars rovers have studied Mars. We have lots of information about Mars without humans travelling there.

Unmanned spacecraft can operate unharmed in a lot of conditions that would kill humans. By using remote sensors and computers they can send back information on:

- temperature
- magnetic field
- radiation
- gravity
- gases in the atmosphere
- composition of the rocks
- appearance of the surroundings (using TV cameras).

Manned missions

OCR B   P2   ✓
EDEXCEL P1   ✓

Spacecraft have put men and women in orbit and on the Moon. There are plans to send humans to Mars, but the difficulties of space missions to other planets are extreme. These include:

● Enough food, water oxygen and fuel must be carried for the entire trip, including delays.
● The distance means that emergency supplies could not be sent in time to be of use.
● An artificial atmosphere must be set up inside the spacecraft, and levels of carbon dioxide and oxygen monitored.
● Interplanetary space is very cold. There must be heating to keep astronauts warm. In direct radiation from the Sun the spacecraft will heat up, so cooling is required.
● There will be very low gravity during the journey. Bones lose density and muscles waste away under these conditions. A special exercise programme is needed using exercise machines.
● Astronauts must be shielded from cosmic rays and from the radiation released from the Sun when there is a solar flare.

Comparing manned and unmanned missions

OCR B   P2   ✓

Is it best to send unmanned space probes or a manned mission to find out about Mars?

Points to consider are:

● The costs of unmanned missions are less.
● There are no lives at risk if something goes wrong with an unmanned mission.
● Everything must be planned before an unmanned mission leaves – no adjustments, repairs or changes can be made unless they are programmed into the computers and can be done remotely.
● Most people are more interested in manned missions. Unmanned missions do not inspire people in the way that manned missions do.

The Moon

OCR B   P2   ✓

The current theory of how the Moon was formed is that the Earth collided with another planet, about the size of Mars. Most of the heavier material of the other planet fell to Earth after the collision and the iron core of the Earth and the other planet merged. Some less dense material was thrown into orbit and formed the Moon.

Evidence for this theory is:

● Samples of Moon rocks brought back to Earth by astronauts show that Moon rocks are the same as Earth rocks – unlike rocks from other planets and moons.

- The Moon is made of less dense rocks – it only has a small iron core, unlike other planets, moons and asteroids.
- The Moon's rocks are igneous although there has been no recent volcanic activity.

PROGRESS CHECK

1. List two ways that scientists have collected information about Mars.
2. Telescopes can be Earth based or launched into space. Give one problem using:
   a) An Earth based telescope.
   b) A space based telescope.
3. How do scientists think the Moon formed?
4. Give an advantage and a disadvantage of manned space missions compared to unmanned space missions.
5. What evidence do we have that the Moon formed during the collision of a planet with Earth?

5. The Moon only has a small iron core and its rocks are the same as Earth rocks. It has no volcanic activity but has igneous rocks.
4. Examples: manned are more interesting/inspirational for people. People can respond to changes or make repairs and unmanned space probes can't. But manned cost more, lives are at risk if something goes wrong.
3. Earth collided with a planet – debris formed Moon.
2. a) Atmospheric effects (pollution, clouds, dust).
   b) Expense of launch, or difficult to maintain or repair.
1. Telescopes and unmanned space probes.

13.3 A sense of scale

LEARNING SUMMARY

After studying this section, you should be able to:

- State approximate sizes and distances of objects in the Universe.
- Use the light year as a unit of distance.
- Explain how brightness and parallax can be used to measure the distance to stars.

The light year

OCR A	P1	✓
OCR B	P2	✓
EDEXCEL	P1	✓
WJEC	P1	✓

To remember the increasing size; A, (no B), C, D, E. (asteroid, comet, dwarf Pluto, Earth).

A **light year** is the distance light travels in a year. Light travels through space, which is a vacuum, at 300 000 km/s. Light from the Sun arrives on Earth after about 8 minutes. After a year, light from the Sun will have travelled a distance = 300 000 km/s × (the number of seconds in a year). This distance is about 9.5×10^{12} m – about nine and a half million million kilometres. (You don't need to remember this number.)

Distances to stars and galaxies are so large that we measure them in light years. The nearest star to Earth is the Sun. The second nearest is about 4 light years from Earth.

Increasing size	Object	Size or distance	Approximate age
	Asteroids and meteors	Usually less than 1 km diameter	
	Comets	Usually less than 15 km diameter	
	Dwarf planet, Pluto		
	The Moon	Smaller than Earth (diameter is about a quarter of the Earth's)	4500 million years
	Earth	Diameter 12 760 km	4500 million years
	Largest planet, Jupiter	Diameter over 10 times the Earth's	
	Sun	Diameter over 100 times the Earth's	5000 million years
	Earth's orbit		
	Solar System	Diameter about ten thousand million km (10 000 000 000 km) Diameter about 10 light years	4600 million years
	Next nearest star (after the Sun)	About 4 light years	
	Milky Way galaxy	Diameter about 100 000 light years	
	Milky Way to nearby galaxies	About 100 000 light years	
	The observable Universe	About 14 thousand million light years	About 14 thousand million years

Looking back in time

OCR A   P1   ✓

The light year is a unit of distance, not a unit of time.

When you look through a telescope and see a star 100 light years away, what you see – the light entering your telescope – left the star 100 years ago. So looking at very distant planets is like looking back in time. Distant objects look younger than they really are. If an alien 950 light years away could look at Earth through its telescope on the right day in 2016 it could watch the Battle of Hastings in 1066.

Brightness

OCR A   P1   ✓

A very bright star may look bright because:

- It is bigger than other stars.
- It is hotter than other stars.
- It is closer than other stars.

> **KEY POINT**
>
> The brightness can be used to work out the distance to a star. The further away the star, the dimmer it is.

If there are reasons to believe stars are similar (for example, they are the same colour) then a difference in **brightness** can be used to measure the distance.

Parallax

OCR A   P1   ✓

You can see the **parallax** effect from a train or car window; objects close to you seem to move and change position more quickly, when compared to distant objects.

When two observations of the night sky are made at different times of the year, the Earth has moved. A star that is close to Earth will have changed its position when compared to distant stars in the background. The amount the nearby star has moved is used to calculate how far it is from Earth.

This method uses the fact that the Earth orbits the Sun. One observation of the night sky is made and then a second six months later. The Earth has changed its position in space by a distance equal to the **diameter** of its orbit. However, most stars are so far away that the distance moved is too small to measure.

Parallax.

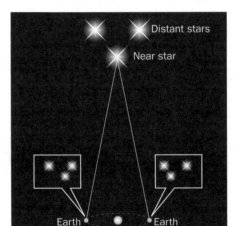

Another difficulty for astronomers is the amount of **light pollution** from the Earth. All the light from our cities shines into the night sky and makes it difficult to pick up the very weak signals from distant stars and galaxies.

The difficulties in making observations lead to uncertainty in our measurements of the distances to stars and galaxies.

PROGRESS CHECK

1. List the following objects in order of increasing size: a comet, the Universe, the Earth, the Moon, the Milky Way, the Sun.
2. How long does it take light to cross the Solar System?
3. A student notices that looking out of a bus window a lamp post appears to move against the background more than a bus stop sign. Which is closer?
4. Why does the Sun look different to other stars?
5. Explain one problem with using the brightness of a star to work out its distance from Earth.
6. Explain why the parallax method can only be used for nearby stars.

6. Distant stars don't appear to move when the Earth changes its position in 6 months.
5. You don't know how bright the star really is.
4. It's much closer.
3. Lamp post.
2. About 10 years.
1. Comet, Moon, Earth, Sun, Milky Way, Universe

13.4 Stars

LEARNING SUMMARY

After studying this section, you should be able to:

- Explain how we get information about stars.
- Describe how stars are formed.
- Describe main sequence stars.
- Explain what happens to stars like the Sun.
- Explain what happens to very massive stars.

How we know about stars

OCR A   P1   ✓
WJEC   P1   ✓

All the information we have about objects outside the Solar System comes from observations made with telescopes. What we know depends on the **electromagnetic radiation** from the stars and galaxies.

All around the Universe there are new stars being formed, **main sequence stars** in the stable part of their 'lifetime' and older stars coming to the end of their time as a star. By observing all of these scientists have worked out the 'life history' of stars.

To find out what stars are made of scientists look at the **spectral lines** (see page 240) in the spectrum of radiation from a star. These are used to identify the elements present in the star.

The lifetime of a star

OCR A   P1   ✓
EDEXCEL P1   ✓

Formation:

- Stars begin as large clouds of dust, hydrogen and helium called an **interstellar gas cloud** or a **nebula**.
- Gravity makes the nebula contract, this makes it heat up and it becomes a **protostar**.
- When it is hot enough **hydrogen nuclei fuse** together to form **helium nuclei**. This is called **nuclear fusion**. Energy is released as light and other electromagnetic radiation. A **star** has formed.

Stable lifetime, fusing hydrogen:

- The star is one of a large number of **main sequence stars** like our Sun. Stars spend a long time fusing hydrogen. Our Sun will do this for ten thousand million years.
- What happens when a star has fused most of its hydrogen depends on the mass of the star.

Final stages of a small star like our Sun:

- The star cools, becoming redder and expands to form a **red giant**. The core contracts and **helium nuclei fuse** to form carbon, oxygen and nitrogen.
- After all the helium has fused the star contracts and the outer layers are lost. As these outer layers move away they look to us like a disc that we call a **planetary nebula**.

To remember the stages in the lifetime of a star use a mnemonic, for example:

New play mates say red giants play nicely with dwarfs.

Nebula, protostar, main sequence, red giant, planetary nebula, white dwarf.

● The remaining core becomes a small, dense, very hot **white dwarf**. The star will then cool over a very long time and become a **brown** or **black dwarf**.

The life cycle of a star of mass similar to our Sun.

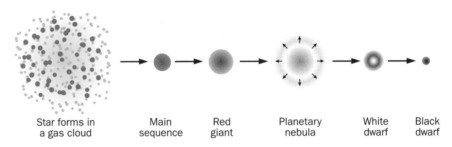

| Star forms in a gas cloud | Main sequence | Red giant | Planetary nebula | White dwarf | Black dwarf |

Final stages of a more massive star:

● The star cools and expands to form a **red supergiant**. The core contracts and **fusion** in the core forms carbon and then heavier elements up to the mass of iron.

● When the nuclear fusion reactions are finished the star cools and contracts, which heats it again until it explodes. The explosion is called a **supernova** and is the largest explosion in the Universe. All the elements heavier than iron that exist naturally on planets were created in supernova explosions.

● The core is left as a **neutron star**. It is very dense. It has a large mass, but a very small volume. If the star is very massive, the core is left as a **black hole**.

The life cycle of a more massive star.

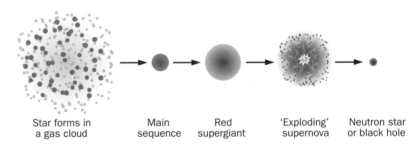

| Star forms in a gas cloud | Main sequence | Red supergiant | 'Exploding' supernova | Neutron star or black hole |

Learn the names of all the different stages in the 'lifetime' of a star and make sure that you can use them correctly to describe what happens at each stage.

Fusion in stars

OCR A   P1   ✓

The particles of dust and gases in the interstellar gas clouds are attracted by gravitational forces between the particles. This is why the cloud contracts. As the core gets hotter the atoms collide at high speed, losing their electrons. The temperature has to be high enough to force the nuclei close together for **fusion** to occur. When light nuclei fuse they release energy.

In a main sequence star the high pressure in the core is balanced by the gravitational forces. The largest stars fuse hydrogen the most quickly so, surprisingly, more massive stars have shorter lifetimes. Only the most massive stars can cause larger nuclei to fuse, forming elements like magnesium and silicon, but even they cannot form nuclei more massive than iron.

Black holes are so dense that even light cannot escape from their strong gravitational fields.

1. What is a planetary nebula?
2. When our Sun has completed the whole 'lifetime', what will be left at the end?
3. Which is brighter, a new main sequence star, a new white dwarf or a new supernova?
4. What is the difference between a red giant and a red supergiant star? Describe what each will become.
5. How were elements in your body like the carbon and oxygen formed?
6. Why is a black hole black?

1. The outer layers of a red giant star that has used up its helium that are drifting away into space in all directions.
2. A brown or black dwarf.
3. A supernova.
4. A red supergiant is more massive, and after helium fusion is complete it goes on to fuse other nuclei until it produces iron. Finally it explodes as a supernova. A red giant stops after helium fusion is complete, producing a planetary nebula and a white dwarf.
5. By nuclear fusion inside red giant and red supergiant stars.
6. Because no light can escape it as there is such a strong gravitational attraction.

13.5 Galaxies and red-shift

After studying this section, you should be able to:

- Explain what spectral lines are.
- Explain how spectral lines can be used to identify elements in stars.
- Explain what a red-shift is.
- Describe what Hubble discovered about distant galaxies.

Galaxies

AQA	P1	✓
OCR A	P1	✓
OCR B	P2	✓
EDEXCEL	P1	✓
WJEC	P1	✓

Galaxies are collections of thousands of millions of stars. There are thousands of millions of galaxies in the Universe. All the galaxies are moving away from us, and from each other.

Our Sun is a star in the **Milky Way galaxy**. To see the Milky Way from Earth (it looks like a milky strip of stars in the sky) you need to be far away from the light pollution of towns and cities. The Milky Way galaxy is shaped like a flat disc with spiral arms. Between galaxies there are empty regions that are hundreds of millions of light years across.

Remember 'thousands of millions' of stars in a galaxy *and* galaxies in the Universe.

How science works

OCR A	P1	✓
OCR B	P2	✓
EDEXCEL	P1	✓

The **scientific community** shares ideas in meetings called **conferences** and in **published journals**. They evaluate each other's work. This process is called **peer review**.

In 1920 scientists had questions about our galaxy and the Universe.

- What were **spiral nebulae?**
- Was our galaxy, the Milky Way, the only galaxy?
- How big was the Milky Way galaxy?

Two scientists held a **Great Debate**.

Harlow Shapley argued that the Milky Way was the only galaxy. He thought spiral nebulae were gas clouds. **Heber Curtis** argued that spiral nebulae were other galaxies at great distances away from the Milky Way.

There was not enough evidence to prove who was right. At the time most scientists thought that Shapley made a better case.

In 1924 Edwin Hubble used a new telescope and a new method of measuring distances. This new evidence showed that the distances to spiral nebulae were much greater than the size of the Milky Way.

He published his results and they were **evaluated** and **reproduced** by other scientists. Distances to more spiral nebulae were measured. They were outside the Milky Way. The scientific community accepted Curtis was right.

New explanations

OCR A	P1	✓
OCR B	P2	✓
EDEXCEL	P1	✓

When new data disagrees with an accepted explanation, scientists do not immediately give up their accepted explanation. They wait until they have an explanation that fits the data better before they give up the accepted explanation.

Absorption spectra and red-shift

AQA	P1	✓
OCR A	P1	✓
OCR B	P2	✓
EDEXCEL	P1	✓
WJEC	P1	✓

Spectral lines are lines in the spectrum of radiation from a hot object like a star. Dark lines are wavelengths that have been **absorbed** by the atoms of gases the radiation has passed through, usually in the outer, cooler parts of the stars. Bright lines are wavelengths emitted by the atoms of hot gases.

Each **element** has a different set of absorption lines, so the lines can be used to identify the elements present in the stars. The **absorption spectrum** has been described as a 'fingerprint' of the element. This is because each element has a unique pattern of absorption lines.

Absorption spectrum of sunlight compared with hydrogen and sodium.

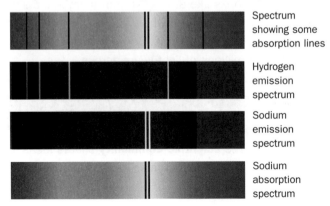

Spectrum showing some absorption lines

Hydrogen emission spectrum

Sodium emission spectrum

Sodium absorption spectrum

For visible light, red has the longest wavelength and violet the shortest. If the wavelength is longer than expected this is called a **red-shift**. If a wavelength is shorter than expected, this is called a blue-shift.

A red-shift is a shift towards the red end of the spectrum. Infrared radiation would be shifted towards microwaves not towards red light. A blue shift means the radiation source is moving towards the observer.

If a source of wave is stationary, the waves move out from the source at the same rate in all directions. If the source of waves is moving the wave is either stretched or squashed, depending on which way the source is moving. In the second diagram below, the source of waves is moving away and the wavelength appears longer. If the source were moving towards the observer, the wavelength would appear shorter.

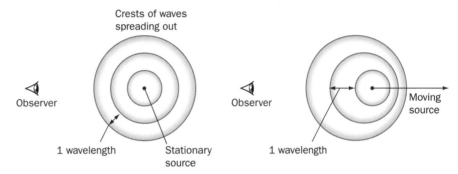

Waves from a moving source.

A red-shift in the light from a star shows that the distance between us and the star is increasing. The bigger the red-shift the faster the star is moving away. Hubble discovered:

KEY POINT

- The light from all the **distant galaxies** is red-shifted – so they are all moving away from us.
- The further away the galaxy, the bigger the red-shift, so the faster the galaxy is moving away.

Red-shift and the Doppler Effect

AQA	P1	✓
OCR A	P1	✓
OCR B	P2	✓
EDEXCEL	P1	✓

The change in wavelength, because a source of waves is travelling towards or away from an observer, is called the **Doppler Effect**. When the wavelength increases the frequency decreases. This is why a siren drops in frequency as it travels away and increases in frequency as it approaches.

Light from stars and galaxies is red-shifted or blue-shifted depending on whether they are moving towards us or away from us. The shift moves all the dark spectral lines by the same amount.

PROGRESS CHECK

1. What do we know about the movement of distant galaxies?
2. What is 'peer review'?
3. From the absorption spectra, is sodium vapour present in the Sun?
4. If the Sun was moving away from us which way would the spectral lines move?
5. Light from the Andromeda galaxy is blue-shifted. What does this tell you about the galaxy?
6. What information can astronomers get from line spectra?

13.6 Expanding Universe and the Big Bang

LEARNING SUMMARY

After studying this section, you should be able to:

- Explain how red-shift implies an expanding Universe.
- Explain how the expanding Universe implies a Big Bang.
- Describe how scientists develop new theories.
- Describe the evidence for the Big Bang theory.

The expanding Universe

AQA	P1	✓
OCR A	P1	✓
OCR B	P2	✓
EDEXCEL	P1	✓
WJEC	P1	✓

Hubble made two important observations:

- The light from all the distant galaxies is red-shifted.
- The further away the galaxy the bigger the red-shift.

KEY POINT

This means:

- All the distant galaxies are moving away from us.
- The further away the galaxy, the faster it is moving away.

We would not see these patterns in the red-shifts just because we, or the galaxies, are moving through space, but it is what we would see if space was expanding.

The difference between a moving star and expanding space.

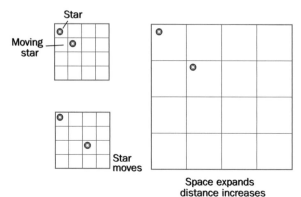

Space expands
distance increases

This is why scientists think we live in an **expanding Universe**. The Universe is everything that exists. There is nothing outside the Universe – not even empty space.

Space is expanding.

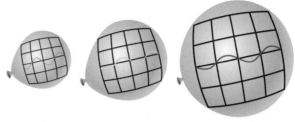

| Blue light | Red-shifted to yellow | Red-shifted to red |

To help you to remember about space expanding and the two effects that Hubble observed, imagine blowing-up a balloon with galaxies drawn on it. The galaxies drawn on the balloon will all spread out, moving away from each other and those furthest apart will separate more quickly because the plastic surface is expanding.

Cosmological red-shift

AQA	P1	✓
OCR A	P1	✓
OCR B	P2	✓
EDEXCEL	P1	✓
WJEC	P1	✓

All of the space in the Universe is expanding, but we do not notice this in the Solar System. This is because gravity is an attractive force that stops mass spreading out when space expands.

Stars and the nearest galaxies may show red-shifts or blue-shifts because they are moving through space and these are sometimes called Doppler shifts. Distant galaxies show red-shifts because space is expanding, so these are sometimes called cosmological red-shifts.

Spectral lines from galaxies.

Moving towards you: blue-shift

At rest

Moving away from you: red-shift

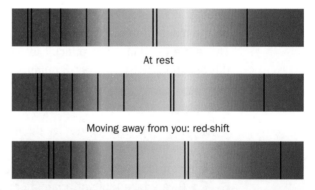

The Big Bang

AQA	P1	✓
OCR A	P1	✓
OCR B	P2	✓
EDEXCEL	P1	✓
WJEC	P1	✓

> **KEY POINT**
>
> The fact that the Universe is expanding is strong evidence for the fact that it started as a small point. Starting from today and working backwards scientists calculate that the Universe began with a 'Big Bang' about 14 thousand million years ago. This is called the **Big Bang Theory**.

The Big Bang Theory started as a **hypothesis** – a suggested explanation thought up creatively to account for the data. Scientists then used it to make a **prediction**. They said that the Big Bang would have produced radiation that, by now, would be found in the microwave region of the spectrum. It would come from all parts of the Universe. Scientists called this the **cosmic microwave background radiation (CMBR)**.

Cosmic microwave background radiation

AQA	P1	✓
OCR B	P2	✓
EDEXCEL	P1	✓
WJEC	P1	✓

Scientists began searching for the CMBR. In 1965, two scientists discovered it accidently. They were using a radio telescope and could not account for an annoying microwave signal that seemed to come equally from all directions. It was the CMBR. The Big Bang Theory was the only theory that could explain this.

Do not confuse the CMBR with radioactive background radiation, which is ionising radiation from radioactive materials.

The steady state theory

EDEXCEL	P1	✓

The **Steady State Theory** is an alternative theory that suggests the Universe is expanding, but has always looked the same. It will continue to look the same, because new matter is being created at various places. There were already some problems with data that could not be explained by the Steady State Theory and the discovery of the CMBR led to the general acceptance of the Big Bang Theory.

Questions that can not be answered

AQA	P1	✓
OCR A	P1	✓
EDEXCEL	P1	✓

Scientists may never be able to answer some questions like 'What happened before the Big Bang?' because they can't collect data from before the Big Bang.

Scientists can't answer some questions because of difficulties in collecting the data they need. For example, whether the Universe will continue to expand, or whether it will slow down and stop, or whether it will start to contract, depends on the mass of the Universe and the distance to the edge of the Universe. These are very large and difficult to measure, so scientists can not yet answer the question, 'What will be the ultimate fate of the Universe?'

PROGRESS CHECK

1. What explanation do scientists have for the red-shifts in radiation from all the distant galaxies?
2. How long ago was the Big Bang?
3. Give an example of a question science can't answer.
4. What effect was predicted by scientists if the Big Bang theory was true?
5. What led to the acceptance of the Big Bang Theory and why?

5. The discovery of the cosmic microwave background radiation because other theories could not explain it.
4. Cosmic microwave radiation left over from the Big Bang.
3. What happened before the Big Bang?
2. 14 thousand million years ago
1. The Universe is expanding.

Sample GCSE questions

1 **(a)** Write these objects in order of increasing size. The first has been done for you **[3]**

A = comet **B = diameter of Earth's orbit** **C = galaxy**
D = the Sun **E = the Universe**

| A | D | B | C | E |

> D anywhere before B = 1 mark, B anywhere before C = 1 mark, C anywhere before E = 1 mark.

(b) The light received from the Andromeda galaxy shows a blue-shift. What does this tell us about the Andromeda galaxy? **[1]**

It is moving towards the Earth.

(c) The diagram shows the spectra of light from two distant galaxies.

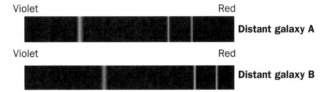

(i) Which galaxy is furthest away, A or B?

B

(ii) Explain how you can tell.

The light from galaxy B has a larger red-shift than the light from galaxy A. This means it is moving away from us faster and the further away a galaxy is the faster it is moving away. **[2]**

> One mark is for identifying and explaining that galaxy B has the larger red-shift. The second mark is for explaining why this means it is further away.

(d) This graph shows the speed of distant galaxies plotted against their distance from Earth.

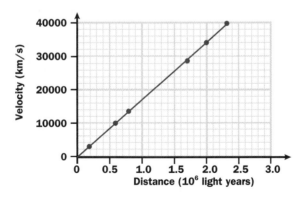

(i) Describe the relationship shown by the graph. **[2]**

The speed of a distant galaxy is proportional to its distance away from the Earth.

> A straight line through the origin means that one variable is proportional to the other. This is the best way to describe the relationship. You could also say that as one variable doubles the other doubles. Identifying that the speed increases as the distance increases would gain only one of the marks.

(ii) Use the graph to estimate the speed of a galaxy that is 1.3×10^6 light years from Earth. **[1]**

22 000 km/s

> Don't forget the units. It is a good idea to use a ruler to mark the value you are reading from the graph.

Sample GCSE questions

(e) Scientists have used this information to form a theory about the beginning of the Universe. Name and describe the theory, explaining a prediction made using the theory and how this lead to its acceptance by many scientists. *The quality of your written communication will be assessed in this answer.* **[6]**

The theory is the Big Bang Theory (1 point). The theory says that the Universe started to expand from a small point (1 point) about 14 thousand million years ago (1 point). Scientists predicted that there should be radiation left over from the big bang (1 point) which would be in the microwave region of the electromagnetic spectrum, called cosmic microwave background radiation (1 point). When scientists discovered the cosmic background radiation (1 point) most scientists accepted the theory.

2 (a) How do scientists get information about which elements are present in a star? **[3]**

They look at the electromagnetic radiation from the star. They see spectral lines which are dark lines corresponding to wavelengths (or frequencies) absorbed by the elements present in the star. The element always has the same spectral lines so they can be used to identify the element.

(b) Betelgeuse is a red giant star. Give two differences between Betelgeuse and our Sun. **[2]**

1. Betelgeuse is much larger than the Sun.
2. Betelgeuse is much cooler than the Sun.

(c) Draw a ring round the main sequence star that will end up as a supernova. **[1]**

The Sun   A star with smaller mass than the Sun

(A star 20 times more massive than the Sun)

(d) Explain what happens as a star leaves the main sequence and ends up as a supernovae. *The quality of your written communication will be assessed in this answer.* **[6]**

When the star has finished fusing hydrogen (1 point) to helium (1 point) it cools and expands (1 point) to form a red supergiant (1 point). The core contracts (1 point) and fusion in the core forms carbon (1 point), oxygen and nitrogen (1 point) and then heavier elements up to the mass of iron (1 point).

When the nuclear fusion reactions are finished (1 point) the star cools and contracts (1 point), which heats it again until it explodes (1 point). The explosion is called a supernova (1 point).

Marks will be awarded depending on the number of relevant points included in the answer and the spelling, punctuation and grammar. In this question there are 6 relevant points so 5 or 6 points with good spelling punctuation and grammar will gain full marks.

Remember that the electromagnetic radiation is the only information we have from stars. Many stars emit wavelengths outside the range of visible light, so em radiation is a better answer than light.

You could also say that Betelgeuse fuses helium, whereas the Sun fuses hydrogen.

Marks will be awarded depending on the number of relevant points included in the answer and the spelling, punctuation and grammar. In this question there are 12 relevant points so 10 or 12 points with good spelling punctuation and grammar will gain full marks.

Exam practice questions

1 **(a)** What is the difference between the geocentric and heliocentric models of the Solar System? **[2]**

....

....

....

(b) When Copernicus found evidence for a heliocentric model, the new evidence was not accepted for many years.

Why did it take so long for new evidence to be accepted? **[1]**

....

....

[Total = 3]

2 The current theory of how the Moon was formed suggests that a planet collided with the Earth and the less dense rocks were thrown up as the Moon. Give two pieces of evidence that support this theory. **[2]**

1. ....

2. ....

3 In the 20th century scientists collected data about the planet Mars.

(a) State whether they used

(i) Telescopes: ....

(ii) Unmanned space missions: ....

(iii) Manned space missions: .... **[1]**

(b) Describe the advantages and the disadvantages of unmanned space missions when compared to manned space missions. *The quality of your written communication will be assessed in this answer.* **[6]**

....

....

....

....

....

....

....

....

....

[Total = 7]

Exam practice questions

4 (a) What is a light year? [1]

....

(b) Explain why the distance to the Sun is measured in kilometres but the distance to other stars is measured in light years. [1]

....

....

[Total = 2]

5 Draw one straight line from each box on the left to match the object to its size. [3]

Object   **Size**

Diameter of the Earth		10 light years
Diameter of the Solar System		4 light years
Diameter of the Milky Way galaxy		12 760 km
Distance to the nearest star		100 000 light years

6 This is the spectrum of a nearby star.

These are the line spectra of some elements on Earth:

(a) Which of the elements are present in the star? [4]

....

Exam practice questions

When we observe light from a distant star we see a red-shift in the wavelength.

(b) What is meant by red-shift? **[1]**

....

(c) What does it tell us about the star? **[1]**

....

[Total = 6]

7 **(a)** Scientists have a theory about how the Universe was formed called the Big Bang theory. Describe the theory and explain the evidence they have for the theory. *The quality of your written communication will be assessed in this answer.* **[6]**

....

....

....

....

....

....

(b) At a conference some scientists present evidence that does not agree with the Big Bang theory. They say the Big Bang theory is wrong. Describe what scientists should do when they disagree about a theory. **[3]**

....

....

....

(c) Scientists have a theory that answers the question 'How did the Universe begin?' Explain whether they can answer the question 'Why was the Universe created?' **[2]**

....

....

....

[Total = 11]

Answers

Note: For questions involving QWC, marks will be awarded if:
- All information in answer is relevant, clear, organised and presented in a structured and coherent format.
- Specialist terms are used appropriately.
- There are few, if any, errors in grammar, punctuation and spelling.

Chapter 1

1. (a) (i)

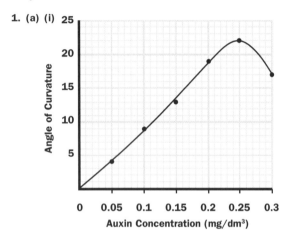

(Marks awarded for suitable scale on *y* axis, Points correctly plotted; best curve drawn.)

(ii) Increased auxin concentration causes more curvature.
Levels off/decreases at high concentrations.
Figures quoted from graph.

(b) (i) It causes cells to elongate.
More on the side where the block is placed.

(ii) Light; negative geotropism/gravitropism.

(iii) Leaves can trap more sunlight/more photosynthesis.
So more food production/more growth.

(c) Rooting of cuttings/weedkillers/seedless fruits/control of fruit ripening.

2. (a)

(b) The lens is too powerful (does not refract the light enough).
The light is focussed behind the retina.

Chapter 2

1. (a)

The chemicals made by the bacteria that are making Vijay feel ill	Antibiotics
An injection that could have stopped Vijay getting the disease	Vaccination
The medicine given to Vijay to kill the bacteria	White blood cells
The cells produced by Vijay's body to kill the bacteria	Toxins

(b) Destroyed by hydrochloric acid.

(c) Sebum on skin/enzyme in tears/mucus in the breathing system/skin.

(d) Proved that it worked/showed that it was not harmful.

2. (a) (i) It often contains a weakened form of the microbe.
The person gets a mild form of the disease.

(ii) Two from: worried about the side effects.
Three sets of side effects at once may damage the child.
Reference to autism.

(b) Two from: one vaccine protects children more quickly and effectively than one, as child is protected from start.
Cheaper.
Takes less time.
May not come back for other injections.

(c) Contains three different weakened pathogens/antigens.
Each one stimulates the production of a different antibody.
These antibodies/memory cells will stay in the blood.

Chapter 3

1. (a) Peter's gametes: X and Y.
Correct offspring: XX, XX, XY, XY.

(b) (i) All countries.
All ratios after the age of 65 show less than one man to each woman.

(ii) India.
The ratio of boys to girls at birth is highest/above one to one.

(iii) Imbalance in the sex ratio in the country leading to possible drop in population.

2. (a) See predators approaching/see prey.

(b) (see QWC guidance on page 250) All apes were born with slightly different bones/mutations.
The apes that could stand the best could see further and were more likely to survive.
They could reproduce and pass on their genes.
Over many generations the population gradually became more upright.

(c) Unlikely that tool use was the reason for man being upright.
Because fossil was upright but could not have used tools as the brain was too small.

Chapter 4

1. (a) A = nitrates; B = nitrogen gas; C = ammonium compounds.

(b) (i) Fungi.

(ii) Any three from: a reasonable temperature.
A suitable pH.
Oxygen.
Moisture.

(c) (see QWC guidance on page 250) Lives in root nodules.
Mutualistic relationship.
The plant gains nitrogen compounds from the bacteria.
The bacteria gains some carbohydrates from the plant.

Chapter 5

1. (a) 10

(b) 20

(c) (2, 8)

(d) Period 2; Group 8

2. (a) $Mg(s) + Cl_2(g) \rightarrow MgCl_2(s)$

Answers

(b) $4Fe(s) + 3O_2(g) \rightarrow 2Fe_2O_3(s)$

3. (a) Gas

    (b) A molecule

    (c) $3H_2$ and $2NH_3$

    (d) Water or H_2O

Chapter 6

1. (a) Photosynthesis

    (b) Oxygen

    (c) There will be fewer green plants; so less photosynthesis

2. (a) Fractional distillation

    (b) Different boiling points

    (c) Nitrogen and oxygen

3. (a) Nitrogen

    (b) 21%

    (c) Any suitable answer e.g. carbon dioxide

4. (a) Does not decompose naturally

    (b) Toxic gases may be released into the atmosphere

    (c) Re-use or recycle

5. CFCs break down and release chlorine atoms (radicals); which destroy ozone molecules and make the ozone thinner

6. David is correct, except for one value (8 km); Improvements could be made by: measuring more than one gas, monitoring over a longer time period, calculating or basing claims on average levels (any two)

7. There is less photosynthesis; Less carbon dioxide removed from air; Less oxygen made; The burning of the trees puts carbon dioxide into the air; Removes oxygen

8. (a) Helium does not burn; Hydrogen burns explosively

    (b) Argon is too dense

Chapter 7

1. (a) Ethanol

    (b) Ethene

    (c) Ethene

2. (a) C_4H_{10}

    (b) Butane is saturated

    (c) Alkanes

    (d) Add bromine solution; butene will decolourise it

3. (a) The fractions can be separated and collected because hydrocarbons; boil at different temperatures

    (b) Any one from: Breaking up large hydrocarbon molecules into small hydrocarbon molecules; To match supply and demand; To make more petrol; To make ethane

    (c) Small molecules have fewer forces of attraction between molecules than large molecules; Less energy is needed to separate them

Chapter 8

1. (a) An ore contains enough of a metal; to make extraction economically viable

    (b) Carbon

2. Aluminium can only be extracted by electrolysis; Aluminium oxide cannot be reduced by carbon because carbon is less reactive than aluminium; Iron is extracted by heating the iron oxide with carbon; because carbon is more reactive than iron

3. (a) Any two from: It is stronger; It is easier to shape; It is more flexible

    (b) Tin

(c) Any two from: It is hard; It is strong; It has a low melting point; It is gas proof.

4. (a) The cation (metal ion) present in a salt

    (b) Sodium ions are present

    (c) Both give a green flame colour

    (d) The wire must be free from any salts previously tested; which might give false flame colours

Chapter 9

1. (a) Hydrochloric acid

    (b) H^+ (or H_3O^+)

    (c) Hydrochloric acid

    (d) Ethanoic acid is weaker; and will not react as much with metals inside the kettle

2. (a) Hydrogen

    (b) The pH increases

    (c) Magnesium sulfate

    (d) Any two from: Magnesium oxide, magnesium hydroxide or magnesium carbonate

3. (a) Calcium carbonate

    (b) It is heated; with clay

    (c) At least one point from environmental, economic and social, plus any additional point, from:
Environmental: The effect on native animal habitats / landscape; Noise and air pollution; Additional traffic
Economic: Costs involved in quarrying and processing; Effect on local businesses
Social: Availability of workforce; How the quarry can be used afterwards

Chapter 10

1. (a) the amount of wind (or wind speed)

    (b) C

    (c) (i) the appliances used at that time of day, e.g. cooker

        (ii) at night everything might be switched off

        (iii) If the wind drops below the maximum the turbine will produce less; The turbine will not cope with higher than average demand.

    (d) To cope with peaks in demand, or can be used when there is no wind (or to give a more constant supply)

    (e) (i) 500 000   **(ii)** 1 500 000

    (f) The time for the turbine to save the amount of money that it cost to buy and install

2. C

3. (a) efficiency = (8W ÷ 100W) × 100% = 8%

    (b) It is transferred to heat.

    (c) 40% of electrical power, $P = 8$ W, $40P \div 100 = 8$ W, $P = (100 \times 8$ W$) \div 40 = 20$ W

    (d) 3 × 100W × 7 = 300 × 7 W h = 0.3 × 7 kWh = 2.1 kWh

4. Answer should describe advantages and disadvantages of nuclear and gas power stations and compare the two.

Chapter 11

1. (a) 45 cm ÷ 5 = 9 cm

    (b) $v = f\lambda$ or wave speed = frequency × wavelength, 9 cm × 4 Hz = 36 cm/s

    (c) The waves will speed up

2. (a) Diffraction

    (b) The wave crests will be closer together (1 point) and the

Answers

harbour entrance is now greater than the wavelength (1 point) so the diffraction effect will be less (1 point). More like (b) on page 199. A diagram must be labelled and clearly show these points if they are not written. Marks will be awarded depending on the number of relevant points included in the answer and the spelling, punctuation and grammar. In this question there are only 3 relevant points so all 3 points with good spelling punctuation and grammar will gain full marks.

Chapter 12

1. radio, infrared, visible light, ultraviolet
2. Radio waves are blocked by the ionosphere.
3. They both have a lens to focus the picture on the light sensitive material (retina or screen) at the back. The light sensitive screen produces an electric signal.
4. A beam of microwaves transmitted through the atmosphere to a receiver will be absorbed by the water droplets so that if the beam is reduced or blocked there is rain present.
5. D
6. Example similarities: Both heat food by causing molecules to vibrate. Both heat using electromagnetic radiation. Both rely on conduction to spread heat through the food and cook the inside. Example differences: grill uses infrared, microwave oven uses microwaves. Infrared vibrates molecules on surface, microwaves penetrate about 1 cm into the food and vibrate the water molecules.
7. The hills have gaps roughly the same size as the wavelength of the radio waves so they are diffracted – they spread out around the hills. The microwaves for phones have smaller wavelength and are not diffracted so the straight beams are blocked.
8. Example answer: The hole in the ozone layer was caused by gases called CFCs (1 point) which react with the ozone (1 point), leaving a gap in the ozone layer (1 point). The ozone layer protects life on Earth from the high energy ionising (1 point) ultraviolet radiation (1 point) from the Sun. The hole in the ozone layer leads to more ultraviolet radiation reaching the Earth's surface (1 point) and causing skin cancer and cataracts (1 point). The governments of the world have passed laws (1 point) banning CFCs and the ozone hole is starting to reduce in size (1 point).
Marks will be awarded depending on the number of relevant points included in the answer and the spelling, punctuation and grammar. In this question there are 9 relevant points so 8 to 9 points with good spelling, punctuation and grammar will gain full marks.
9. True: a, b, f. False: c,d,e.

Chapter 13

1. (a) The geocentric model is that the Earth is at the centre and the planets and stars move around it. The heliocentric is that the Sun is at the centre of the solar system and all the planets including Earth orbit around it in approximate circles.
   (b) because the idea conflicted with people's religious beliefs.
2. Two of: The Moon has less dense rocks and only a small iron core. The Earth and Moon rocks are the same. The Moon has igneous rocks but no sign of recent volcanic activity.
3. (a) (i) yes (b) (ii) yes (c) (iii) no

(b) The advantages of unmanned missions are: The costs of unmanned missions are less than manned missions, because there is no need to take food, water, oxygen and other supplies people need. There are no lives at risk if something goes wrong with an unmanned mission, but there are with a manned mission. The disadvantages of an unmanned mission are that everything must be planned before an unmanned mission leaves – no adjustments, repairs or changes can be made unless they are programmed into the computers and can be done remotely. Also, most people are more interested in manned missions. Unmanned missions do not inspire people in the way that manned missions do.
Marks will be awarded depending on the number of relevant points included in the answer and the spelling, punctuation and grammar. There must be advantages and disadvantages given for full marks.

4. (a) A light year is the distance travelled by light through space, or a vacuum, in a year.
   (b) The Sun is much closer than the other stars, it is much less than 1 light year away.
5. Diameter of the Earth = 12 760 km, Diameter of the Solar System = 10 light years, Diameter of the Milky Way galaxy = 100 000 light years, Distance to the nearest star = 4 light years.
6. (a) A and D
   (b) All the spectral lines are shift towards the red end of the spectrum
   (c) It means that the star is moving away from us.
7. (a) The Big Bang theory is that the Universe started to expand from a small initial point about 14 thousand million years ago. It is still expanding. The evidence is that the electromagnetic radiation from all the distant galaxies is red–shifted, and the further away the galaxy is the more its radiation is red shifted. This shows that all the distant galaxies are moving away from us and those further away are moving fastest. Scientists predicted that there should be cosmic microwave background radiation left from the big bang, and this was found in the 1960s.
   Marks will be awarded depending on the number of relevant points included in the answer and the spelling, punctuation and grammar.
   (b) They should try to repeat their findings and other scientists should try to reproduce them. They should look for another explanation, but not discard the theory until they can work out a new one that accounts for all the data.
   (c) They cannot answer this question because they cannot collect data or find evidence to answer it. It has more to do with religious belief than cause and effect. It cannot be tested.

Notes

Index

Index

1	2											3	4	5	6	7	0
																	4 **He** helium 2
7 **Li** lithium 3	9 **Be** beryllium 4											11 **B** boron 5	12 **C** carbon 6	14 **N** nitrogen 7	16 **O** oxygen 8	19 **F** fluorine 9	20 **Ne** neon 10
23 **Na** sodium 11	24 **Mg** magnesium 12											27 **Al** aluminium 13	28 **Si** silicon 14	31 **P** phosphorus 15	32 **S** sulfur 16	35.5 **Cl** chlorine 17	40 **Ar** argon 18
39 **K** potassium 19	40 **Ca** calcium 20	45 **Sc** scandium 21	48 **Ti** titanium 22	51 **V** vanadium 23	52 **Cr** chromium 24	55 **Mn** manganese 25	56 **Fe** iron 26	59 **Co** cobalt 27	59 **Ni** nickel 28	63.5 **Cu** copper 29	65 **Zn** zinc 30	70 **Ga** gallium 31	73 **Ge** germanium 32	75 **As** arsenic 33	79 **Se** selenium 34	80 **Br** bromine 35	84 **Kr** krypton 36
85 **Rb** rubidium 37	88 **Sr** strontium 38	89 **Y** yttrium 39	91 **Zr** zirconium 40	93 **Nb** niobium 41	96 **Mo** molybdenum 42	[98] **Tc** technetium 43	101 **Ru** ruthenium 44	103 **Rh** rhodium 45	106 **Pd** palladium 46	108 **Ag** silver 47	112 **Cd** cadmium 48	115 **In** indium 49	119 **Sn** tin 50	122 **Sb** antimony 51	128 **Te** tellurium 52	127 **I** iodine 53	131 **Xe** xenon 54
133 **Cs** caesium 55	137 **Ba** barium 56	139 **La*** lanthanum 57	178 **Hf** hafnium 72	181 **Ta** tantalum 73	184 **W** tungsten 74	186 **Re** rhenium 75	190 **Os** osmium 76	192 **Ir** iridium 77	195 **Pt** platinum 78	197 **Au** gold 79	201 **Hg** mercury 80	204 **Tl** thallium 81	207 **Pb** lead 82	209 **Bi** bismuth 83	[209] **Po** polonium 84	[210] **At** astatine 85	[222] **Rn** radon 86
[223] **Fr** francium 87	[226] **Ra** radium 88	[227] **Ac*** actinium 89	[261] **Rf** rutherfordium 104	[262] **Db** dubnium 105	[266] **Sg** seaborgium 106	[264] **Bh** bohrium 107	[277] **Hs** hassium 108	[268] **Mt** meitnerium 109	[271] **Ds** darmstadtium 110	[272] **Rg** roentgenium 111							

Elements with atomic numbers 112–116 have been reported but not fully authenticated

*The Lanthanides (atomic numbers 58–71) and the Actinides (atomic numbers 90–103) have been omitted.

Cu and **Cl** have not been rounded to the nearest whole number.